# AN ATLAS OF ULTRASTRUCTURE

## JOHANNES A. G. RHODIN, M.D.

Professor of Anatomy,
New York University School of Medicine, New York City;
Docent of Anatomy, Karolinska Institutet, Stockholm, Sweden

**W. B. SAUNDERS COMPANY** PHILADELPHIA AND LONDON / 1963

*Dedicated to my wife*

*GUNVOR*

*with love and admiration for
her incredible patience*

# PREFACE

The need for an atlas of ultrastructure has been evident for some time. However, since the field of electron microscopy of cells and tissues has been opened up to research comparatively recently, and since the techniques employed have not been perfected to the extent that anyone could undertake such a project without the risk of overburdening himself, an atlas such as the present one has not appeared. However, with the perfection of preparation techniques, such as the introduction of epoxy resins for embedding, the construction of reliable and easily managed microtomes for sectioning, the adaptation of various heavy metals for increasing the contrast of the fine cellular details, and the perfection of the electron microscope itself, it is now possible to carry out, within a relatively short time, the type of investigation presented in this atlas.

This atlas is not intended primarily for electron microscopists, since the experienced and well-informed morphologist, familiar with recent advances in techniques using electron microscopy for the study of mammalian tissues, already knows and can easily find the references required for extended reading and planning of continued investigations in this field. In addition, many of these references provide far more detailed descriptions with wider functional considerations than does this present work.

This atlas tries to bring together in a simple and clear fashion the wealth of information that presently is available concerning mammalian ultrastructure. Light micrographs and line drawings have not been included, since any current textbook of histology provides the student with this kind of illustrative material. However, a comprehensive knowledge of the normal histology of the mammalian body is essential before studying this work. The atlas is intended as a supplement to ordinary textbooks of histology and should help the student to bridge the gap that now exists between light microscopy and electron microscopy, as indicated by the great number of high magnification illustrations one usually finds in electron microscopy publications. Therefore, a large number of low-magnification illustrations are included as well as, wherever space has permitted, sets of pictures with serially increased magnifications. With few exceptions, the bibliography includes only electron microscopical publications. The incorporation of an extensive bibliography is intended to help those who are interested in an extended reading, and who would like to have easy access to the references of the original sources.

JOHANNES A. G. RHODIN

# ACKNOWLEDGMENTS

The experimental work done by myself and utilized in this atlas was aided by Research Grants A–2705, RG–6597, and Training Grant 2G–297 from the National Institutes of Health, United States Public Health Service; a grant from the Muscular Dystrophy Associations of America, Inc.; and the receipt of an Investigatorship from the Health Research Council of the City of New York under contract I–186.

Throughout the entire project, the valuable and skillful technical assistance of Mrs. Inger Terzakis has enabled me to carry out the analysis of the great variety of tissues included. I most gratefully acknowledge her never failing cooperation in tissue preparation, sectioning, and photography, and in the preparation of the bibliography. To Mr. Eugene Minner and Mr. Norman Katz I am indebted for assistance in the work with the electron microscope and the photographic printing of the original illustrations. Mrs. Helen Stark, my secretary, has been most helpful in preparing the manuscript and checking the references, and I wish to express my deep gratitude to her.

To my friends, professional and personal, without whom I could not have progressed this far, I extend my deep thanks and appreciation. In particular, I should like to acknowledge my debt to Dr. Fritiof S. Sjöstrand, Professor of Zoology, University of California at Los Angeles, for providing my earliest opportunity to learn the techniques of electron microscopy and for his guidance in those early years of ultrastructural analyses. I thank Dr. Donal Sheehan, Professor and Chairman, Department of Anatomy, New York University School of Medicine, for his encouragement in pursuing this type of research, and Dr. Edward J. Reith, Associate Professor of Anatomy, Department of Anatomy, New York University School of Medicine, for many valuable discussions in connection with the analysis of the various tissues. Several colleagues at New York University School of Medicine have been most helpful in providing me with human specimens, and I would like to thank Dr. Howard C. Baron, Department of Surgery, for the specimen of parathyroid gland; Dr. John F. Daly, Professor of Otorhinolaryngology, for the specimens of parotid gland and esophagus, and for help with the preparation of the guinea pig cochlea; Dr. Gordon W. Douglas, Professor of Obstetrics and Gynecology, for the placenta; and Dr. Robert S. Hotchkiss, Professor of Urology, for the ductuli efferentes of the human testis. Special thanks are due to Dr. John Lind, Professor of Pediatrics, Karolinska Hospital, Stockholm, Sweden, who kindly assisted in obtaining the human fetal teeth.

# ACKNOWLEDGMENTS

It is with great appreciation I acknowledge the permission to reproduce the following illustrations: page 35 (top), from Rhodin, Del Misier, and Reid (1167), courtesy of New York Heart Association, Inc.; page 51 (bottom left and right) from Rhodin (1159), courtesy of the American Physiological Society; page 83, from Rhodin in The Encyclopedia of Microscopy, G. L. Clark, Ed., New York, 1961, courtesy of Reinhold Publishing Corp.; pages 95, 97, 99, and 101, from Rhodin (1160), courtesy of Blackwell Scientific Publications Ltd.; page 131 (top), from Rhodin and Terzakis (1169), courtesy of Academic Press Inc.; and page 135, from Rhodin and Reith (1168), courtesy of American Association for the Advancement of Science.

Finally, I want to thank the W. B. Saunders Company for their faith in and enthusiasm for the work during the entire preparation of this atlas.

JOHANNES A. G. RHODIN

# MATERIALS AND METHODS

All statements are based on work with the mouse unless otherwise specified. The entire mammalian body has not been covered in this work. Thus, tissues such as the pituitary, thymus, adrenal medulla, and prostate gland remain to be elucidated. Furthermore, several tissues and organs have been dealt with quite briefly, and it is obvious that a more detailed discussion is necessary in order to enable the student to fully understand the complexity of the structures involved.

The specimens were prepared according to techniques currently employed in electron microscopy. The material was fixed in 1 per cent osmium tetroxide solution in a veronal acetate buffer (Palade, 979) modified either according to Sjöstrand (1342) or Millonig (863). Epon 812 (Luft, 802) or methacrylate (Newman, Borysko, and Swerdlow, 941a) was used as the embedding medium. The sections were cut on the LKB Ultrotome microtome (Hellström, 564). Various methods of staining the sections with heavy metals were tried. The most useful were those developed by Watson (1484, 1485), Lever (775), and Millonig (864). The electron micrographs were taken with the Siemens Elmiskop I electron microscope. The legends of each illustration indicate the embedding process and stain by the following abbreviations:

Meth. : Methacrylate (941a)
Ep. : Epon 812 (802)
LA. : Lead tartrate (864)
LH. : Lead hydroxide (775)
UA. : Uranyl acetate (1484)

*References:* GENERAL 345, 514, 564, 814, 843, 854, 876, 886, 969, 1044, 1229, 1316, 1333, 1482.
FIXATION 601, 801, 863, 979, 1005, 1116, 1145, 1342, 1518.
EMBEDDING 214, 394, 420, 713, 797, 802, 882, 883, 941a, 1218.
STAINING 232, 651, 750, 775, 826, 838, 864, 869, 1029, 1031, 1337, 1443, 1484, 1485, 1489.

# CONTENTS

# CONTENTS

TRACHEA

LUNG TISSUE

KIDNEY

TESTIS

OVARY

CONTENTS

# An Atlas of
# Ultrastructure

The ultrastructure of the cell is a rather complex picture and enumerable details are revealed which the light microscope is unable to resolve. Rarely does one find any single cell type that displays the great assortment of cell organelles and cell inclusions which the study of many cell types can bring together. The megakaryocyte is a unique case, however, since its cytoplasm contains many of the membranous systems, organelles, and inclusion bodies that one finds elsewhere and has, therefore, been selected as an introduction to details of the mammalian cell. The various cellular components will be dealt with separately and their occurrence and possible functions pointed out as the tissues are studied individually.

The cell nucleus ($Nu$) with its finely granular nucleoplasm is enveloped by a triple-layered membrane ($NuM$). The cytoplasm is likewise granular, owing to the ribosomes ($Ri$), which occur singly or in clusters or are attached to flat membranous sacs ($Re$) and then are referred to as rough-surfaced endoplasmic reticulum. Near the nucleus is the Golgi complex ($Go$) comprised of smooth membranes, large vacuoles, small granules, and vesicles. Aggregates of small vesicles are sometimes surrounded by a membrane and are called multivesicular bodies ($Mv$). These bodies bear slight resemblance to membrane-bound structures with a dense content, which properly are referred to as granules ($G$) and usually represent secretory products. Other spherical bodies are actually mitochondria ($Mi$) with internal membranes. The entire cell is enveloped by the cell membrane or plasma membrane ($Cm$), which can be infolded and encountered deep within the body ($Cy$). Smooth membranes also surround small, clear, spherical spaces, which may be referred to as large vesicles ($Ve$), or the membranes may surround irregular spaces, in which case the structure can be called a smooth-surfaced endoplasmic reticulum ($Sm$). Occasionally a connection is established between elements of the smooth and the rough-surfaced endoplasmic reticulum ($Re$-$Sm$).

Megakaryocyte. Spleen. Magnification 20,000×. Ep. UA. LH.

*References:* 38, 103, 222, 362, 402, 644, 858, 918, 931, 1111, 1150, 1244, 1311, 1345, 1346, 1348, 1548, 1551.

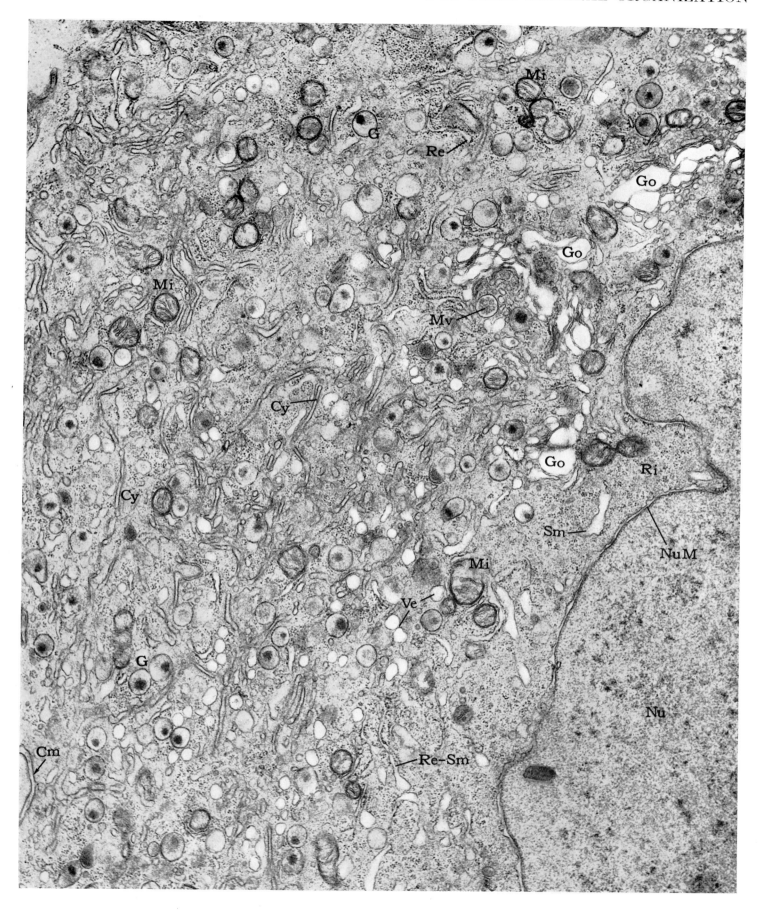

The free surface of epithelial cells is differentiated into specialized structures of different shapes, depending on the function and location of the cell.

*1 and 2:*     MICROVILLI. Almost every epithelial cell is provided with short, slender microvilli on its free surface. These structures vary considerably in length and width, but an average of 0.5 $\mu$ in length and 0.1 $\mu$ in width is representative. Since the microvillus is an extension of the cell, it is covered by the plasma membrane, a triple-layered structure with a lightly stained layer between two heavily stained layers. This constitutes the so-called *unit membrane*. In addition, microvilli of certain cells have an *extraneous coat* with a furry or spikelike appearance, seen in longitudinal (1) as well as in tangential (1) and cross sections (2).

Gallbladder. Magnification (1) 52,000$\times$; (2) 61,000$\times$. Ep. LH.

*3 and 4:*     STRIATED BORDER. The striated border is referred to both as a brush border and as microvilli. It seems appropriate to exclude the name microvilli and to use this term only for short, irregularly arranged extensions of the cell surface. The striated border is composed of extremely regular, evenly spaced, and equally long cell processes, which average 1 $\mu$ in length and 0.15 $\mu$ in width. However, this appearance may vary from one location to another, as, for instance, in various parts of the intestines, but the striated border is characterized by the dense arrangement of the processes as compared with the microvilli. Between the bases of the individual components of the striated border are small tubular invaginations that serve as small pockets by which large molecules can be taken into the cell. This process is usually referred to as *micropinocytosis*, or membrane flow, and the small pockets are called *micropinocytotic vesicles*. The villi of the striated border, as are the microvilli, are covered by the unit membrane, here resolved in the cross section of the striated border (4). A faint extraneous coat can be seen, but it is not nearly so pronounced as in microvilli. The cytoplasm of the striated border is denser than the rest of the apical cytoplasm and sometimes has a slightly fibrillar nature, continuing down into the apex of the cell for a short distance. The fine fibrils probably have a cytoskeletal function in helping maintain rigidity within the cell processes.

Small intestine. Magnification (3) 57,400; (4) 66,600$\times$. Ep. LH.

*5 and 6:*     STEREOCILIA. Stereocilia are extremely long, slender cell processes with an average length of 8 $\mu$ and a width of 0.1 $\mu$. They occur only in the epididymis and vas deferens. The stereocilia differ from striated borders and microvilli not only in their extreme length but also in the repeated branching near their bases. They are covered by the unit plasma membrane (6) with a thin extraneous coat and display a core of filaments ($Fi$), which are slightly coarser than those found in the elements of the striated border. The nature of the small local distentions along individual stereocilia is unknown.

Ductus epididymis. Magnification (5) 16,500; (6) 87,000$\times$. Ep. UA.

*7 and 8:*     CILIA. The cilia are approximately 8 $\mu$ long and 0.3 $\mu$ wide and thus are the thickest of all the processes that extend from the free cell surface. Each cilium is covered by the unit membrane of the plasma membrane and contains longitudinally arranged, coarse filaments. Close examination of cross-sectioned cilia (8) reveals that the filaments are arranged as follows: peripherally ($Pf$) located are nine double filaments and centrally ($Cf$) are two single ones. The center of each filament has the same density as the rest of the ciliary cytoplasm. The peripheral filaments originate in the basal corpuscle ($Bc$), which is located below the cell surface within the apical cytoplasm. The peripheral filaments descend beneath the basal corpuscle as fine fibrillar rootlets ($Ro$). From some of the peripheral filaments projects a lateral knob ($Kn$) composed of fine, often banded fibrils. The two central filaments ($Cf$) terminate at the level of the cell surface and do not descend into the basal corpuscle as distinctly discernible structures in sections of human cilia. Irregular microvilli ($Vi$) occur between the cilia. The filaments of the cilium are contractile elements, and the complicated phases of the ciliary beat are most likely controlled by the basal corpuscle.

Human trachea. Magnification (7) 30,000$\times$; (8) 62,700$\times$. Ep. LH.

*References:* 69, 105, 229, 233, 286, 287, 328, 356, 359, 364, 368, 1066, 1120, 1165, 1186, 1189, 1192, 1193, 1194, 1255, 1574.

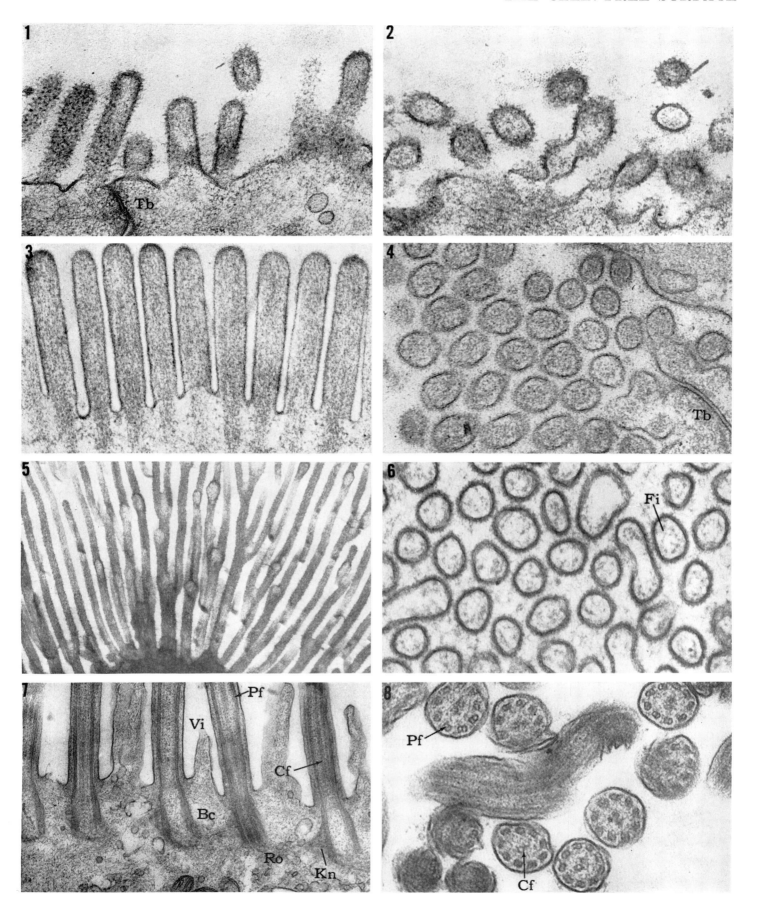

The lateral cell surface shows several peculiarities, all of which seem to serve to hold cells together. There are three main types of attachment: terminal bars, desmosomes, and cell invaginations. The plasma membrane and the intercellular space are each designed differently in relation to these attachment areas, which all occur in pairs.

*Top Left:*

TERMINAL BARS (*Tb*). These structures are located only near the free surface of the cell where adjoining cells (*C1* to *C3*) meet. The intracellular aspect of the plasma membrane (*Cm*) is invested by a continuous band of amorphous, dense substance, which extends around the entire cell circumference. The intercellular space is decreased to the smallest recorded dimension between the two adjoining terminal bars (see also Figures 1 and 4 on page 5).

Pancreas with lumen (*Lu*) of secretory capillary. Magnification 34,700×. Ep. LH.

*Top Right:*

DESMOSOMES. Desmosomes (*Des*) may be found at any point on the lateral cell surfaces. Two cells (*C1* and *C2*) of the tracheal stratified epithelium are shown in which the cell surface is provided with lateral processes and desmosomes of varying sizes (*Des1—Des2*). The desmosome is a local, buttonlike specialization of the plasma membrane (*Cm*) and the intercellular space (*Is*). When the unit membrane enters the region of a desmosome (asterisk), the dense interfacial component continues unchanged, whereas the cytoplasmic component increases in thickness and density. Cytoplasmic material having a high density and a fibrillar and lamellated appearance is added at the intracellular surface. The intercellular space becomes wider within the region of the desmosome (best seen in upper left picture) and still another thin membrane is interposed. A simpler intercellular arrangement is seen at the arrows where a fusion of the outermost components of the unit membranes has occurred. This corresponds to the arrangement seen within the terminal bar rather than that seen within the desmosome.

Human esophagus. Magnification 111,000×. Ep. UA.

*Bottom Left and Right:*

CELL INVAGINATIONS. Invaginations (*Iv*) of the lateral cell surfaces of adjacent cells (*C1* to *C2*) occur frequently. These invaginations are either small fingerlike projections (left) or are deep elaborate ridges (right), which might lodge an assortment of cell organelles. The plasma membrane (*Cm*) does not show any particular specialization in relation to the invaginations, and neither does the intercellular space. However, this space is wider in relation to the desmosomes (*Des*) and narrower within the zone of the terminal bar (*Tb*). The function of the invaginations may be to secure a firmer intercellular relationship, but in case of elaborate foldings it may reflect a means of increasing the cell surface for exchange purposes.

*Left:* Uterine gland epithelium. Magnification 58,000×. Ep. LH. *Right:* Kidney tubular epithelium. Magnification 25,300×. Ep. LH.

*References:* 115, 363, 367, 715, 846, 900, 1043, 1055, 1456, 1458, 1459, 1508.

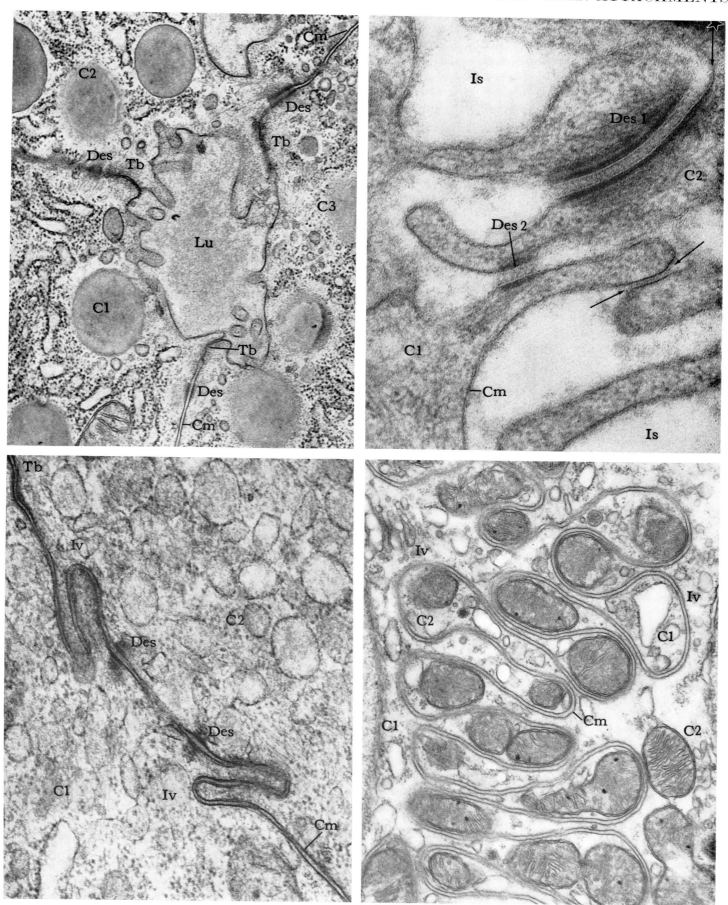

# THE CELL: ENDOPLASMIC RETICULUM AND GOLGI COMPLEX

The cytoplasm contains mainly two kinds of membranous systems, neither of which has any obvious and easily recognizable structural continuity with the plasma membrane. Both systems of membranes are involved in secretory activities, and it seems that the one is related to the other structurally as well as functionally.

*Top:*

ENDOPLASMIC RETICULUM. The most common representative of the endoplasmic reticulum is the so-called rough-surfaced endoplasmic reticulum (*Re*). It consists of sheaths of thin paired membranes, which enclose a narrow central space, the cisterna. The cytoplasmic aspects of the membranes are studded with small particles, the so-called ribonucleoprotein particles (*RNP*) or ribosomes. (For a detailed description of the rough-surfaced endoplasmic reticulum, see page 76.) The number of membranes varies from one cell type to the other. In cells engaged in heavy protein synthesis, such as the exocrine cells of the pancreas (this illustration), the rough-surfaced endoplasmic reticulum dominates the cell and forms a complex of membranes and cisternae throughout the entire cell with the exception of spaces occupied by nuclei (*Nu*) and mitochondria (*Mi*).

Section through bases of exocrine cells of the pancreas. Magnification 7600×. Ep. LH.

*Bottom:*

GOLGI COMPLEX. The Golgi complex is located near the nucleus, usually surrounding one pole like a halo. The appearance of the Golgi complex varies greatly from cell to cell and from tissue to tissue. It is well developed in most secretory cells and is practically absent or quite rudimentary in the cells of stratified squamous epithelia. The Golgi complex consists of a system of paired, smooth-surfaced membranes and small vesicles (*Ve*). Some of the pairs of membranes may become distended to form large vacuoles (*Va*). The number and length of the membranes vary presumably because of a difference in the functional state of the complex. There is good structural evidence that a communication exists between the cisternae (*Ci*) of the rough-surfaced endoplasmic reticulum (*Re*) and the Golgi vesicles (asterisk). Furthermore, the small vesicles are seen to connect with the Golgi vacuoles (arrow). The vacuoles subsequently become filled with a slightly dense material and seem to develop into prezymogen granules (1 to 4), which in turn mature to secretory or zymogen granules (*G*). In contrast to the mitochondria (*Mi*), these granules do not show any peculiar inner structures. It is commonly accepted that the ribosomes (*Ri*) and the endoplasmic reticulum (*Re*) elaborate the precursors of the secretory granules that at a later stage appear within the Golgi area and develop into mature granules.

Exocrine cell of the pancreas. Magnification 32,000×. Ep. LH.

*References:* ENDOPLASMIC RETICULUM  177, 505, 544, 557, 983, 984, 985, 986, 987, 989, 991, 992, 996, 1105, 1107, 1114, 1117, 1354b.

GOLGI COMPLEX  32, 33, 34, 220, 223, 224, 226, 227, 253, 453, 454, 481, 482, 504, 508, 718, 822, 1065, 1069, 1100, 1354a, 1354c, 1426, 1584.

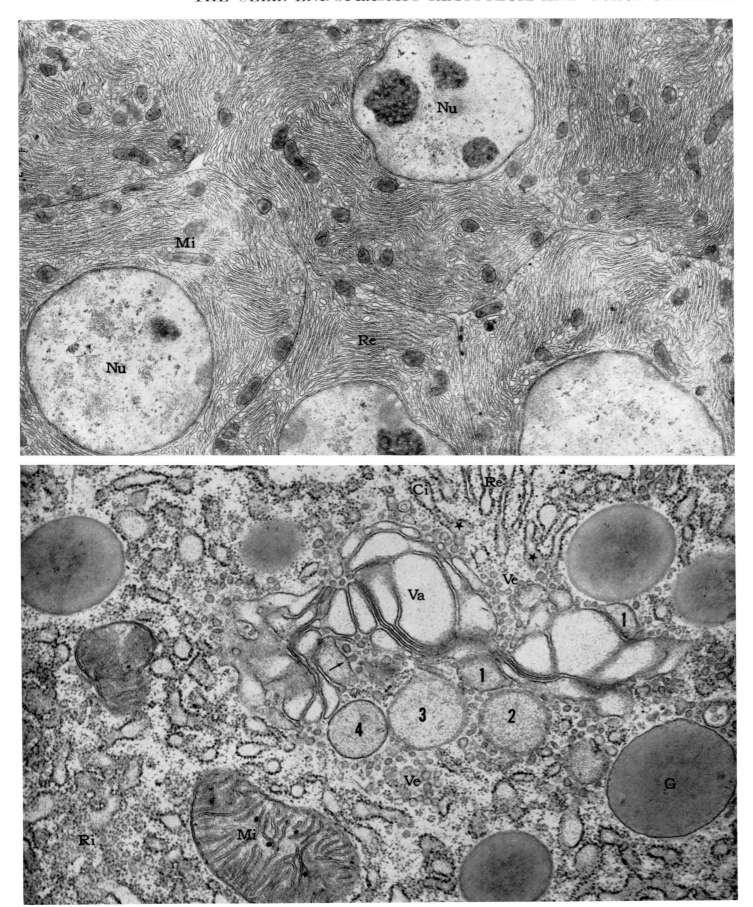

The mitochondria are discrete bodies within the cell. They may vary in number, size, and shape, but their ultrastructure is sufficiently peculiar to make the mitochondria stand out clearly against other cell organelles. Some of the most typical mitochondria in a series of different cell types have been selected in order to demonstrate the slight variation in ultrastructure.

*Top Left:*

KIDNEY TUBULAR CELL. Kidney mitochondria are usually oval or elongated. Each mitochondrion is surrounded by a triple-layered membrane ($Om$), and the interior is traversed by inner membranes ($Im$), plates, or cristae, which also show the triple layering. The light membranous layer of the outer membrane, sandwiched between two dense layers, occasionally is connected with the same layer of the inner membrane (asterisk). The mitochondrion contains a finely granular matrix ($M$) in which intensely dense granules ($D$) of varying sizes are located. The mitochondria are the carriers of most cellular oxidative enzymes, and it is believed that the membranous structures of their interior represent either the enzymes proper or the surfaces upon which the enzymes and the metabolites interact.
Magnification 90,000×. Ep. LH.

*Top Right:*

LIVER PARENCHYMAL CELL. The mitochondria of the liver cells are irregularly shaped, and the inner membranes rarely are seen to reach across the entire mitochondrial matrix in a longitudinal section ($Le$) of the mitochondrion. A cross-sectioned mitochondrion ($Cr$) may not look as if it contained any inner membranes at all because of the plane of section that passes through the mitochondrial matrix between two cristae.
Magnification 34,000×. Ep. LH.

*Bottom Left:*

GALLBLADDER EPITHELIUM. The inner membranes of these mitochondria follow irregular courses, and they seem to make frequent interconnections throughout the mitochondrial matrix. They also establish connections with the outer membrane (asterisk). At the lower end of the mitochondrion, the outer membrane seems to be missing. However, the membrane has been sectioned obliquely and therefore does not stand out sharply.
Magnification 81,000×. Ep. LH.

*Bottom Right:*

OVARIAN THECA LUTEIN CELL. The mitochondria of most endocrine cells show a marked difference in the organization of their inner structure. It seems that most mitochondrial membranes have acquired a tubular shape, since mitochondria may be seen where the tubules are either cross sectioned ($Cr$) or longitudinally sectioned ($Le$). The tubules seem to be arranged circularly ($Cir$). The mitochondrial envelope is clearly triple layered, but rarely does one come across the point of connection between the outer membrane and the inner tubules.
Magnification 49,000×. Ep. LH.

*References:* 46, 161, 171, 228, 250, 419, 422, 447, 486, 489, 590, 765, 766, 794, 925, 930, 932, 937, 980, 981, 990, 1121, 1145, 1238, 1331, 1344, 1354b, 1492, 1493, 1517.

Page 10

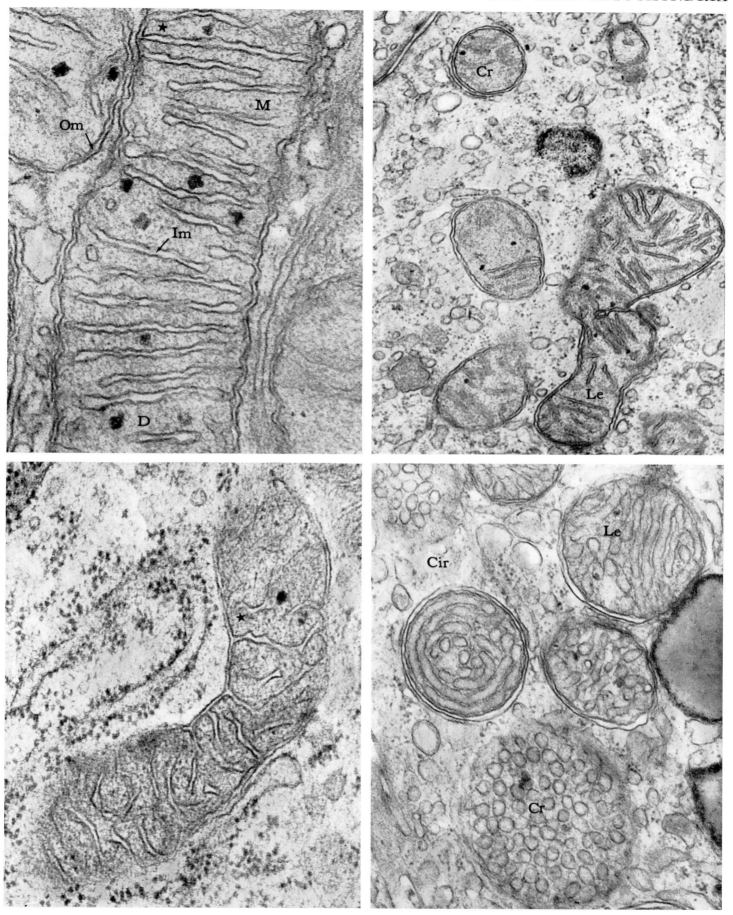

The cytoplasm usually contains a variety of organelles or inclusion bodies, some of which are more clearly defined and easier to identify than others. Some of the more prominent examples have been selected here, but it should be kept in mind that the origin of some of these inclusions and their functional role in the cell metabolism are only vaguely understood at the moment.

*Top Left:*

MICROBODIES ($Mb$). These are small oval bodies that are surrounded by a single thin membrane in contrast with the nearby triple-layered mitochondrial ($Mi$) outer membrane. The microbody lacks inner membranes but usually displays a matrix of medium density in which more intensely stained areas can be encountered. The origin of the microbody is unknown, but it may develop from projections of the smooth-surfaced endoplasmic reticulum ($Sm$) or from vesicular structures containing an accumulation of dense material ($X$). The typical microbody has been identified only in cells of the liver, kidney, and adrenal cortex. Other nearby structures are ribosomes ($Ri$) and peribiliary granules ($Ft$), which seem to contain an accumulation of ferritin particles.

Liver cell. Magnification 46,000×. Ep. LH.

*Top Right:*

LYSOSOMES ($Ly$). Bodies having a highly pleomorphic appearance with large or small, dense granules ($Ly\ 1$) and short, irregular or long, concentrically arranged membranes ($Ly\ 2$) are usually referred to as lysosomes. They do not show the orderly, fine structure of nearby mitochondria ($Mi$). Similar bodies were first isolated from fractionated liver cells, and a biochemical analysis of the lysosome fraction disclosed a high content of several hydrolytic enzymes. Structurally, this kind of inclusion body can be identified in almost any kind of cell. Cells with phagocytizing functions, such as macrophages, are particularly rich in lysosomes. The lysosomes undoubtedly represent sites in the cell where a breakdown of materials occurs, whether this material is phagocytized or takes its origin from within the cell itself.

Kupffer cell in liver sinusoid. Magnification 46,000×. Ep. LH.

*Bottom Left:*

LIPID GRANULES. These are easily identifiable because of their high electron density ($Li$), large size, and irregular outlines. They are extremely numerous in the endocrine cells of the adrenal cortex and in the lutein cells of the ovary. The lipid granules of liver and pancreatic cells often have a close relationship to neighboring mitochondria (arrows), and this relationship has been interpreted as the structural evidence for enzymatic interaction between the mitochondrion ($Mi$) and the lipid.

Liver cell. Magnification 46,000×. Ep. LH.

*Bottom Right:*

GLYCOGEN GRANULES. The glycogen granules ($Gl$) are easily identified after staining with lead, for instance. Their diameter is slightly larger than that of the nearby ribosomes ($Ri$) and averages 200A. The glycogen granules usually occur in clusters and stain more intensely than the ribosomes. Other nearby structures are mitochondria ($Mi$) and a small microbody ($Mb$).

Liver cell. Magnification 30,000×. Ep. LH.

*References:* MICROBODIES 186, 1145, 1235.
LYSOSOMES 71, 186, 243, 244, 337, 340, 868, 926, 1171, 1172, 1173.
LIPID GRANULES 338, 856, 1564.
GLYCOGEN 145, 281, 282, 667, 1144, 1419, 1420.

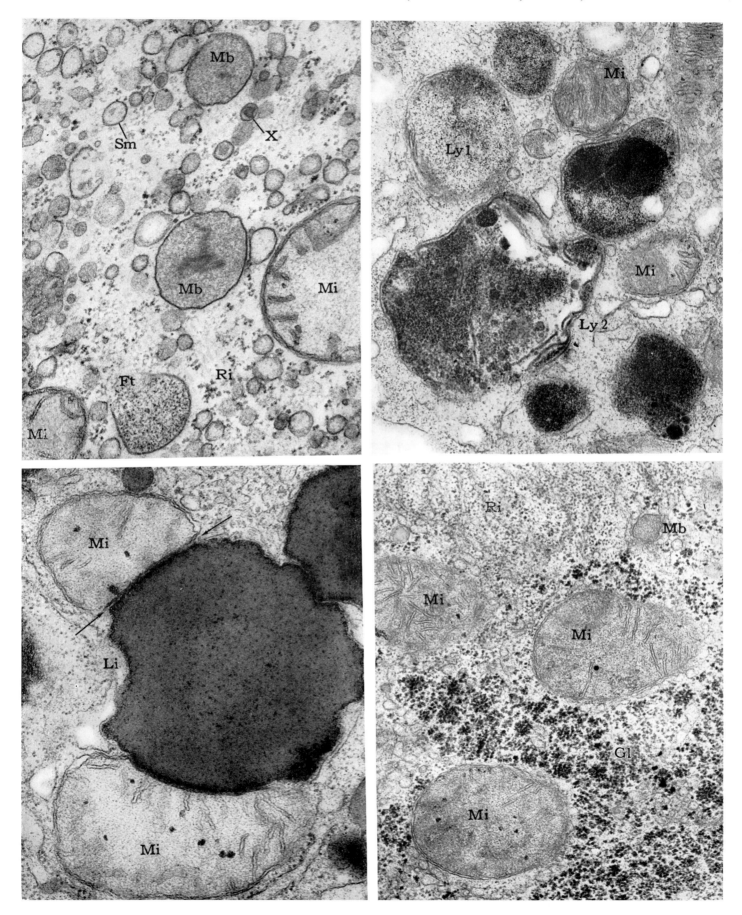

*Top Left
and Right:*

THE NUCLEUS. The shape and size of the nucleus vary from one cell type to the other, but the nucleoplasm (*Npl*) is invariably enveloped by a triple-layered membrane (*NuM*). The three components of the nuclear membrane have a different arrangement from, for instance, the triple-layered membrane of the mitochondrial envelope. The outermost layer of the nuclear membrane seems to have more of a cytoplasmic component, since ribosomes (*Ri*) occasionally are attached to the cytoplasmic aspect (*Cyto*) of the membrane. The innermost layer of the nuclear membrane is smooth. A less dense layer is sandwiched between the two dense ones. In sections that are perfectly perpendicular to the nuclear membrane (left), the inner and outer components are seen to fuse and to form a single layer for a short distance (*Fe*). In sections that are tangential to the nuclear membrane (right), the fusions are identified as rings (*Fe*), most of which have a central knob (*Kn*). These structures are usually referred to as nuclear pores, but since they are actually fenestrations in the nuclear envelope that are closed by a diaphragm, it is more likely that they are not merely openings but are regions of the nuclear membrane with special function.

*Top Left:* Dust cell lung tissue. Magnification 54,000×. Ep. LH. *Top Right:* Spermatocyte. Magnification 45,000×. Ep. LH.

*Bottom Left:*

THE NUCLEOLUS. The nucleoplasm has a finely granular structure of medium density except in the nucleolus, which is characterized by high density. The nucleolus has an irregular or spherical shape and seems to consist of a meshwork of threads or dense material, called a nucleolonema (*Nem*). Some areas of the nucleolus show a more distinct and coarser granularity than the rest (*Chr*) and represent chromatin. Similar aggregations of granules can also be identified elsewhere in small islands throughout the nucleoplasm.

Oocyte. Magnification 15,000×. Ep. LH.

*Bottom Right:*

THE CENTROSOME. Each cell has a centrosome consisting of two bodies, the centrioles, which are located near each other. Each centriole has a fine structure similar to the basal corpuscle of a cilium. The centriole, therefore, is composed of filaments—usually nine groups of three each, arranged in a circle. The long axis of one centriole is always perpendicular to that of its counterpart in a centrosome. The centrosome of a spermatid (this illustration) has been selected to demonstrate the various details. In one of the centrioles, the groups of three filaments are cross sectioned (*FiC*), whereas in the other centriole, they have been sectioned longitudinally (*Fil*). In this particular instance, one of the centrioles serves as point of origin (asterisks) for the outgrowing tail (*Ta*) of the maturing spermatid.

Spermatid. Magnification 89,000×. Ep. LH.

*References:* NUCLEUS 2, 12, 36, 49, 54, 57, 72, 183, 377, 436, 437, 457, 458, 465, 509, 673, 815, 839, 849, 850, 891, 892, 967, 1016, 1017, 1070, 1112, 1402, 1403, 1404, 1481, 1483, 1486, 1488, 1520, 1529.
NUCLEOLUS 79, 100, 234, 607, 611, 1388, 1572.
CENTROSOME 1, 7, 545, 1553.

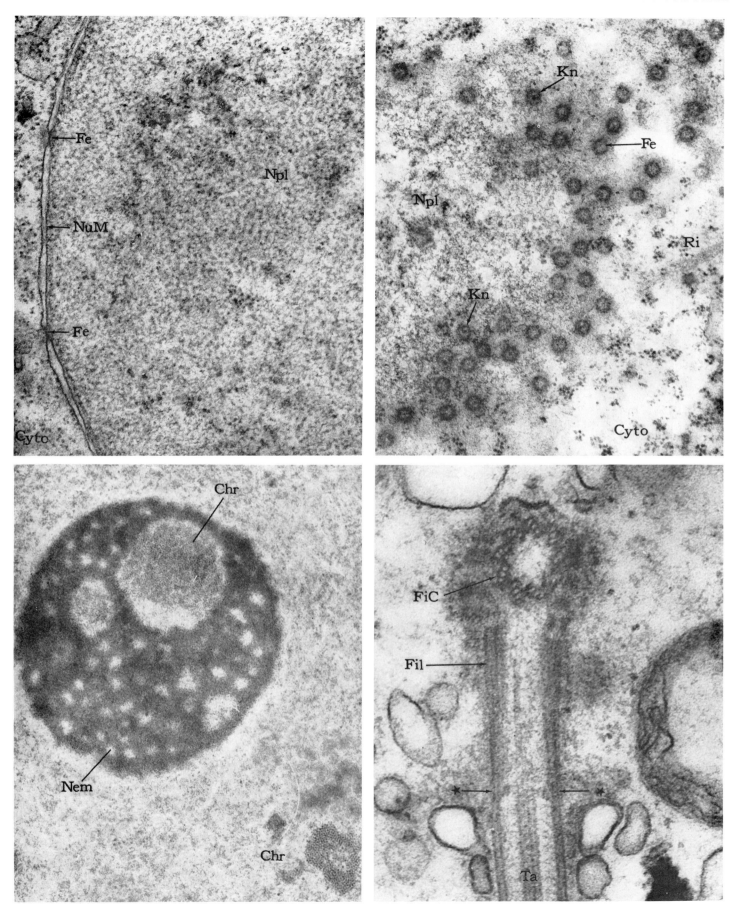

*Top:*

Connective tissue, whether of the areolar (loose) or fibrous (dense) type, is composed mainly of fibroblasts (*Fib*) and collagenous fibrils (*Co*). The fibroblasts are elongated cells with extremely long and finely branched cell processes. Depending on the location, the fibroblasts may be arranged in an orderly fashion, as, for instance, in the tendons or in the corneal stroma, or they may be less regularly arranged, as in the *submucosa of the urinary bladder* (this illustration). The collagenous fibrils are grouped in bundles, which run in various directions and thus appear to be sectioned either across (*Cr*) or lengthwise (*Le*). Occasional unmyelinated nerves (*Ne*) are present.

Urinary bladder. Magnification 8000×. Ep. LH.

*Bottom Left:*

Detail of fibroblasts in the submucosa of the urinary bladder. The largest diameter of the cell is at the nucleus (*Nu*). The cytoplasm of active fibroblasts is rich in rough-surfaced endoplasmic reticulum (*Re*) and free ribosomes (*Ri*). Mitochondria (*Mi*) and lysosomes (*Ly*) are common components of the fibroblast. The prominence of ergastoplasm (*Re* and *Ri*) is clearly evidence for the secretory function of the fibroblast. How and where the secretory precursors are formed is not clear, but the cisternae of the endoplasmic reticulum are probable sites. The secretory product itself appears extracellularly—here represented by the collagen fibrils (*Co*). Pinocytotic vesicles (*Pi*) indicate an active exchange of fluid and substances between the cell and its environment.

Urinary bladder. Magnification 20,000×. Ep. LH.

*Bottom Right:*

Detail of collagen fibrils in the sclera of the eye. The fibrils that are sectioned longitudinally (*Le*) show periodic cross-bandings, which repeat at intervals of about 700A in the mature fibrils. The individual bands have been interpreted as a reflection of the sequence of amino acid units along the parallel chains of collagen molecules. The thin bands are spaced differently but are repeated with great uniformity. The repetition of bandings is inverted in some fibrils (arrows), and this may indicate the source of the great strength of the collagen fiber. The cross-sectioned (*Cr*) fibrils do not show any easily discernible structural pattern.

Sclera. Magnification 150,000×. Ep. UA.

*References:* 62, 163, 164, 241, 391, 405, 406, 495, 496, 648, 649, 682, 796, 847, 911, 968, 971, 1032, 1033, 1118, 1128, 1163, 1227, 1228, 1270, 1286, 1289, 1477, 1478, 1538, 1540, 1541.

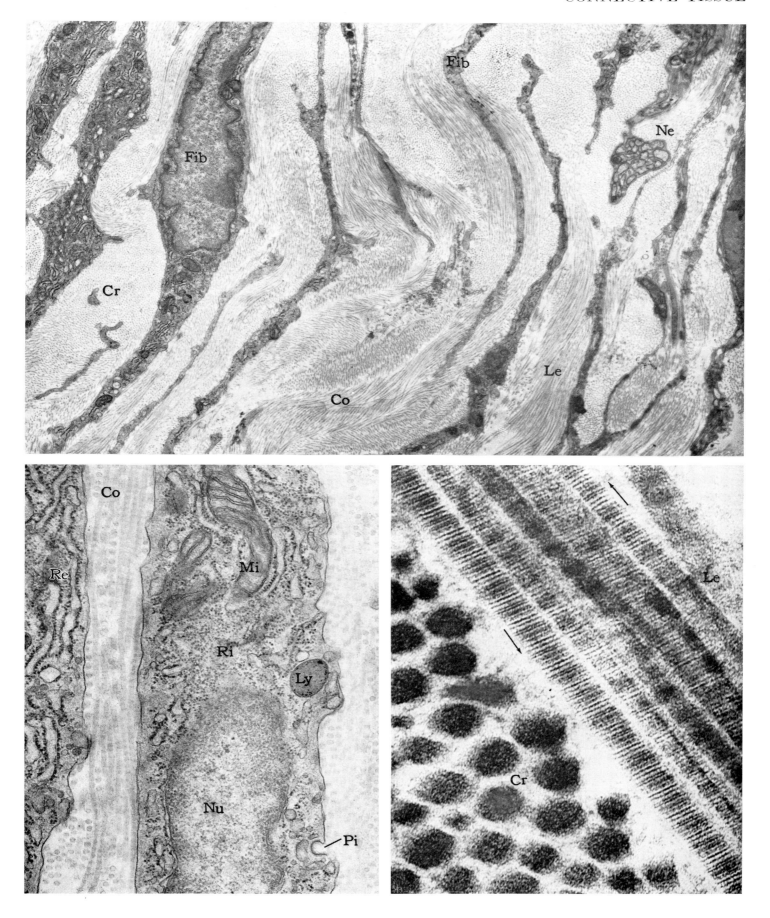

*Top:*    Cartilage consists of irregularly shaped cells, the chondrocytes, and an interstitial substance (*Is*). The chondrocyte has a fairly large nucleus (*Nu*) and numerous small surface processes projecting into a clear space, the lacuna (*Lac*), which surrounds the chondrocyte. The chondrocytes are isolated from each other by the intercellular substance, but several cells may be located in the same lacuna. This group is then referred to as a cell nest (*Nest*). The cytoplasm of the chondrocyte has clear spaces, which are accumulations of glycogen (*Gl*). The intercellular substance (*Is*) is composed of a meshwork of reticular and fine collagenous fibrils.

Epiphyseal cartilage of developing bone in the femur of a mouse embryo.
Magnification 3500×. Ep. UA.

*Bottom Left:*    The cytoplasm of the chondrocyte is rich in rough-surfaced endoplasmic reticulum (*Re*) and ribosomes. It has a fairly large Golgi complex (*Go*), some mitochondria (*Mi*), and lipid droplets (*Li*). After staining with lead salts, the glycogen (*Gl*) stands out as dense accumulations of coarse granules. The intercellular substance is finely fibrillar (*Is*). The nucleus (*Nu*) occupies the major part of the cell.

Hyaline cartilage of a tracheal ring. Magnification 9500×. Ep. LH.

*Bottom Right:*    The intercellular substance (*Is*) of the hyaline cartilage is composed of extremely fine reticular filaments. The fibrillar network is coarser within the lacunae (*Lac*) close to the surface processes of the chondrocytes (*Ch*). The territorial peripheries of two adjoining chondrocytes are seen at the asterisks.

Hyaline cartilage. Trachea. Magnification 45,000×. Ep. UA.

*References:*    9, 142, 473, 700, 701, 702, 829, 1319, 1321, 1322, 1332, 1409, 1586.

Page 18

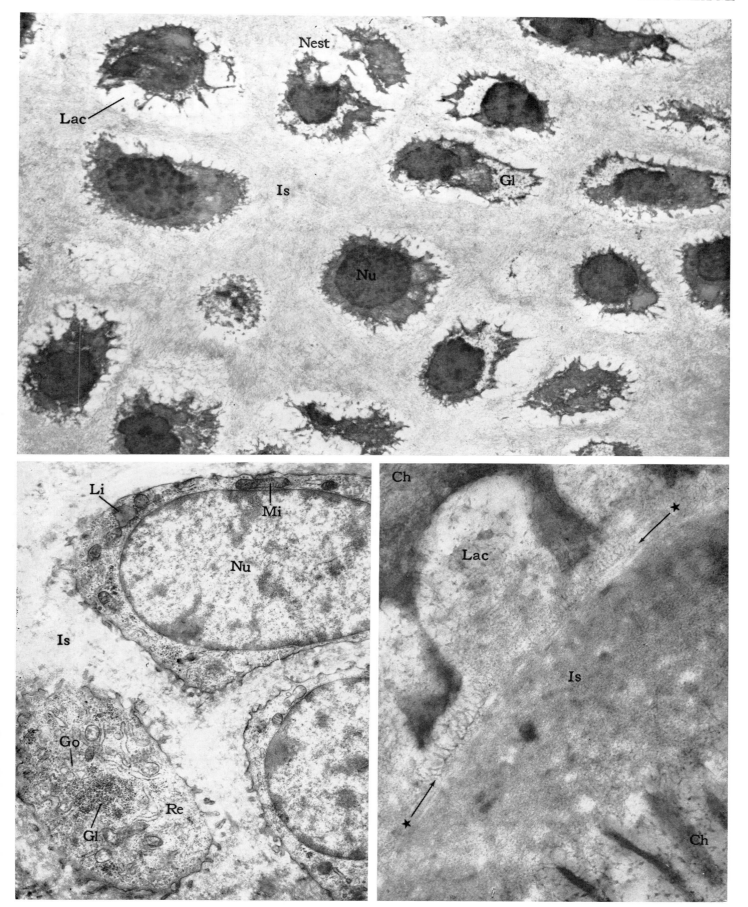

*Top:* The developing bone tissue consists of osteoblasts, an intercellular matrix (*Is*) with numerous fine collagenous fibrils (*Co*), and the mineralized bone matrix (*Cal*). The osteoblast with its nucleus (*Nu*) displays a well-developed, rough-surfaced endoplasmic reticulum (*Re*) with dilated cisternae (*Ci*) and a substance of medium density. The Golgi area (*Go*) is fairly large, and a relatively small number of mitochondria (*Mi*) are located in the cytoplasm. The plasma membrane (*Cm*) borders on the intercellular space (*Is*) in which numerous fine collagenous fibrils (*Co*) can be seen. As the mineralization (*Cal*) proceeds, progressively more of the collagen becomes obscured.

Distal end of the tibia of the newborn mouse. Magnification 16,000×. Ep. LH.

*Bottom Left:* The calcification continues until the osteoblast is completely surrounded by mineralized matrix (*Cal*), at which point the cell usually is referred to as an osteocyte. The nucleus (*Nu*) and the rough-surfaced endoplasmic reticulum (*Re*) of the osteocyte can still be seen, but the intercellular space (not occupied by calcium crystals) has decreased to a narrow zone around the cell, the lacuna (*Lac*), and small channels, the canaliculi (*Can*), which interconnect the lacunae.

Tibia of the newborn mouse. Magnification 10,000×. Ep. LH.

*Bottom Right:* This section shows at higher magnification the early stage of calcification of the bone matrix. The cisternae (*Ci*) of the rough-surfaced endoplasmic reticulum with the attached ribosomes (*Ri*) may elaborate precursors to the bone matrix, which become liberated (*Lib*) at the cell surface (*Cm*) and give rise to the collagen fibrils (*Co*). The next step is the appearance of small areas of high electron density that contain small needlelike crystals, most probably representing the apatite crystals (*Cal*). In fully calcified bone, these crystals are parallel with and located in the collagen fibrils.

Tibia of the newborn mouse. Magnification 82,000×. Ep. UA. LA.

*References:* 144, 283, 407, 408, 409, 410, 417, 477, 532, 699, 702, 816, 828, 1122, 1196, 1197, 1198, 1199, 1200, 1320, 1323, 1324, 1491, 1524.

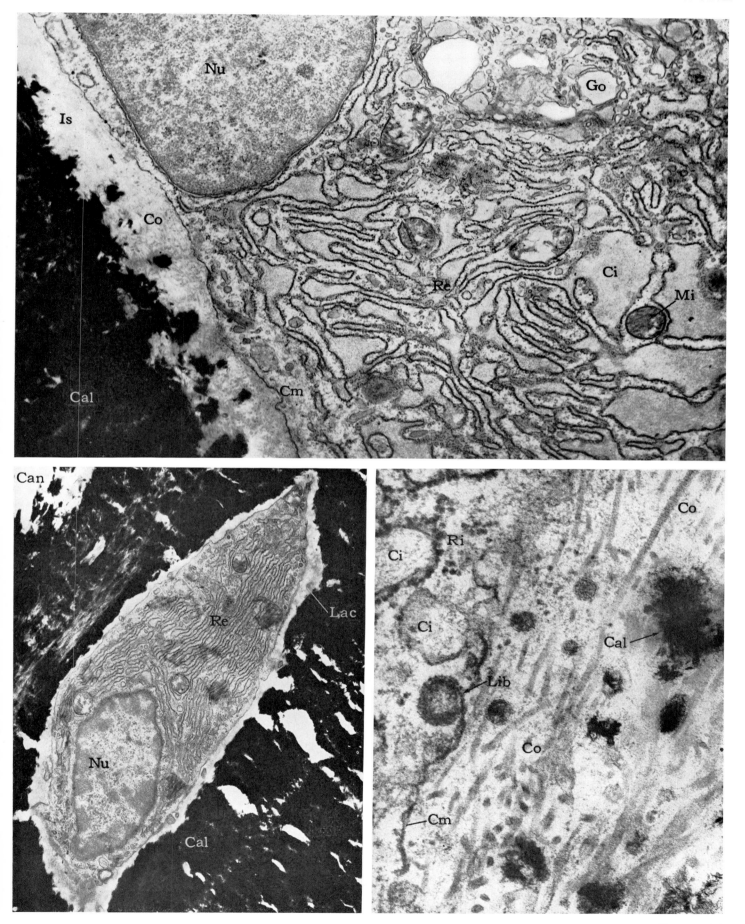

*Top:*  Sagittal section of a developing lower molar tooth in the human embryo at about the fourth month, showing the uppermost portion of the developing decidual tooth at the late "bell" stage. The ameloblasts (*Am*) have started to elongate and the nuclei are beginning to line up along the basal (proximal) end of the cell, which borders on the stratum intermedium (*StI*). The distal end of the ameloblasts contains dense aggregates in the cytoplasm, and wide, clear intercellular spaces appear. The layer of odontoblasts (*Ob*) is rather undifferentiated, but the nuclei of the odontoblasts have a tendency to withdraw from the future line of junction (*DeJ*) between the enamel and the dentin of the adult tooth. The relatively light zone on the odontoblastic side of the junction is traversed by numerous fine cell processes emanating from the odontoblasts (*Ob*). The cells of the stratum intermedium (*StI*) are polyhedral, while the cells of the stellate reticulum (*StR*) in the enamel pulp are small and are provided with long, branching processes. A similar structural appearance characterizes the mesothelial cells of the dental pulp (*Dp*).

Human embryo. Molar tooth. Magnification 3000×. Ep. UA.

*Bottom Left:*  Detail of an area similar to the one indicated by the square in the top picture, showing the dentinoenamel junction of the developing human molar tooth. The thin processes of the odontoblasts (*Ob*) and the distal ends of the ameloblasts (*Am*) are separated by a thin basement membrane (*Bm*). Fine collagenous (*Co*) fibrils, which occur between the odontoblasts, attach at the basement membrane. The distal ends of the ameloblasts (*Am*) contain mitochondria (*Mi*) and dense secretory granules (*G*). In addition, a coarse granulation characterizes the cytoplasm. Some of this seems to represent ribosomes, but it cannot be excluded that the cytoplasm also contains glycogen particles. Similar particles (*Stm*) are deposited in the intercellular space (*Is*) where they form the precursor of the enamel matrix.

Human embryo. Molar tooth. Magnification 20,000×. Ep. LA.

*Bottom Right:*  Area similar to that in the picture at the left from the developing lower molar tooth of a newborn mouse. The basement membrane of the dentinoenamel junction (*DeJ*) is obscured by the heavy mineralization. This is most pronounced in the predentin (*P*), which is almost completely calcified, whereas the matrix of the enamel (*E*) displays a different degree of calcification characterized by long, dense profiles of inorganic material.

Newborn mouse. Molar tooth. Magnification 20,000×. Ep. LA.

*References:* 24, 372, 642, 768, 787, 857, 878, 934, 1011, 1013, 1015, 1059, 1125, 1126, 1138, 1139, 1140, 1141, 1213, 1214, 1215, 1239, 1274, 1296, 1297, 1298, 1299, 1327, 1334, 1368, 1406, 1487, 1490, 1571

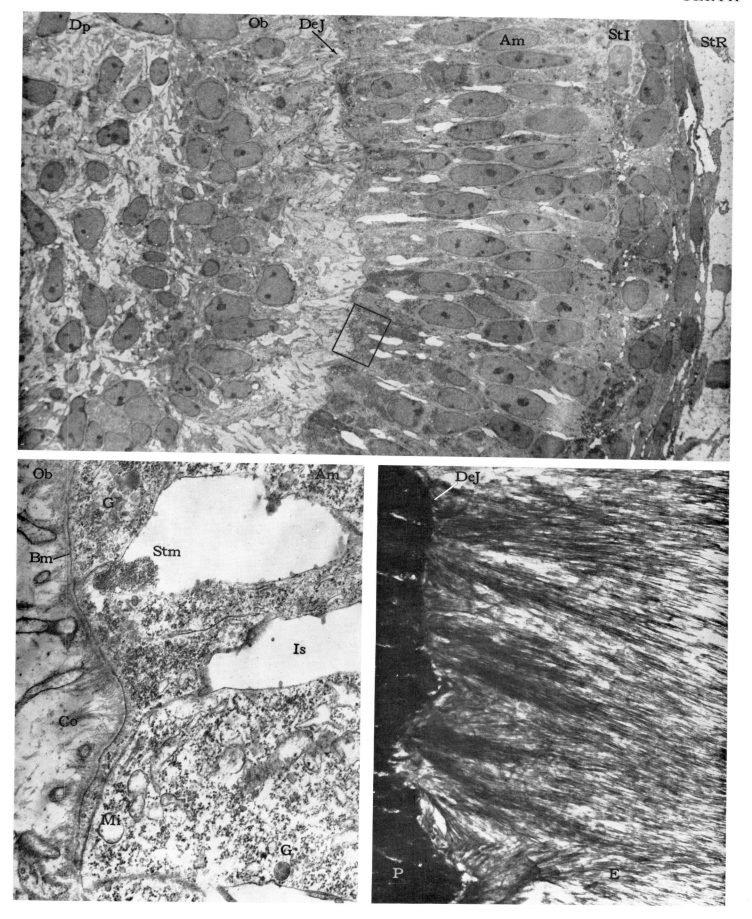

*Top:*

Smooth muscle cells have an elongated, spindlelike shape with a centrally located nucleus (*Nu*). The cells are densely packed and can be studied quite advantageously in sections of the relaxed intestine (this illustration) that contain the peripheral longitudinal muscle layer (cross sectioned) and the inner circular layer (sectioned lengthwise). Capillaries (*Ca*) and cells (*Ne*) that accompany unmyelinated nerves are often present between the muscle layers.

Small intestine. Magnification 1200×. Ep. UA.

*Bottom Left:*

Detail of three longitudinally sectioned, intestinal smooth muscle cells (1 to 3). Near the nucleus (*Nu*) are located mitochondria (*Mi*) and a small Golgi complex (*Go*). The plasma membrane runs uninterrupted and smooth for distances of several microns, but it can also be seen to dip into shallow pockets, pinocytotic vesicles (between 1 and 2). The intercellular space (*Is*) is narrow and is almost completely filled by the thin basement membrane, which coats each smooth muscle cell. The intercellular space is bridged here and there by short cell processes that establish lateral connections (*Lc*) between cells (2 and 3).

Small intestine. Magnification 25,000×. Ep. LH.

*Bottom Right:*

Detail of cross-sectioned smooth muscle cells in the vas deferens. Myofibrils are not easily demonstrated in smooth muscle cells. In low-magnification illustrations (top), the striations seen are cell boundaries, and inside the cell body only a general longitudinal orientation of cellular components is seen. High magnification shows filaments that seem to have at least two dimensions. The coarse filaments have an angular shape and a mean diameter of about 100A, whereas the fine filaments with an average diameter of about 40A seem to be concentrated in small, dense, oblong areas (fusiform densities) but can also be found between the coarse filaments.

Unmyelinated nerves (*Ne*) appear between the muscle cells and are also seen to penetrate individual cells as the nerve ending is approached. The intercellular space (*Is*) is occupied by basement membrane-like material.

Vas deferens. Magnification 40,000×. Ep. UA.

*References:* 76, 135, 139, 311, 440, 442, 444, 445, 446, 534, 535, 536, 548, 647, 827, 1034, 1124, 1159, 1170, 1264, 1326, 1417, 1565, 1566.

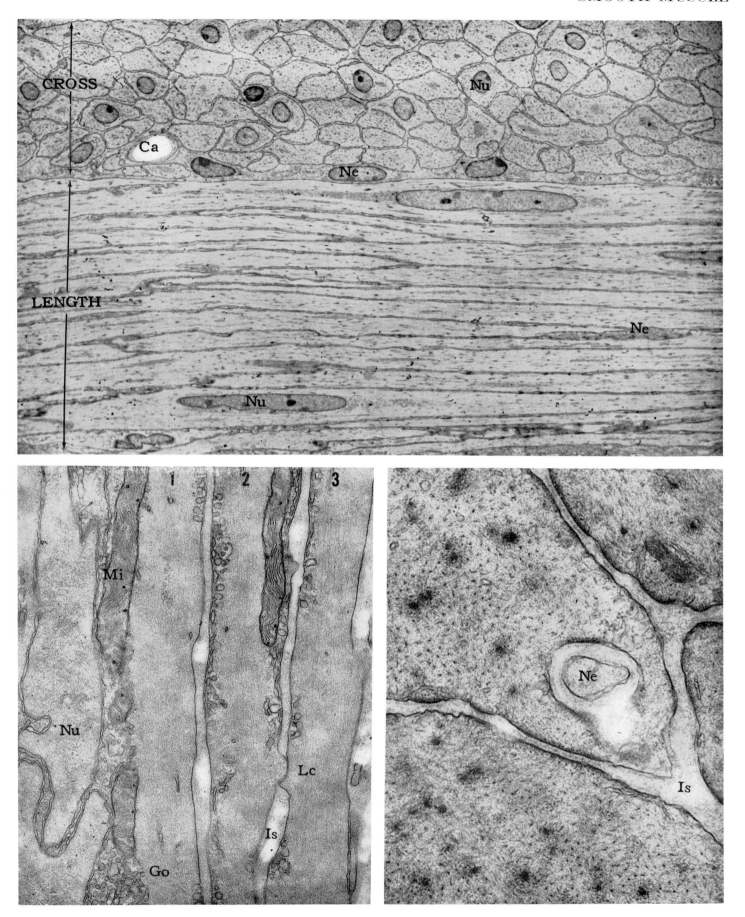

The striated skeletal muscle cell is an extremely long cell with several nuclei (*Nu*), usually located at the cell surface. The end of the cell tapers off gradually and is anchored to an adjacent cell by means of collagen fibrils (*Co*). Most of the cell volume is occupied by the contractile elements of the cytoplasm, the myofibrils, which are composed of small subunits, the myofilaments. The myofibrils display a regular cross banding, which can be seen in both relaxed and contracted muscle cells. Although the myofibrils are separate threadlike units, the cross banding of one myofibril appears at approximately the same level as that of an adjacent myofibril in the relaxed state; this gives a striated appearance to the entire muscle cell.

Generally, there are two kinds of bands. The dense ones are called A-bands and the light ones, I-bands. Moreover, each dense A-band has a light, central H-zone, and the light, I-band centrally displays a distinct dark line, the Z-membrane. A sarcomere extends from one Z-membrane to another. When contraction takes place, it is mostly the light A-bands that are involved and one can see (at the far right) that they have almost disappeared. When counting the number of Z-membranes present within the same distance in a relaxed (left) and in a contracted (right) muscle fiber (indicated by the numbered scales), one concludes that the right fiber has contracted to about half the length of the left one. Closer examination reveals that the A-bands have also decreased slightly in length although considerably less than the I-bands.

Skeletal muscle of the leg. Magnification 2800×. *Left:* Ep. UA. *Right:* Meth. unstained.

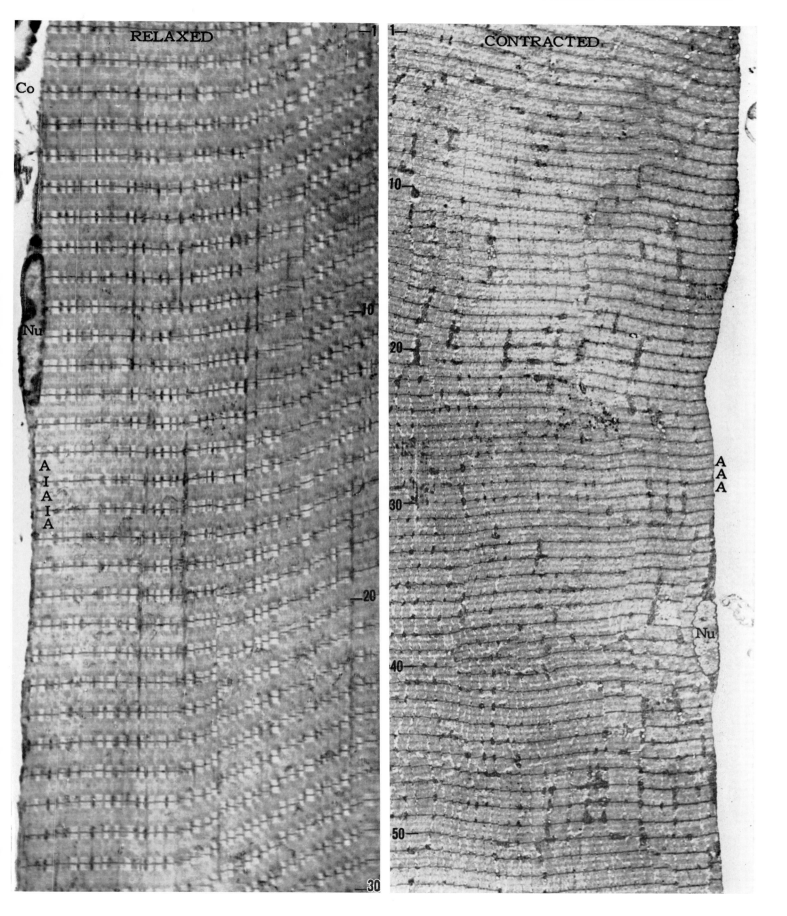

*Top:*    Detail of a longitudinally sectioned striated muscle of the thigh. The myofibrils run from left to right. The Z-membranes (*z*) are prominent in the middle of the I-bands (*I*). The light H-zone within the A-band is not clearly seen, but the faintly dense M-stripe (*M*) can be resolved. Still another fine line, the N-line (*N*), can be recognized on either side of the Z-membrane. A sarcomere (*Sa*) extends from one Z-membrane to the next.

The distribution of small mitochondria (*Mi*) is quite extensive throughout the muscle fiber, and particular attention should be paid to their location at the Z-membranes. Lipid inclusions (*Li*) occur frequently.

Thigh muscle. Magnification 8000×. Ep. UA.

*Bottom:*    Cross section of a striated muscle through the A-bands. This section indicates the extent to which elements of the specific muscular smooth-surfaced endoplasmic reticulum, the sarcotubules (*Tu*), form a continuous system around and between individual myofibrils (*Mf*). It is believed, although not fully proved, that the sarcotubules are derived from, and even may represent, intracellular tubular invaginations of the plasma membrane. Around the nucleus (*Nu*) is a small portion of the cytoplasm, devoid of myofilaments, in which a few small mitochondria (*Mi*) are located. The muscle cell is surrounded by the sarcolemma (*Sr*), which is composed of the plasma membrane and a thin basement membrane.

Thigh muscle. Magnification 20,000×. Ep. LA.

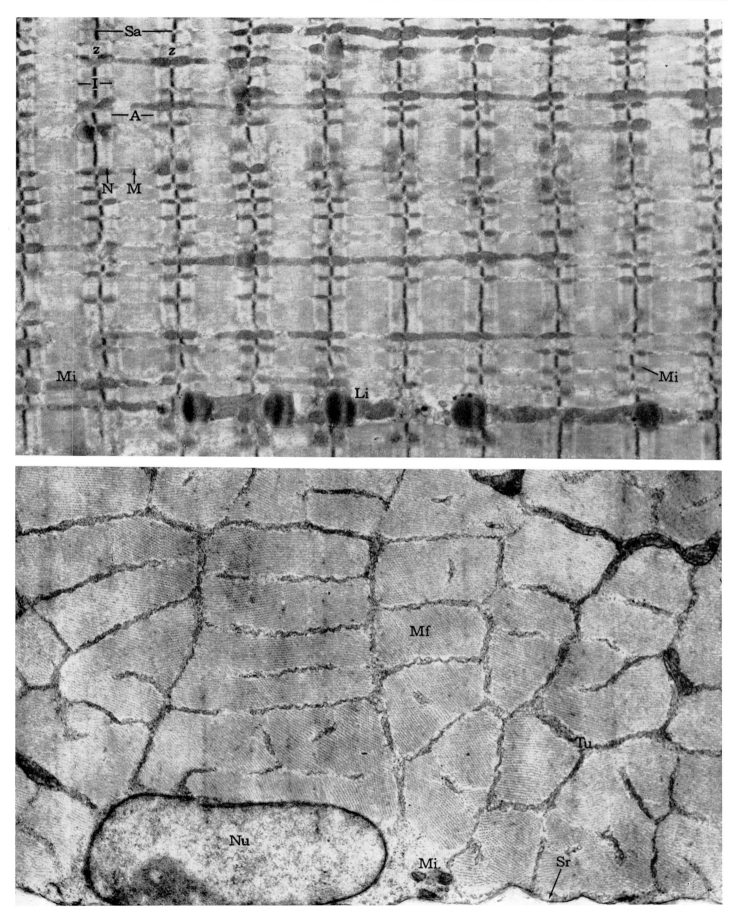

*Top Left:*    Detail of longitudinally sectioned myofibrils. The myofilaments vary in thickness and mutual arrangement within the different zones of the sarcomere. Some filaments display an increased thickness within the M-stripe (*M*), and there appears to be a splitting or lateral junction of the filaments at the level of the Z-membrane (*Z*) and the N-line (*N*). Fine filaments (one asterisk) and coarse filaments (two asterisks) are seen side by side at the level of the H-zone. Mitochondria (*Mi*) and sarcotubules (*Tu*) are located between the fibrils.

Thigh muscle. Magnification 53,000×. Ep. UA.

*Top Right:*    Detail of cross-sectioned myofibrils, indicating that two sets of myofilaments are clearly present in a striated muscle (circle). The fine filaments average 50A, and the coarse ones about 100A, in diameter. The close apposition of sarcotubules (*Tu*) and myofilaments is evident. It has been assumed that the sarcotubules may facilitate the inward spread of muscular excitation.

Thigh muscle. Magnification 57,000×. Ep. LH.

*Bottom:*    Detail of a *motor end plate*, showing the junction between a motor nerve ending and the striated muscle. The cytoplasm of the nerve ending (*Ne*) contains several mitochondria (*Mi*) and small synaptic vesicles (*Ve*). The axoplasm is bordered by a membrane, usually referred to as the presynaptic membrane (*Psm*). Corresponding to the insertion of the nerve ending, the plasma membrane of the muscle cell, called the postsynaptic membrane (*Ssm*), displays a complex system of narrow, longitudinal infoldings, the so-called junctional folds (*Jf*). The intercellular space or synaptic cleft (*Is*) is occupied by an amorphous substance, which is structurally identical with the basement membrane that forms one component of the sarcolemma. The sarcoplasm contains numerous vesicles (*Ve*) near the junctional folds.

Thigh muscle. Magnification 33,000×. Ep. LA.

*References:*    MUSCLE   10, 17, 53, 70, 73, 108, 109, 146, 292, 370, 459, 470, 476, 533, 587, 588, 589, 613, 618, 619, 620, 621, 622, 697, 698, 708, 832, 835, 836, 889, 906, 1045, 1110, 1113, 1143, 1183, 1243, 1245, 1294, 1351, 1352, 1362, 1375, 1387, 1451.

NEUROMUSCULAR JUNCTION   16, 52, 212, 213, 289, 291, 498, 546, 547, 767, 819, 852, 1130, 1131, 1132, 1133, 1181, 1182, 1191, 1578, 1579, 1580.

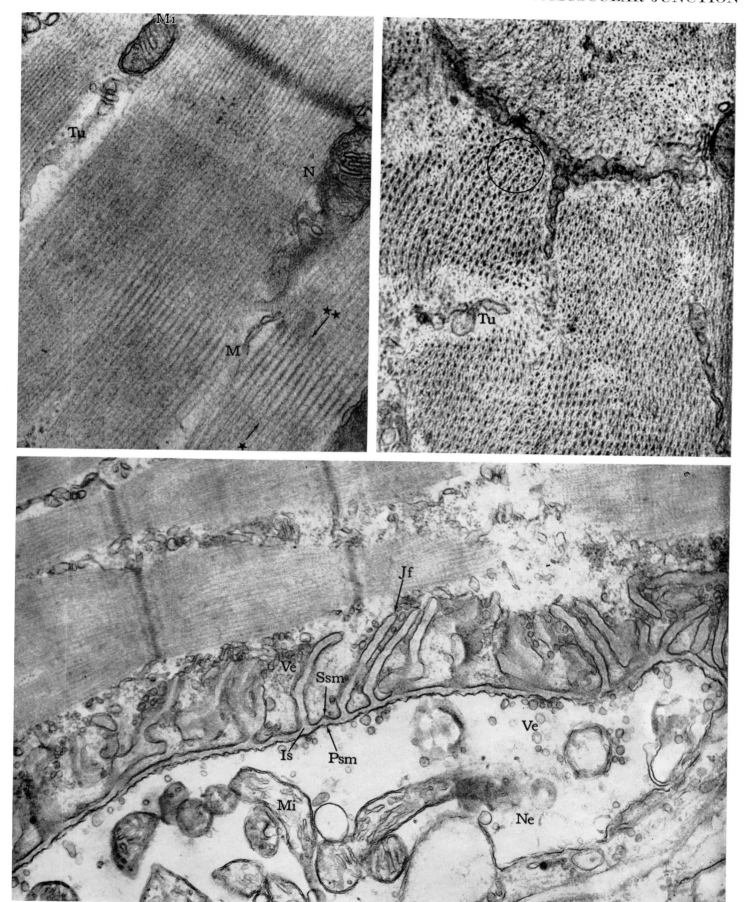

*Top:*

Longitudinally sectioned cardiac muscle cells (*2 to 6*) from the ventricular septum of the steer heart. The cardiac muscle cell is striated, but several features distinguish it from striated skeletal muscle. The cardiac cell is smaller and contains usually one (rarely two) nuclei (*Nu*) located centrally; the surrounding cytoplasm is filled with mitochondria. Furthermore, these cells show an abundant branching, which is indicated (in this illustration) in a few instances by arrows in relation to the numbers (*4* and *6*). The branches meet similar processes of adjacent cells in an end-to-end fashion, and the junction is called the intercalated disk (*Id*). Capillaries (*Ca*) occur frequently between the muscle fibers.

Steer heart. Ventricular septum. Magnification 2000×. Ep. UA.

*Bottom Left:*

Detail of the junction between cells *2* and *3* in the top picture. There is often a steplike arrangement of the intercalated disks (*Id*), probably because of a variation in the degree of contraction of the various myofibrils. The intercellular space (*Is*) is narrow and is occupied by numerous collagen fibrils. It should be noticed that the intercalated disk always replaces one Z-membrane (*Z*) within the individual myofibril. The fine structure of the myofibril coincides with that of the striated skeletal fibers. The mitochondria are, however, less abundant in the cardiac muscle cell, although they may be larger and of a definite spherical shape. The sarcotubular system is well developed but not prominent in these illustrations.

Steer heart. Ventricular septum. Magnification 10,000×. Ep. UA.

*Bottom Right:*

Detail of a segment of an intercalated disk from the ventricular septum of the steer heart. The plasma membrane of the ends of the cells on the left (*2*) and on the right (*3*) is elaborately folded, forming small cellular protrusions that interdigitate. The cytoplasmic aspect of each plasma membrane is provided for short distances with a dense, amorphous substance that serves as points of anchorage for the approaching myofilaments. The entire structural complex is reminiscent of desmosomes as they appear in, for instance, the epidermis or the esophagus, here serving as points of origin or termination for tonofilaments (cf. page 133). The intercellular space (*Is*) narrows to about 100A within the intercalated disk. Since this muscle is highly contracted, the H-zone of the A-bands has almost disappeared, but the M-stripe (*M*) is seen clearly. The mitochondria (*Mi*) have irregular inner membranes. Fine sarcotubules (*Tu*) and ribosomes (*Ri*) are seen between the myofibrils.

Steer heart. Ventricular septum. Magnification 31,000×. Ep. LA.

*References:* 4, 29, 56, 91, 107, 158, 159, 290, 371, 490, 491, 577, 581, 675, 692, 694, 780, 781, 782, 783, 855, 884, 889, 898, 1060, 1061, 1062, 1096, 1123, 1285, 1335, 1336, 1353, 1354, 1364, 1384, 1386, 1425, 1455, 1462, 1496, 1593.

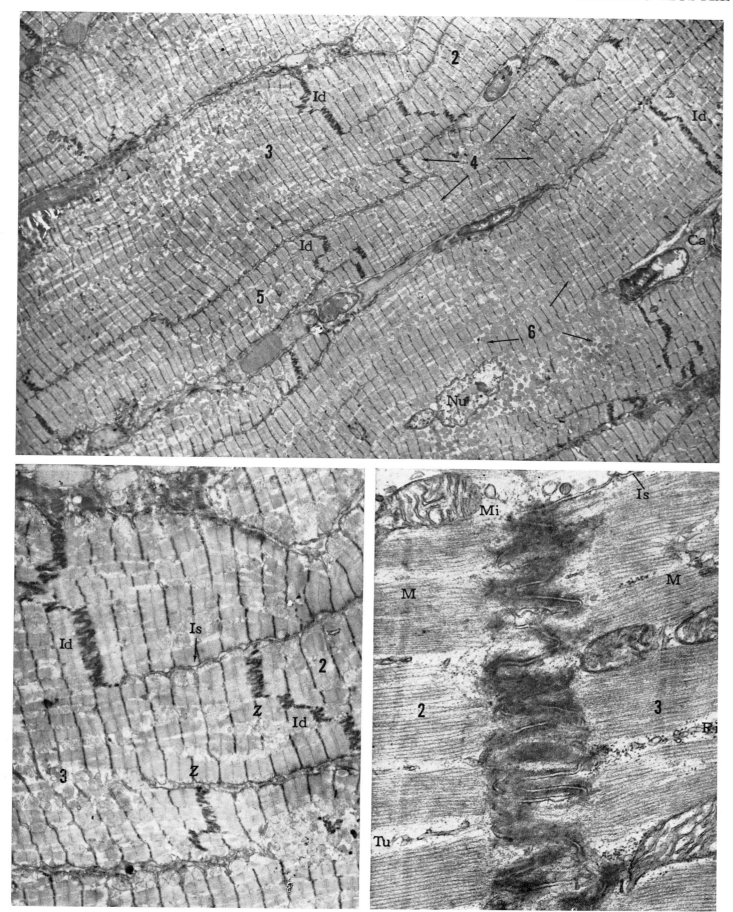

*Top:*              Longitudinally sectioned cells (2, 3, and 4) in the atrioventricular bundle (common bundle or bundle of His) of the steer heart. These cells are longer and wider than ordinary cardiac muscle cells, but they contain short myofibrils (*Mf*) with striations similar to those of cardiac cells. The nucleus (*Nu*) may be found anywhere in the cell. The cytoplasm is granular and most of it is occupied by fine glycogen granules (*Gl*). Mitochondria are lined up mainly along the cell borders (arrows). The cells are connected in a staggered fashion to form long, thin bundles throughout the conduction system. The small bundles are embedded in and frequently pierced by connective tissue elements (*Co*). A thin basement membrane surrounds each small bundle of cells but does not penetrate between adjacent cells.

              Steer heart. Common bundle. Magnification 2200×. Meth. Unstained.

*Bottom:*          Detail of the border cytoplasm of two adjacent cells (2 and 3) in the common bundle of the steer heart. The cell membrane (*Cm*) has a wavy and irregular course. At intervals, desmosomes (*Ds*) secure the attachment between the two conduction cells. This arrangement is reminiscent of the structure of the intercalated disks of the cardiac muscle cell, but seems to be of a more primitive form since it is almost identical with the cell-to-cell relationship in the heart muscle of the embryo. Mitochondria (*Mi*) and small glycogen (*Gl*) particles can be identified as well as longitudinally (*Le*) and cross-sectioned (*Cr*) myofilaments.

              The similarity between the conduction cell and the cardiac muscle cell makes it certain that the bundle of His is composed mainly of cells with the features of striated muscle.

              Steer heart. Common bundle. Magnification 26,000×. Ep. LA.

*References:*   140, 570, 899, 1167, 1453, 1454.

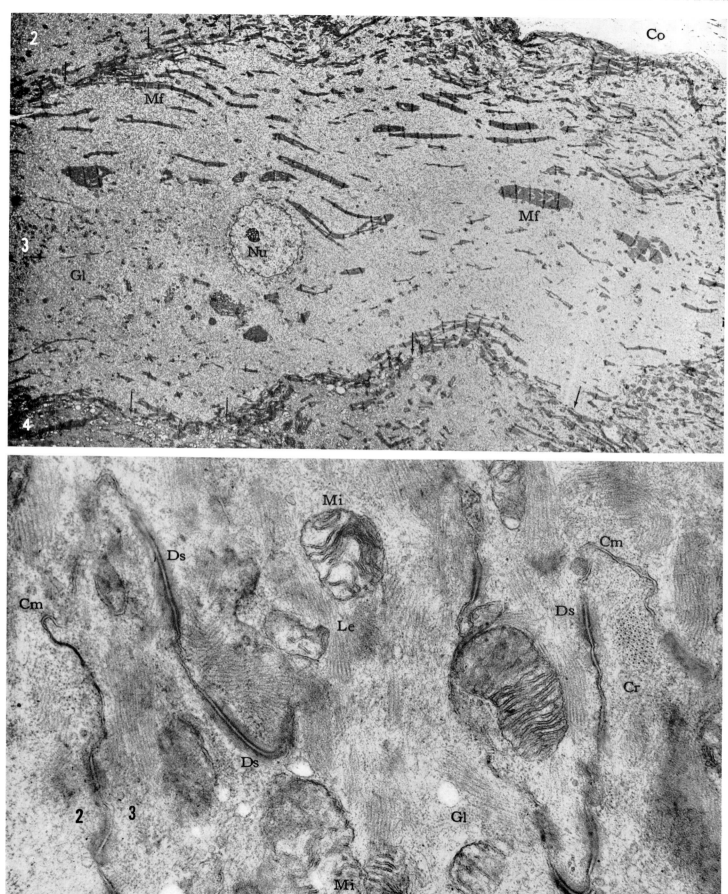

*Top:*  The nervous tissue consists of nerve cells (*Ne*) or neurons, which have a cell body with a nucleus and several cytoplasmic extensions, of which one is long—the axon (*Ax*)—and the others, short and branched—the dendrites (*De*). In the pyramidal cell layer of the cerebral cortex (this illustration), as elsewhere in the central nervous system, the neurons are surrounded by glial cells with pale neuroglial processes (*Gi*).

Cerebral cortex. Pyramidal cell layer. Magnification 2000×. Ep. UA.

*Bottom:*  The complexity of the molecular layer of the cerebral cortex is the result of the high degree of branching of axons (*Ax*) and dendrites of the neurons and the cell processes of the neuroglia (*Gi*). This arrangement makes possible a wide synaptic interrelation between these cells. The glial cells surround the capillaries (*Ca*) of the cortex.

Cerebral cortex. Molecular layer. Magnification 2000×. Ep. LH.

*References:* CENTRAL NERVOUS SYSTEM   31, 110, 130, 131, 253, 266, 267, 268, 269, 344, 348, 434, 502, 503, 540, 804, 807, 808, 809, 810, 811, 812, 813, 837, 940, 965, 1127, 1224, 1275, 1276.

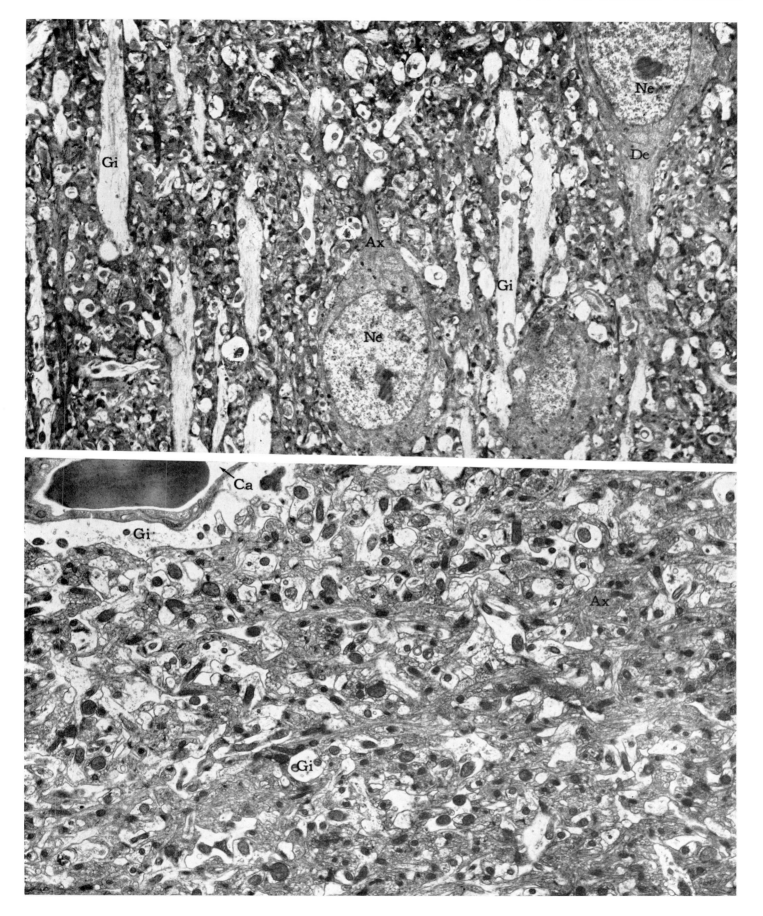

*Top:*    All nerve cells have a fairly large nucleus (*Nu*) with a distinct nucleolus (*No*). The cytoplasm around the nucleus (perikaryon) contains chromophile substance, which is composed of rough-surfaced endoplasmic reticulum (*Re*) and ribosomes (*Ri*). The entire complex is usually referred to as Nissl (tigroid) bodies. Mitochondria (*Mi*) and a Golgi complex (*Go*) are commonly observed, but rarely does one find centrioles (*Ce*). The transition between the perikaryon and the axon (*Ax*) is called the axon hillock (asterisks). The axioplasm contains more neurofilaments (*Fi*) than the perikaryon, less ribosomes, and no rough-surfaced endoplasmic reticulum.

Cerebral cortex. Pyramidal cell layer. Magnification 30,000×. Ep. LH.

*Bottom:*    Detail of the molecular layer of the cerebral cortex. Most of the nerve fibers are non-myelinated (*At*), contain fine neurofilaments and mitochondria (*Mi*), and terminate in bulb-like formations in which numerous synaptic vesicles (*Sy*) can be seen. Some nerve fibers are myelinated (*Ax*) similar to nerve fibers in peripheral nerves. Their axioplasm has a delicate fibrous appearance in contrast to the cross-sectioned glial processes (*Gi*), which are finely stippled. It should be kept in mind that the fine structure of the central nervous system has not been studied sufficiently to permit detailed interpretations of the neuroglial relationships; likewise presently existing fine structural studies do not make it possible at this moment to ascribe precise functions to the various types of glial cells that have been described elsewhere.

Cerebral cortex. Molecular layer. Magnification 30,000×. Ep. LH.

*References:*    NERVE CELL    58, 255, 274, 284, 386, 464, 507, 541, 542, 582, 604, 614, 823, 851, 1009, 1010, 1014, 1047, 1220, 1577.
GLIA    129, 483, 575, 605, 943, 944, 1052, 1053, 1177.
SYNAPSE    248, 260, 261, 263, 264, 270, 478, 484, 485, 487, 672, 995, 1000, 1002, 1178, 1523.

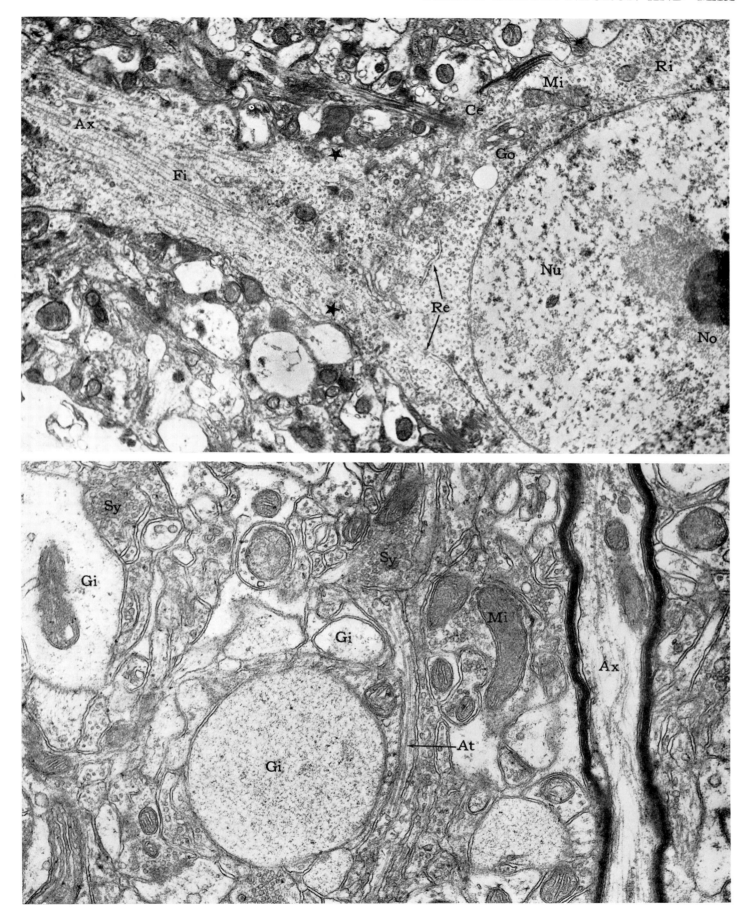

Some nerve cells are located in ganglia outside the central nervous system. In the spinal ganglia most of the neurons are unipolar, in the ganglia of the acoustic nerve they are bipolar, and in the autonomic ganglia most of the nerve cells are multipolar with numerous branched dendrites (*De*) and a single thin axon (probably at the asterisk), which forms the postganglionic unmyelinated nerve fiber.

The ganglion cell is comparatively large. In this preparation of a presumably terminal parasympathetic ganglion in the cat pancreas, the cell achieves a maximum diameter of about 25 microns. The nucleus is large and spherical and is located eccentrically. The perikaryon displays an assortment of evenly distributed cell organelles. The mitochondria (*Mi*) are irregularly shaped. The great number of dense granules (*Ly*) most probably correspond to the pigments described in light microscopy; their fine structure indicates that they represent lysosomes. Golgi complexes (*Go*) are found at various sites and are composed mostly of vesicles. Rough-surfaced endoplasmic reticulum (*Re*) rarely occurs in stacks to form true Nissl bodies but more frequently appears as short, isolated pairs of membranes surrounded by an abundance of ribosomes (*Ri*), a component that is common throughout the entire perikaryon.

The ganglion cell is completely encapsuled by the satellite cells (*Sat*), which structurally and functionally are the equivalent of the Schwann cell of the peripheral nerve axons. The nucleus of the satellite cell (*Sat*) is smaller and denser than that of the ganglion cell and has a slightly elongated shape. The cytoplasm is comparatively light and has most of the usual cell organelles concentrated near the nucleus. Adjacent plasma membranes (*Cm*) of the neuron and the satellite cell are separated by a small intercellular space, which does not show up in this low magnification picture. Peculiar structures of as yet unknown function are found in the satellite cytoplasm and consist of a row of tiny vesicles (*Rv*), which often are seen to fuse for short distances and give the impression of long cytoplasmic membranes. The endoneurium is formed by numerous fine collagenous and reticular fibrils (*Co*). Between the ganglion cells throughout the ganglion is seen an abundance of delicate unmyelinated nerve fibers (*Ne*) and light, thin branches of satellite cells (*Sat*). Most of these nerves probably represent dendrites and preganglionic fibers, which synapse in a tangled fashion, thus giving rise to the dense glomeruli of the ganglion.

Cat pancreas. Autonomic ganglion. Magnification 8300×. Ep. LH.

*References:* GANGLION  19, 20, 55, 60, 155, 240, 247, 257, 343, 573, 575a, 1012, 1219, 1221, 1222, 1223, 1356, 1440, 1546, 1547.

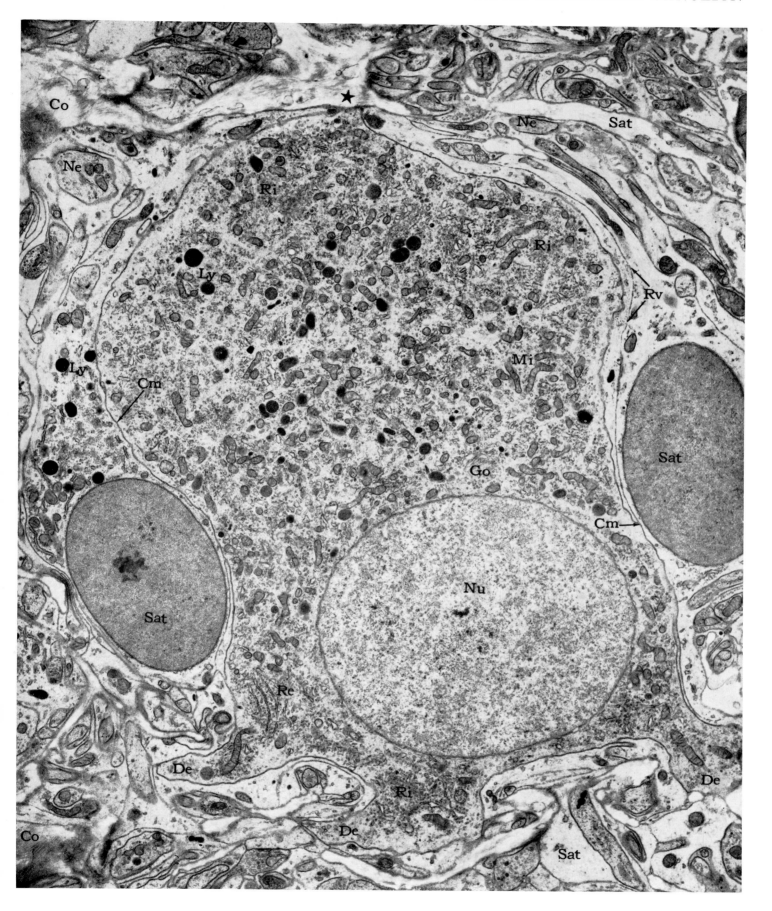

*Top:*     Transverse section of nerve fibers in the sciatic nerve. The nerve fibers are surrounded by the perineurium, which consists of flat, elongated fibroblasts in which nuclei (*Pe*), mitochondria, and lipid inclusions occur. Collagen fibrils (*Co*) form the endoneurium. The peripheral nerves contain a mixture of myelinated (*Mn*) and unmyelinated (*Un*) nerve fibers. The myelinated nerve fiber contains one axon (*Ax*), whereas the unmyelinated ones have several. The axons are surrounded by a myelin sheath (*Ms*), which in turn is derived from the Schwann cell (*Sch*), the nucleus of which protrudes into the endoneurium.

Sciatic nerve. Magnification 9000×. Ep. LH.

*Bottom:*     Longitudinal section of fine myelinated nerves (1 to 5), of which one (3) has been sectioned through the axon (*Ax*). The axioplasm is finely fibrillar with elongated bodies representing mitochondria (*Mi*). The Schwann cell nucleus (*Sch*) makes a local indentation in the myelin sheath. Slitlike interruptions of the myelin sheath represent the incisions or clefts of Schmidt-Lanterman (*SL*). The endoneurium is formed by numerous collagenous fibrils (*Co*).

Sciatic nerve. Magnification 3700×. Ep. LH.

*References:* NERVE FIBERS  342, 471, 576, 693, 964, 1209, 1415, 1428, 1494, 1495.

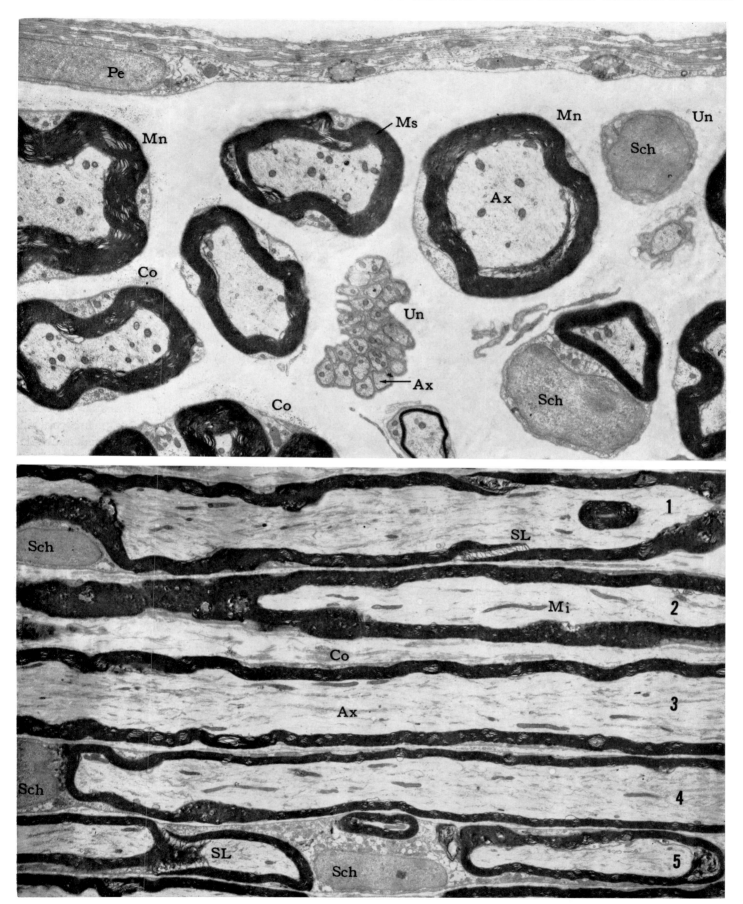

*Top:*  Detail of a thin, cross-sectioned myelinated nerve. The axoplasm (*Ax*), bordered by the membrane of the nerve cell, the axolemma (*AxL*), contains vesicles of varying size (*Ve*), mitochondria (*Mi*), and cross-sectioned, dense neurofilaments (*Fi*). Wrapped around the axon is the myelin sheath, formed by the thinned-out cytoplasm of the Schwann cell (*Sch*). The prominent dense lines of the myelin sheath are formed by a fusion of the two inner layers of the unit plasma membrane. This occurs at the mesaxon (*Mes*) but can also be seen in places where the Schwann cell cytoplasm (*Sch*) has not been flattened out completely (*Fus*). The Schwann cell with its nucleus (*Nu*) and mitochondria (*Mi*) is surrounded by a thin basement membrane (*Bm*), which in turn borders on the collagen (*Co*) of the endoneurium.

Sciatic nerve. Magnification 73,000×. Ep. LH.

*Bottom:*  Detail of a Schwann cell and associated cross-sectioned unmyelinated axons (*Ax*), each of which is bordered by a continuous axolemma (cell membrane). The axoplasm contains small mitochondria (*Mi*), vesicles (*Ve*), dense granules (*D*), and cross-sectioned neurofilaments (*Fi*), most of which display a clear center in contrast to the neurofilaments of the myelinated nerve axons. The Schwann cell nucleus (*Nu*) clearly displays its triple-layered nuclear membrane with occasional nuclear fenestrations (*Np*) bridged by a diaphragm. The cytoplasm of the Schwann cell (*Sch*) envelops the nerve axons completely but is not wrapped around several times as is the case with the myelinated nerve. The cytoplasm is rich in ribosomes (*Ri*) and elements of the rough-surfaced endoplasmic reticulum (*Re*); it contains dense ferritin granules (*Ft*) and a small Golgi complex (*Go*). A thin basement membrane (*Bm*) surrounds the Schwann cell and the axons, creating a border line toward the endoneurium (*Co*).

Sciatic nerve. Magnification 38,000×. Ep. LH.

*References:*  AXON-SCHWANN RELATIONSHIP   154, 262, 293, 309, 310, 460, 461, 462, 463, 805, 1051, 1054, 1179, 1184, 1188, 1263, 1268, 1269, 1447.

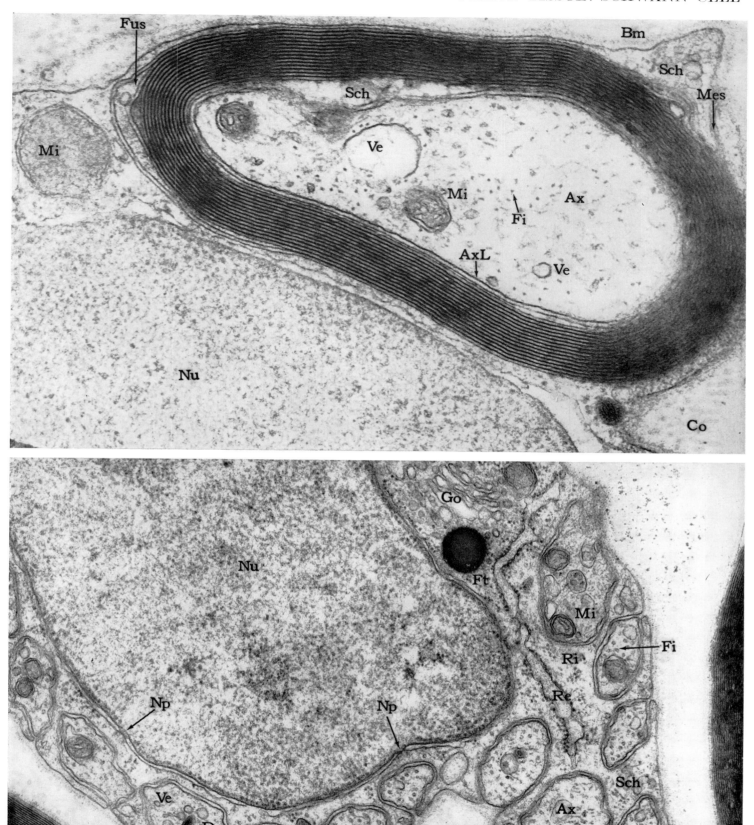

*Left:*         Detail of the longitudinally sectioned myelin sheath of a sciatic nerve. As already pointed out, the prominent dense lines (*Fus*) of the myelin sheath are formed by fusion of the two inner layers of two closely opposed cell membranes. The thin intraperiod lines (*Ip*) are formed by fusion of the two outer layers of two closely opposed cell membranes. Near the axon the Schwann cell cytoplasm is not sufficiently thinned out so that the two inner layers (center of *Sch*) may fuse; of the outer thin membranes, the one at the right (in the bracket marked *Sch*) has fused, but the one at the left does not fuse with the axolemma (*AxL*). The axon (*Ax*) is at the far left, and the endoneurium is at the far right.

Sciatic nerve. Magnification 157,000×. Ep. LH.

*Right:*         Detail of a Schwann cell (*Sch*) and associated longitudinally sectioned unmyelinated axons (*Ax*). The nucleus (*Nu*) and the mitochondria (*Mi*) are located within the same cytoplasm, which extends down (arrows) between the axons. The four membranes, which can be seen clearly in the circle, are the axolemmas and cell membrane of the Schwann cell. However, a second Schwann cell territory is involved in surrounding the axons, since a thin strand of cytoplasm from beyond meets the cytoplasm from above at the asterisk. The axoplasm contains fine neurofilaments (*Fi*), small mitochondria (*Mi*), and a multitude of tiny vesicles (*Ves*), some of which have merged to form elongated tubular strands, which may be a variety of the smooth-surfaced endoplasmic reticulum. A basement membrane (*Bm*) and collagen (*Co*) surround the structural unit.

Sciatic nerve. Magnification 17,000×. Ep. LH.

*References:* MYELIN   204, 382, 383, 384, 397, 398, 399, 400, 401, 403, 404, 1271, 1272, 1273, 1340, 1341.
UNMYELINATED NERVE FIBERS   306, 307, 441, 574

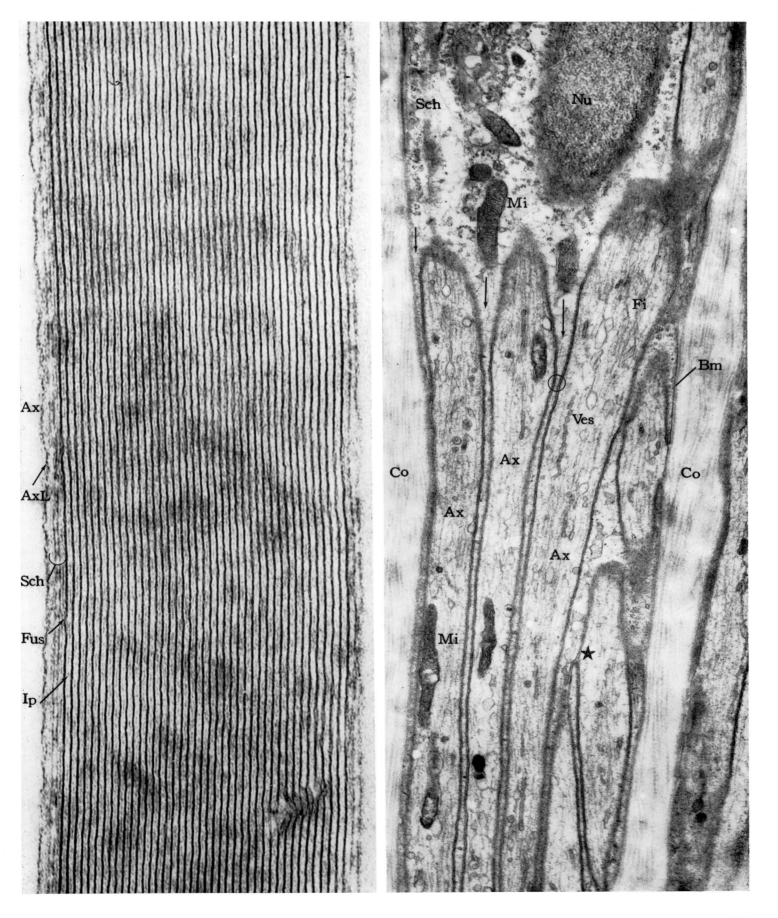

*Left:*    Detail of a *Schmidt-Lanterman cleft* of a myelinated nerve. The axon (*Ax*) and the axolemma (*AxL*) are seen at the far right. Earlier studies using the light microscope suggested that the cleft merely indicates poor preservation of the myelin sheath. This does not now seem likely, since fine details of construction indicate that a local shearing defect in the myelin separates the lamellae widely at the major lines of density (arrows). In other words, the Schwann cell cytoplasm (*Sch*) retains its same volume but stretches in a long, continuous, helical pathway to connect the outer Schwann cell cytoplasm, which contains the nucleus, with the thin layer next to the axon (described previously). The function of these Schmidt-Lanterman clefts is unknown.

Sciatic nerve. Magnification 69,000×. Ep. LH.

*Right:*    Detail of a *node of Ranvier* of a delicate myelinated nerve. This structure is formed by the end of one Schwann cell and the beginning of another. Since the myelin sheath actually is a specialization of the Schwann cell cytoplasm, which has become wrapped around the axon (*Ax*), the myelin spiral can unwind by separating along the fused major lines of density, creating a blunt spiral end of the myelin sheath near the nodal gap. In a section, this end appears as numerous small feet resting against the axolemma (*AxL*). Their number equals that of the major lines of density in the myelin sheath and can easily be counted (26). The axon continues uninterrupted across the nodal gap and is separated from the collagen (*Co*) of the endoneurium by a basement membrane (*Bm*) and small, fingerlike processes (*Fp*) extending from the peripheral Schwann cell cytoplasm.

Nerve impulses seem to travel by saltatory transmission. When electric current flow is recorded in a nerve fiber, it is found to flow in a stepwise fashion along the nerve, reaching a maximum at each node of Ranvier. The action currents developed at each node act as stimulating currents to the adjacent nodes.

Sciatic nerve. Magnification 32,000×. Ep. LH.

*References:* SCHMIDT-LANTERMAN CLEFTS  1187.
NODES OF RANVIER   308, 332, 853, 1039, 1180, 1185, 1190, 1448, 1449.

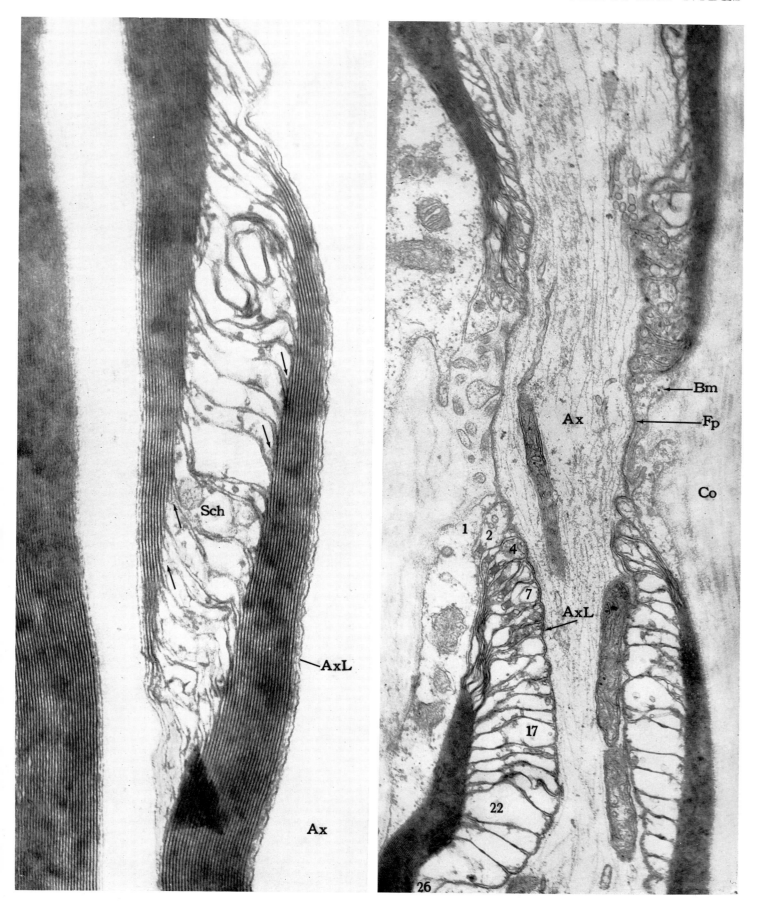

*Top:*

Cross section of a small artery in the mesentery of the intestine. In all arterial vessels, the same general arrangement of layers is seen in the vascular wall. Facing the lumen (*Lu*) is a thin layer of endothelial cells (*Ed*) surrounded by a thin basement membrane, which may contain fibrous elastic components (*In*). The tunica media displays a varying number of helically arranged smooth muscle cells (*Sm*), which in turn are surrounded by a network of elastic fibers, the membrana elastica externa (*Ex*). A tunica adventitia (*Ad*) of areolar connective tissue forms the outermost layer of the vascular wall.

Mesenteric artery. Magnification 2600×. Ep. UA.

*Bottom Left:*

Detail of a longitudinally sectioned arteriole in the adventitia of a femoral artery. The endothelium (*Ed*), bordering on the lumen of the vessel (*Lu*), is stretched out thinly against a basement membrane (*Bm*), which also penetrates between the smooth muscle cells (*Sm*). The fibroblasts (*Fib*) and the collagen fibrils (*Co*) of the adventitial tissue are abundant. Whether the tunica media is composed of one layer of smooth muscle cells or of several layers, the general arrangement and the fine structure of these cells are similar. The cytoplasm contains mitochondria (*Mi*), myofilaments (*Fi*), and dense oblong areas (fusiform densities) peculiar to smooth muscle cells (cf. page 25). Vascular smooth muscle cells also establish lateral connections (*Lc*) through short cytoplasmic processes.

Arteriole. Vasa vasorum. Magnification 15,000×. Ep. LH.

*Bottom Right:*

Detail of the junction of two endothelial cells (*Ed*) of an artery. Numerous pinocytotic vesicles (*Pi*) are present on the luminal (*Lu*), lateral, and basal surfaces of the endothelial cell. In addition, several small vesicles (*Ve*) are scattered throughout the cytoplasm together with occasional lysosomelike bodies (*Ly*). The lateral surfaces of the endothelial cells meet in a jointlike fashion. Terminal bars or desmosomes are not commonly present in the endothelial interrelationship seen in mouse tissue. The elastic components of the membrana elastica interna (*In*) are not preserved adequately to permit a detailed description.

Femoral artery. Magnification 50,000×. Ep. LH.

*References:* GENERAL 358, 361, 413, 522, 578, 662, 665, 668, 670, 683, 684, 821, 885, 1022, 1023, 1048, 1080, 1098, 1159, 1582, ENDOTHELIUM 128, 412, 414, 501, 523, 887, 888, 1401. ELASTIC TISSUE 168, 515, 1049, 1163, 1290, 1446.

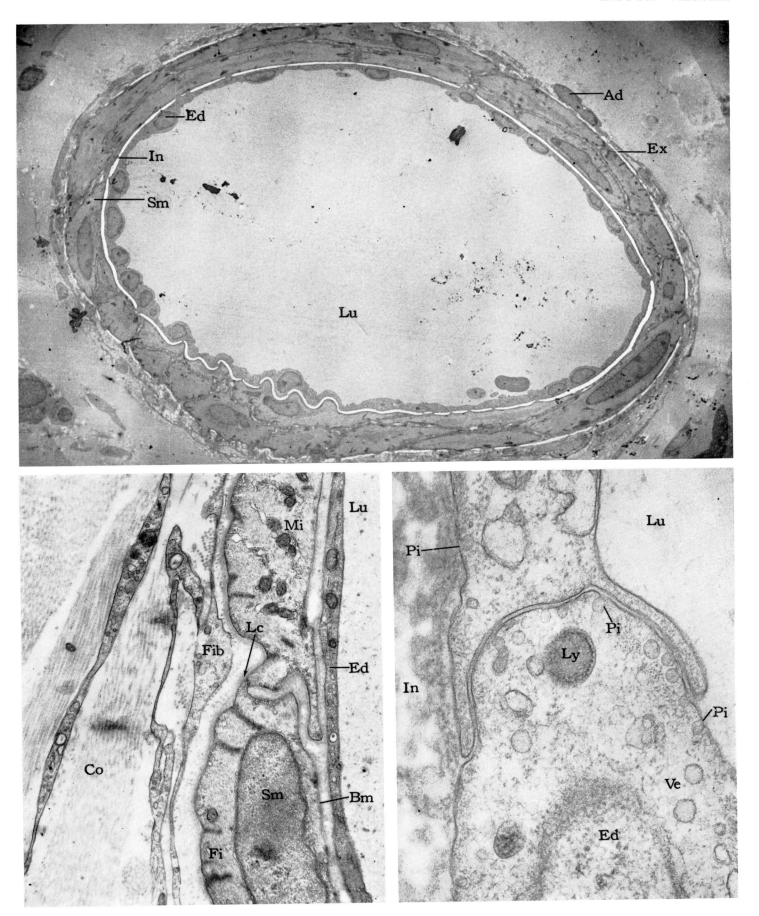

Cross section of a thin capillary in the lamina propria of the gastric mucosa. Blood capillaries are always surrounded by a thin basement membrane (*Bm*) in contrast to lymph capillaries and sinusoids (cf. page 79). The endothelium is extremely thin except for the part of the cell that contains the nucleus (*Nu*), the Golgi complex (*Go*), and most of the mitochondria (*Mi*) that can be identified in the endothelial cytoplasm. Pinocytotic vesicles (*Pi*) are abundant wherever the endothelium exceeds about 0.1 micron in thickness. Whether these vesicles communicate with the Golgi complex or with the endoplasmic reticulum has not yet been established. Discontinuities, referred to earlier as capillary pores, occur frequently along the thinnest parts of the endothelium. A more recent concept of their fine structure indicates that they are merely fenestrations (*Fe*), each of which is bridged by a thin diaphragm. Therefore, blood capillaries do not have true holes in contrast to the cells lining the sinusoids of the liver (cf. page 73). The significance of a closing diaphragm in the fenestrations is of great functional importance, since it indicates the active role played by the endothelium in determining the exchange of substances across the cell.

In the circulating blood appear two components that are of importance in the exchange of oxygen and carbon dioxide and in the coagulation mechanism. The *erythrocyte* (*Er*) is sectioned throughout its full width as is the platelet or *thrombocyte* (*Th*). The red blood cell is enveloped by a thin plasma membrane and has a dense, homogeneous content lacking a nucleus, mitochondria, and other cytoplasmic constituents. Note the close proximity between the red cell membrane and the capillary fenestrations. The platelet also lacks a nucleus but has retained a finely granular cytoplasm with vesicular elements of the smooth-surfaced endoplasmic reticulum, mitochondria, and large dense granules of the type that is abundant in the cytoplasm of the megakaryocyte (cf. page 3).

Lamina propria. Gastric mucosa. Magnification 30,000 ×. Ep. LH.

*References:* CAPILLARY   5, 39, 74, 275, 295, 885, 912, 913, 982, 993, 1021, 1068, 1158.
ERYTHROCYTE   645, 799.
THROMBOCYTE   237, 390, 617, 706, 1092, 1202, 1284.

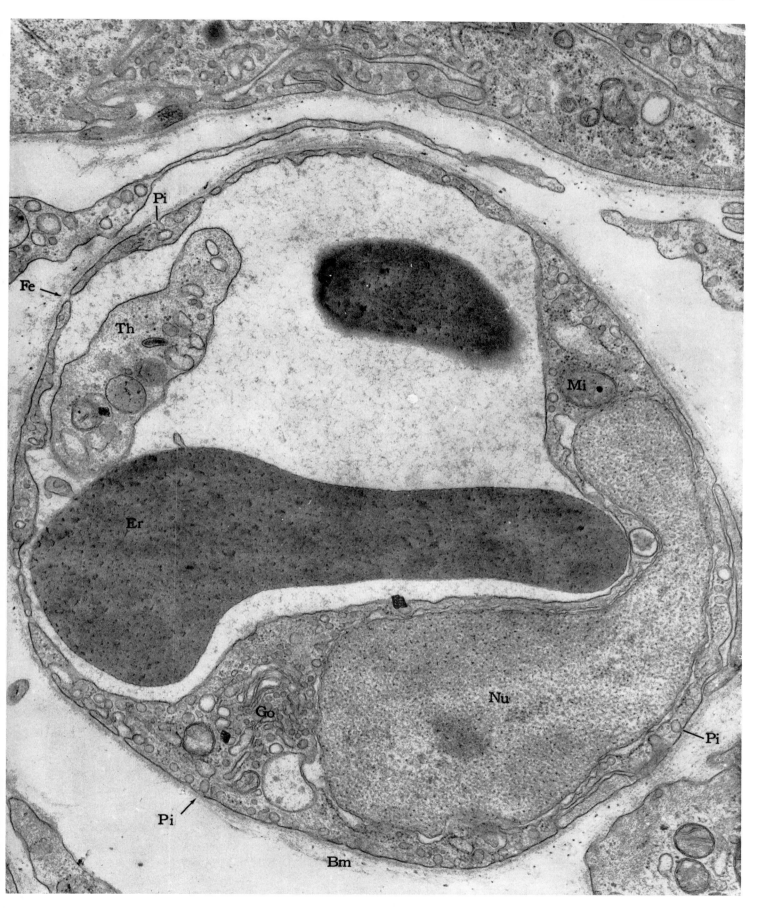

*Top:*

The epithelium of the oral mucosa is of the stratified squamous variety. The structure of the epithelium varies according to the location. Thus, the cells do not undergo keratinization in the epithelium of the inner surfaces of the lips and cheek, whereas keratinization of the soft type occurs in the hard palate, in the gingival margin, and in some areas on the dorsum of the tongue. The ultrastructure of the nonkeratinizing, stratified squamous epithelium is described in relation to the esophagus (page 56) and the cornea (page 144).

This illustration includes the keratinized epithelium on the dorsum of the mouse tongue and the bases of two filiform papillae (*Fip*). The cells between the papillae have irregular outlines and become increasingly more squamous as they move toward the surface. They contain numerous keratohyalin granules (*Ke*), most of which are small. There is a gradual increase in density as the cells become keratinized and lose their keratohyalin granules. At the surface of the tongue, the cells become sloughed off. The dense spheres represent cross-sectioned bacteria (*Bt*). The cells that participate in the formation of the filiform papilla contain large keratohyalin granules (*KE*). The core of each papilla contains a vascular connective tissue in man, whereas in the mouse it is solid and is formed by overlapping keratinized epithelial cells. There is an indication that half of each filiform papilla is formed by cells that have undergone hard keratinization as with that of the hair cortex. This conclusion is arrived at from consideration of the high electron density and the coarse filamentous structure present in the papilla (*Fip*).

Dorsum of the mouse tongue. Magnification 2600×. Ep. UA.

*Bottom:*

The parotid gland is a purely serous type of gland, secreting a watery albuminous fluid. This fluid contains the enzyme amylase, which initiates the digestion of carbohydrates. The serous acini are lined with pyramidal epithelial cells, which rest on a thin basement membrane (*Bm*). The nucleus (*Nu*) is usually located toward the basal region in cells near the secretory stage. Several cells (2 to 4) surround a narrow lumen (*Lu*) into which project tiny microvilli. Intercellular secretory canaliculi (asterisk) penetrate toward the base of the cells. The lateral cell surface (*Cm*) is highly irregular with interdigitating short and narrow cytoplasmic processes. The rough-surfaced endoplasmic reticulum (*Re*) is particularly abundant in the basal cell area, but an abundance of ribosomes (*Ri*) contribute to an overall high degree of cytoplasmic density. The Golgi complex (*Go*) is rather prominent, as is the great number of secretory granules (*G*). These granules show highly irregular outlines and a medium, slightly granular, dense content. Although this cell in many respects resembles the exocrine pancreatic cell (cf. page 77), it differs from it in the way the secretory granules originate and are shaped. The Golgi complex of the parotid cells does not seem to be the immediate precursor of the secretory granules, since they, because of their irregular outlines, more likely seem to be derived directly from the rough-surfaced endoplasmic reticulum. The release of the secretion into the lumen (*Lu*) also seems to be different from that in the pancreas, at least in the salivary glands of some species.

The myoepithelial or basket cell is located between the base of the epithelial cells and the basement membrane (*Bm*). Since the myoepithelial cell has a stellate shape, it most frequently shows up as cross sections of isolated cell processes (*My*). The ultrastructure of the myoepithelial cell definitely puts it in the class of smooth muscle cells.

Human parotid gland. Magnification 12,000×. Ep. LH.

*References:* ORAL MUCOSA   6, 355, 424, 1168, 1366, 1367, 1418.
SALIVARY GLAND   387, 388, 456, 506, 647, 711, 752, 824, 871, 872, 1025, 1026, 1027, 1129, 1293, 1295, 1410, 1411.

Page 54

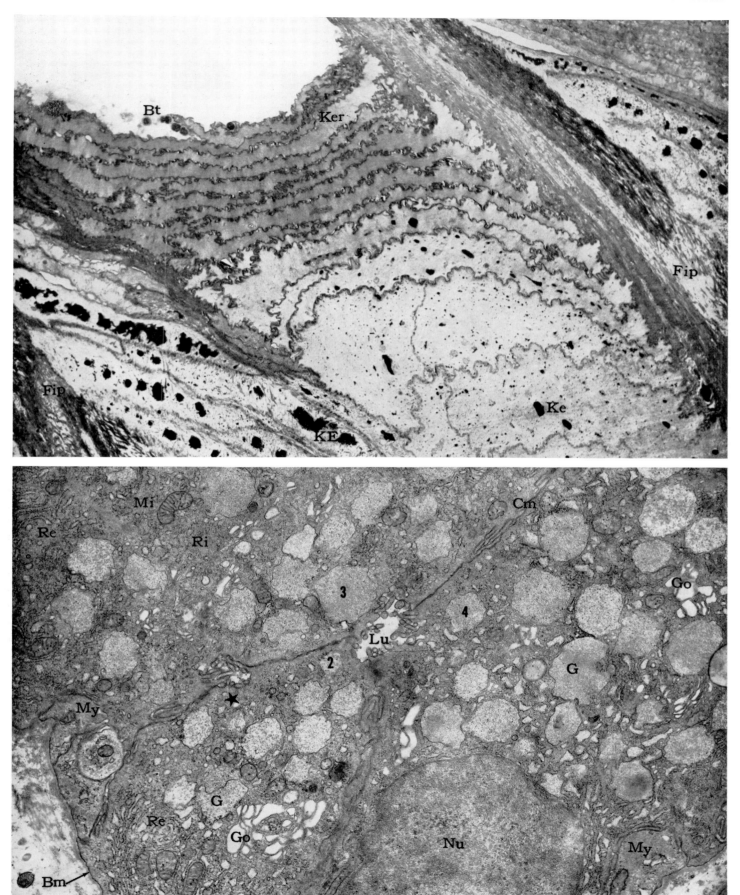

*Top Left:*   The human esophagus (all illustrations on this page) is lined with a typical stratified squamous epithelium, which does not undergo keratinization. The basal cells are of a columnar shape and rest on a thin basement membrane (*Bm*), which separates the epithelium from the lamina propria; these cells are rich in collagen (*Co*) and capillaries (*Ca*). The nucleus (*Nu*) of the basal cell occupies a major part of the cell. In adult tissue, the Golgi complex is rudimentary or absent. There is a continuous migration of cells toward the surface of the epithelium. The cells enlarge and acquire a polyhedral shape upon leaving the basal layer. Intercellular spaces (*Is*) become wide, and desmosomes (*Des*) are more frequent.

Human esophagus. Magnification 3400×. Ep. UA.

*Top Right:*   Farther away from the basement membrane the cells elongate, and as a result nuclei (*Nu*) seem to be scarce. The intercellular spaces (*Is*) gradually close up and the desmosomes (*Des*) decrease in size.

Human esophagus. Magnification 4000×. Ep. UA.

*Bottom:*   Since this is a stratified squamous epithelium that does not undergo keratinization, there is a good opportunity to compare the events that occur as the cells move toward the surface in this epithelium with those in a keratinizing epithelium, such as the epidermis (page 133). The three pictures illustrate, from left to right, the cellular changes occurring in basal, intermediate, and superficial cells of the esophagus.

The cytoplasm is first dense because of a multitude of ribosomes (*Ri*) and tonofilaments (*To*). Gradually these cell constituents become more scarce until the cell is ready to become desquamated at the surface. It should be kept in mind that keratinization does not occur, probably because of the absence of keratohyalin granules in this type of epithelium. The desmosomes (*Des*) (cf. page 7) are attached to the cell by a specialization of the plasma membrane and form points of origin for the tonofilaments. The intercellular space (*Is*) is relatively large except for the points where the paired structure of a desmosome occurs. Again, the desmosomes gradually decrease in number and size as the surface of the epithelium is approached until they finally disappear. The intercellular space, on the other hand, is closing up, and the cells ultimately are prepared for desquamation. (For a study of what occurs immediately before desquamation, consult the description of the corneal epithelium on p. 145.)

Human esophagus. Magnification 28,000×. Ep. UA.

*References:* 915, 1168.

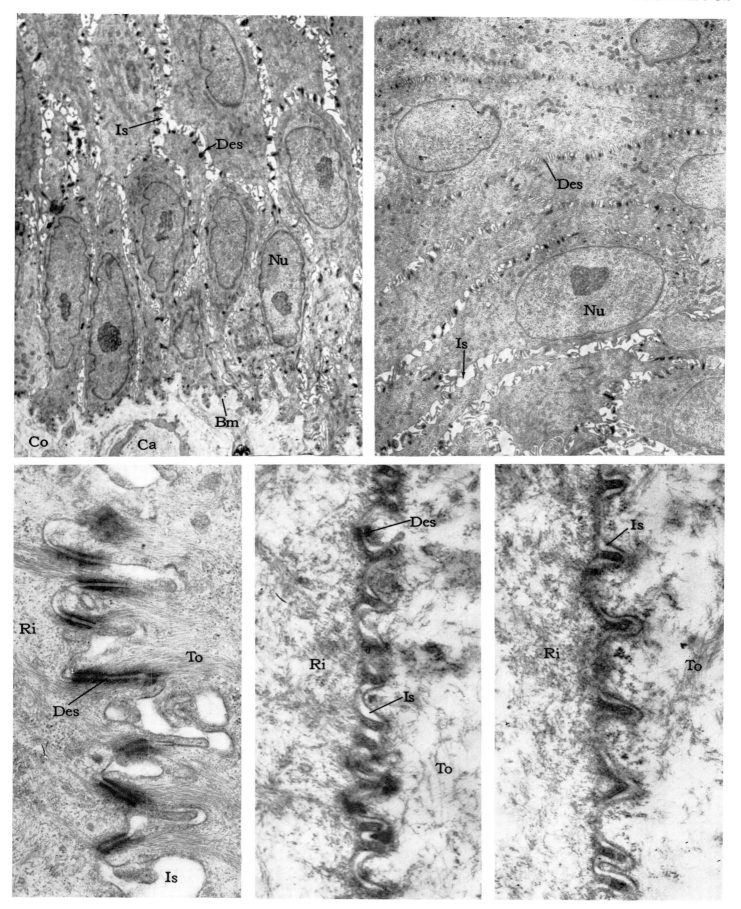

*Top:*    As seen in a longitudinal section of the gastric mucosa, the epithelial cells (*Su*) that line the surface (*Lu*) and the gastric pits (*Pit*) of the fundus of the mouse stomach are of a columnar type. The surface cells are of a tall columnar type with the bases tapering off toward the lamina propria (lower right corner), whereas the cells of the gastric pits are shorter and have a base of approximately the same dimensions as the apex of the cell. The nucleus (*Nu*) is slightly elongated, and the apex of the cell is filled with dense mucous granules. The secretory granules may also be aggregated near the nucleus within the Golgi area of the cell. Small mitochondria (*Mi*) cluster beneath the apical granules, and cells with accumulations of lysosomes (*Ly*) occur infrequently. Wide intercellular spaces (*Is*) can be observed only between the tapering basal ends of the surface cells.

Fundus. Surface epithelium. Magnification 6000×. Ep. LH.

*Bottom:*    The tubular and branching gastric glands open up into the bottom of the gastric pit through a short neck or duct. The necks and the glands are most conveniently studied in cross sections (this illustration). Several cell types are found in these regions. The neck of the gland (*GsN*) is lined predominantly with the so-called mucous neck cells (*Mu*), but occasional parietal cells (*Ox*) are wedged between. The gastric gland proper (*Gs*) is dominated by the chief or zymogenic cells (*Ch*) mixed with parietal cells (*Ox*) and occasional, basally located argentaffine cells (*Ay*). All the cell types mentioned border on the lumen of the tubular gland except for the argentaffine cell, which rarely reaches the lumen. The lamina propria (*Lp*) contains numerous capillaries (*Ca*) and connective tissue elements.

Fundus. Gastric glands. Magnification 2800×. Ep. LA.

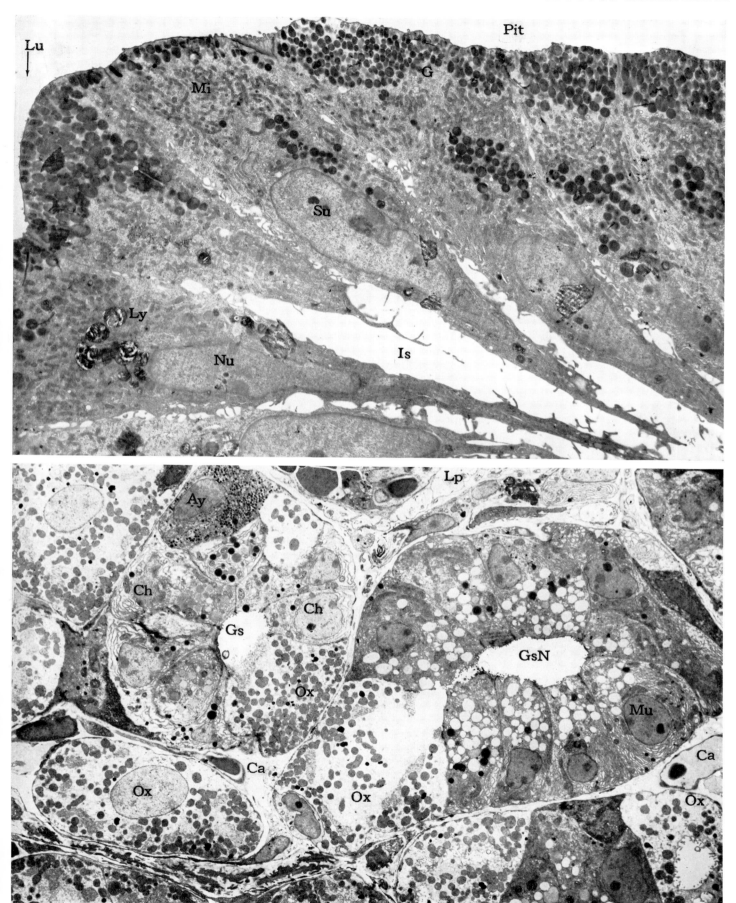

*Top Left:*        The surface cell (*Su*) of a gastric pit (*Pit*) has a concentration of dense mucous granules (*G*) near the cell apex, a characteristic of this cell type. The granules are formed within the Golgi area (*Go*). Two types of mitochondria occur, one of which shows large dense inclusions (*Mi 1*); the other lacks this distinctive feature (*Mi 2*). Only very small microvilli with a thick extraneous coat project into the gastric pit. Rough-surfaced endoplasmic reticulum (*Re*) is sparse in this special kind of mucous cell. The only other site in the mammalian body where similar cells occur is in the uterine glands (cf. page 127).

       Fundus. Surface epithelium. Magnification 14,000×. Ep. LH.

*Top Right:*        The neck of the gastric gland (*GsN*) is lined with a different kind of mucous cell, the mucous neck cell (*Mu*) in which the secretory granules (*G*) do not stain like those of the cells on the gastric surface. The nucleus has a basal location, and the rough-surfaced endoplasmic reticulum (*Re*) is slightly more abundant than in the cells of the gastric surface. The mucous neck cell has an appearance reminiscent of the mucous cells of the oviduct (cf. page 125), none of which resemble the typical goblet cell of the large intestine or the respiratory passages. The mucous neck cell is easily confused with the zymogenic cell of the gastric gland, but the zymogenic granules seem to have different staining properties. The nearby parietal cell (*Ox*) lacks secretory granules.

       Fundus. Gastric gland. Magnification 8300×. Ep. LA.

*Bottom Left:*        The parietal cell, often called an oxyntic cell (*Ox*), is a most peculiar cell with light cytoplasm filled with numerous large, spherical mitochondria (*Mi*). The cytoplasm is traversed by branching, intracellular secretory capillaries often occupied by numerous microvilli (*Vi*) projecting from the wall of the capillary. The parietal cell has a very small Golgi complex (*Go*), composed mostly of small vesicles, and the entire cell cytoplasm is pervaded by similar small vesicles (*Ve*), which supposedly are the structural evidence for a secretory activity in conjunction with hydrochloric acid production.

       Fundus. Gastric gland. Magnification 14,000×. Ep. LH.

*Bottom Right:*        The chief or zymogenic cell (*Ch*) is a typical secretory cell, which closely resembles the exocrine cells of the pancreas. At the base of the cell the rough-surfaced endoplasmic reticulum (*Re*) is abundant. Within the Golgi area (*Go*) arise secretory granules (*G*); their maturation into zymogen granules can be followed by comparing their increasingly intense shades of gray. The apex of the cell borders on the lumen of the gland (*Gs*). A small part of an oxyntic cell (*Ox*) is seen in upper right corner.

       Fundus. Gastric gland. Magnification 14,000×. Ep. LA.

*References:* 111, 153, 157, 221, 499, 517, 518, 519, 520, 560, 561, 562, 563, 586, 627, 709a, 710, 749, 778, 779, 893, 915, 1302, 1303, 1304, 1305, 1306, 1307, 1308, 1309, 1310, 1452.

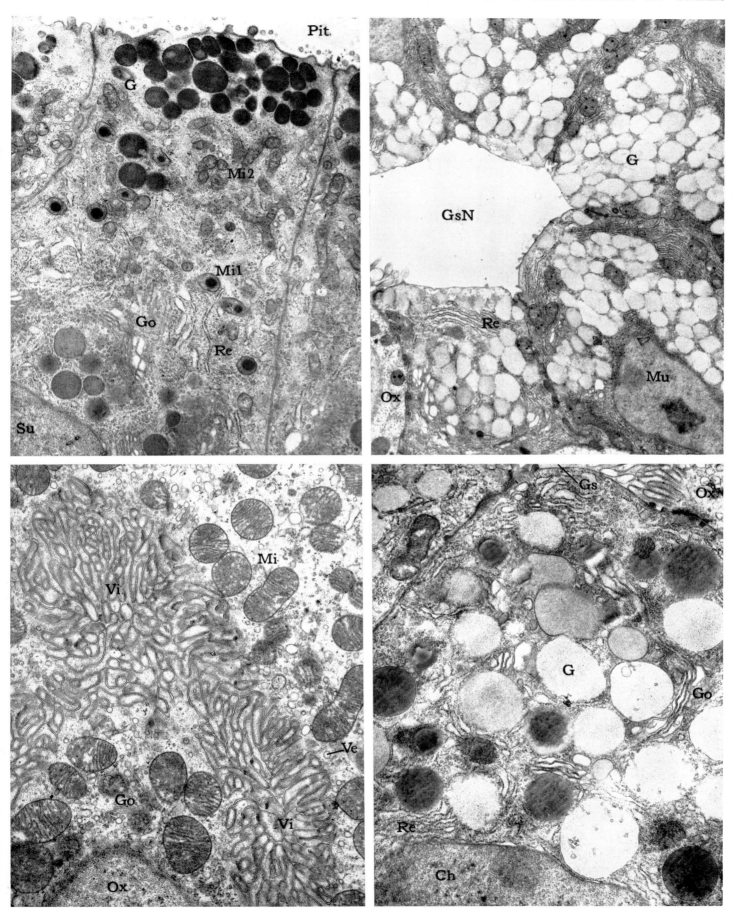

*Top:*

In this cross section of intestinal villi of the jejunal mucosa, it can be seen that the surface cells (*Su*) are of a columnar type with occasional mucous-secreting goblet cells (*Gc*) interspersed. A striated border (*Sb*) lines the luminal surface (*Lu*). The sides of some of the cross-sectioned intestinal villi are closely opposed, and the striated border of one touches that of a neighboring villus. The cell borders (*Cb*) can be seen clearly. The nucleus (*Nu*) is oval with a central location in the cell. The base of the cells is tapered slightly and contacts the thin basement membrane, which in turn borders on the lamina propria (*Lp*) in the core of the villus.

Jejunum. Magnification 2500×. Ep. UA.

*Bottom Left:*

Detail of the luminal part (*Lu*) of two intestinal surface cells. The striated border consists of fingerlike projections emerging from the cell surface. (For a detailed description, see page 4.) Beneath the bases of the villi is a cytoplasmic zone, traversed by a meshwork of fine filaments, referred to sometimes in light microscopy as the "terminal web." Mitochondria (*Mi*) are fairly numerous, and lysosomes (*Ly*) occur frequently, as can be seen in the top picture in which all the dense granules in the cells are lysosomes. Multivesicular bodies (*Mv*) are more abundant than in most cells. The cytoplasm is pervaded by small vesicles (*Ve*), most of which originate from micropinocytotic vesicles between the bases of the microvilli of the striated border. These vesicles transport small absorbed fat particles (asterisks) through the cell and at the lateral cell border deliver the fat into the space between the cell membranes (*Cm*). Ribosomes are not encountered in great abundance, but rough-surfaced endoplasmic reticulum (*Re*) appears in short strands.

Duodenum. Magnification 15,000×. Ep. LH.

*Bottom Right:*

This section shows the bases of a few surface cells with mitochondria (*Mi*) bordering on the basement membrane (*Bm*). It shows clearly how small fat droplets (asterisks) accumulate between the bases of the cells now being liberated from the membranous vesicles (*Ve*). Some are just about to pass through the basement membrane; others have reached the interstitial space of the lamina propria (*Lp*) on their way to a lacteal. Part of a thin blood capillary (*Ca*) is nearby.

Duodenum. Magnification 16,000×. Ep. LH.

*References:* 75, 123, 180, 181, 219, 231, 474, 480, 527, 528, 537, 538, 539, 555, 603, 643, 719, 776, 786, 862, 1004, 1006, 1007, 1008, 1240, 1241, 1242, 1254, 1267, 1427, 1500, 1581.

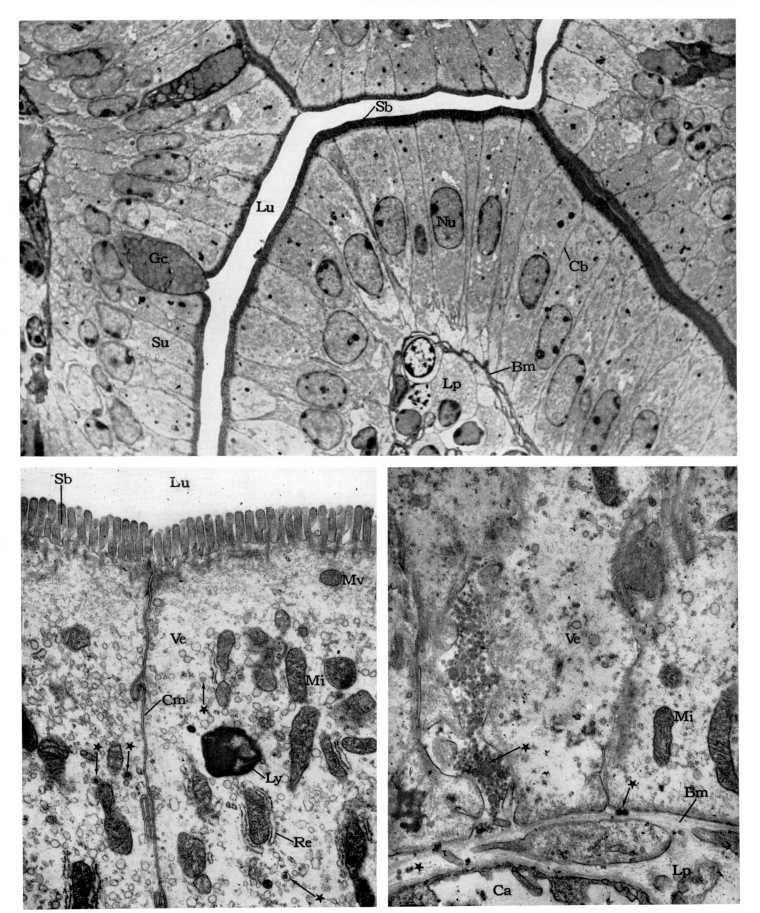

*Top:*	The surface epithelium of the intestinal villi continues down into the crypts of Lieberkühn (*Lie*), which here are seen in cross section. The cells have a definitely undifferentiated appearance (*Ia*), and it is generally accepted that they migrate from the crypts to the surface of the villus, here giving rise to the surface cells. The cells have small microvilli, which project into the narrow lumen (*Lie*) of the intestinal gland. Toward the bottom of the crypt are numerous cells of Paneth (*Pa*) with intensely stained secretory granules. The lamina propria (*Lp*) contains a rich capillary network (*Ca*).

Jejunum. Magnification 3700×. Ep. LA.

*Bottom Left:*	The Paneth cell of the crypts of Lieberkühn has an irregularly shaped nucleus (*Nu*) near the base of the cell toward the basement membrane (*Bm*), which surrounds the intestinal gland. The cytoplasm is characterized by enormously long and whorling strands of rough-surfaced endoplasmic reticulum (*Re*), the cisternae of which seemingly do not tend to become dilated as, for instance, in the pancreas or the thyroid. The cytoplasm of the cell is usually light compared with adjoining undifferentiated cells (*Ia*). Several mitochondria (*Mi*) and occasional lysosomes (*Ly*) are seen. The cell is dominated by the secretory granules, which arise within the Golgi area (not shown). The granules have an extremely electron-dense core surrounded by a clear halo. The entire granular complex is bound by a thin, smooth-surfaced membrane.

Duodenum. Magnification 7000×. Ep. LH.

*Bottom Right:*	In the glands of the stomach, as well as in the crypts of Lieberkühn in the small and large intestines, are small, basally located cells with a large nucleus (*Nu*) and a cytoplasm overfilled with small, intensely stained granules (*G*) among elongated mitochondria (*Mi*). This is the argentaffine cell. Its function is not clear, but the ultrastructure of the granule is closely reminiscent of those occurring in the endocrine cells of the adrenal medulla. It has been suggested that the cell is responsible for the production of serotonin or secretin. The secretory membrane-bound granules arise within the Golgi area (*Go*) and gradually increase in density. The mode of release of their content is not understood, since few of these cells reach the lumen of the gastrointestinal tract, but an intercellular discharge toward the base of the cell in the vicinity of neighboring capillaries is most likely.

Stomach. Fundic gland. Magnification 14,000×. Ep. LH.

*References:*	178, 516, 560, 709a, 867.

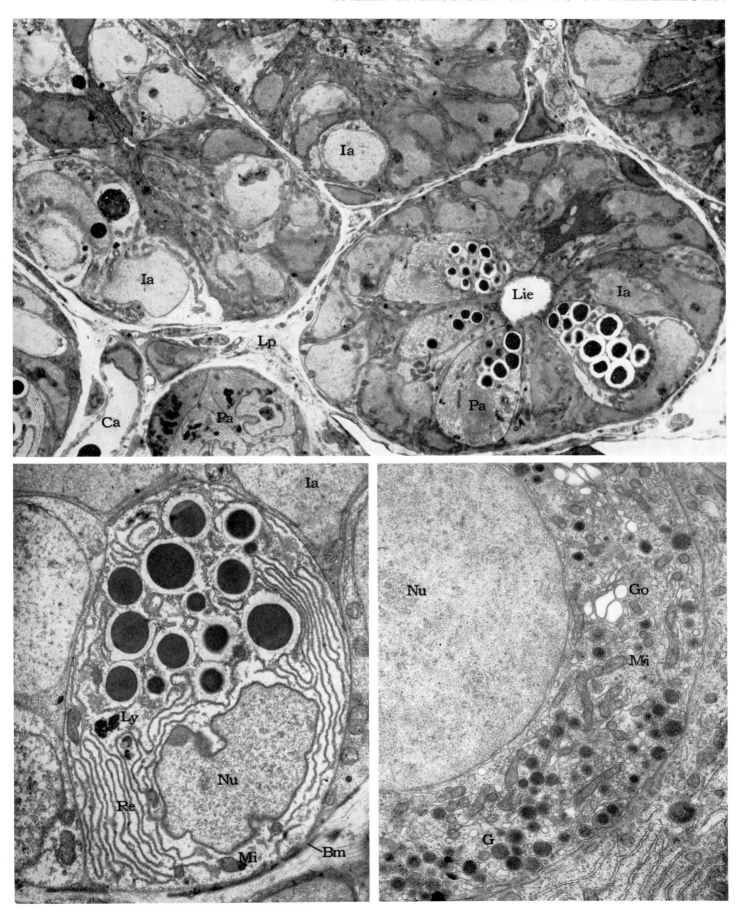

*Top:*

The luminal (*Lu*) surface of the large intestine is covered by tall columnar cells (*Su*). Straight tubular mucous glands, or crypts of Lieberkühn (*Lie*), extend from the surface down through the mucosa. The columnar surface cells (*Su*) have a striated border (*Sb*) at their apices, and generally the fine structure of these cells coincides with what has been described for the surface cells of the small intestine (cf. page 62). The columnar cells are also found down to a certain level in the crypts of Lieberkühn, where mucous cells (*Gc*) and undifferentiated cells (*Ia*) predominate. The goblet cells exhibit various stages of mucus production. Two cells are caught in a stage of discharging mucus into the crypt (arrows). The lamina propria (*Lp*) contains numerous blood capillaries (*Ca*) and an assortment of loose connective tissue elements.

Colon. Magnification 1800×. Ep. UA.

*Bottom Left:*

In order to illustrate the formation and discharge of mucus in the goblet cell, a cell from the human trachea has been selected, since the processes involved are similar in both types of epithelium. The mucous granules originate in and first appear within the Golgi area (*Go*). The usual components of this specialized cytoplasmic region appear as parallel membranes, small vesicles, and vacuoles (*Va*). The larger vacuoles condense and enlarge to establish early forms of mucous granules in a succession—most likely as indicated (1 to 3). At stages 3 and 4, the surrounding vacuolar membrane tends to dissolve. Nearby structures are lysosomes (*Ly*) and mitochondria (*Mi*). The precursors of the mucoid material are probably elaborated by the nearby elements of the rough-surfaced endoplasmic reticulum, which are not seen in this illustration.

Human trachea. Magnification 31,000×. Ep. LH.

*Bottom Right:*

The membranes of the mucous granules disappear, and even the thin cytoplasmic strands (*Cs*) become stretched and disrupted, causing adjacent granules (5) to fuse. The apex of the cell is now transformed into a goblet, and before the discharge of mucus into the lumen (*Lu*) the surface cell membrane (*Cm*) disrupts, giving rise to the stage indicated by the arrows in the top picture. Ciliated cells on either side of the goblet cell are joined to the mucous cell membrane by means of terminal bars (*Tb*).

Human trachea. Magnification 16,000×. Ep. LH.

*References:* 411, 650, 709a, 1003, 1165, 1413.

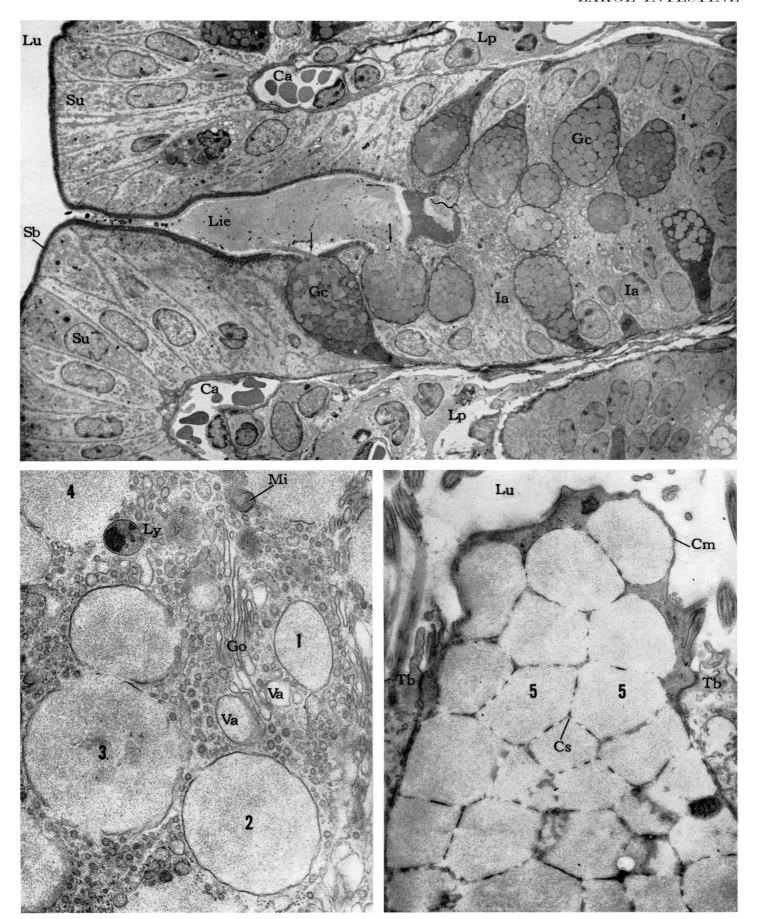

# SEROSA

*Left:*

The serosa or the serous membrane forms the outermost coat of the wall of the alimentary tube. It is composed of a single layer of squamous endothelial cells (*Me*). The serosa borders on the peritoneal cavity (*Pt*) and rests on a layer of delicate fibroelastic tissue with numerous collagen fibrils (*Co*). The mesothelial cells (*Me*) are of a polygonal shape, and the cellular junctions (*Jct*) are provided with terminal bars as attachment devices. The cell body is flat with the largest depth corresponding to the site of the nucleus.

This particular section corresponds to the wall of the gut over an intestinal lymph node. There are few smooth muscle cells (*So*) in the peripheral longitudinal muscle layer, which here are cross sectioned (*Cr*). The smooth muscle cells (*So*) of the inner circular are sectioned longitudinally (*Le*). Delicate nerves (*Ne*) and cells of unknown nature with a light cytoplasm (*X*) are encountered between the muscle layers.

Intestine. Magnification 5000×. Ep. LA.

*Top Right:*

Enlarged detail of the picture at the left. The elongated nucleus (*Nu*) of the mesothelial cell occupies a major portion of the cell depth. Scattered, oval mitochondria (*Mi*) and a small Golgi complex (*Go*) can be identified. Scattered short microvilli (*Vi*) extend from the surface of the mesothelial cell into the peritoneal cavity (*Pt*). Small, pocketlike invaginations (*Pi*) appear at the superficial and basal surfaces. The mesothelial cells of the intestinal serosa rest on a continuous, thin basement membrane (*Bm*), which in turn separates the serous membrane from the collagenous fibrils (*Co*) of the connective tissue and the smooth muscle cells (*So*). A basement membrane is present beneath the visceral mesothelium in the liver, spleen, kidney, adrenal gland, pleura, and pericardium, but is absent beneath the mesothelium of the omentum. The composition of the submesothelial connective tissue varies considerably in relation to the different organs. For instance, it is rich in collagen and fibroblasts within the capsule of the adrenal gland, the kidney, and the spleen, whereas only a few fibroblasts are present in the liver capsule and the pleura, both of which have an abundance of collagenous fibrils.

Intestine. Magnification 10,000×. Ep. LA.

*Bottom Right:*

Detail of a portion of the thin cytoplasmic extension of the squamous mesothelial cell of the intestinal serosa. The microvilli (*Vi*), which protrude into the peritoneal cavity (*Pt*), vary in length. They are covered by the surface plasma membrane (*Cm*) and contain central thin filaments (*Fi*) similar to those occurring in stereocilia (cf. page 5). The surface inpocketings (*Pi*), representing pinocytotic vesicles, are abundant and may be caught within the cell, here possibly acquiring the size of the cytoplasmic vesicles (*Ve*). The basement membrane (*Bm*) is a thin, homogeneous, continuous structure. The mesothelial cell is probably highly permeable and allows fluid to seep through to lubricate the surfaces. It is assumed that the microvilli increase the surface area for exchange of soluble substances between the cells and the peritoneal cavity. Foreign particles can be washed free from the surface shortly after their inoculation. If the particles are small, they are undoubtedly taken up by the pinocytotic vesicles and transferred across the mesothelial cell. However, the vesicles may also indicate an active exchange of fluids and metabolites between the mesothelial cell and the environment as is the case with similar structures in the endothelium of blood vessels and the smooth muscle cell.

Intestine. Magnification 50,000×. Ep. LA.

*References:* 380, 381, 423, 521, 959, 960, 1076, 1380, 1457.

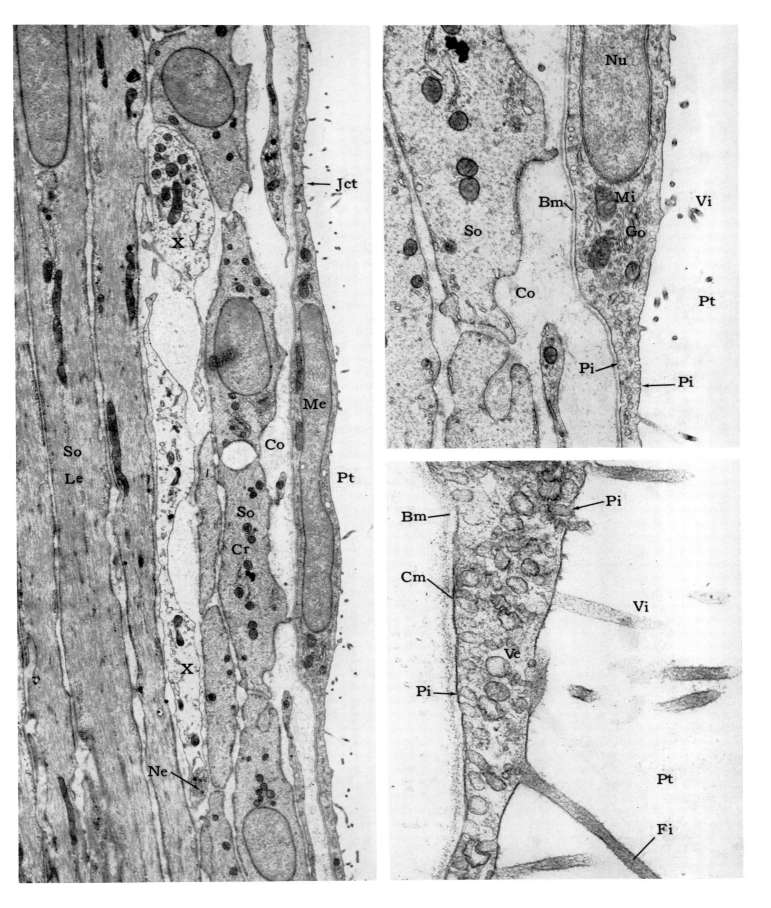

*Top:*

The liver is composed of cords of polyhedral hepatic cells (*Lr*), most of which have one or sometimes two nuclei. The entire mass of liver cells is surrounded by a fibrous capsule (capsule of Glisson) containing bundles of collagenous fibrils (*Co*). It is covered with mesothelial cells (*Me*) wherever it borders on the peritoneal cavity (*Pt*). The major part of the blood enters the liver parenchyma through the branches of the portal vein and is drained by the central veins. Sinusoids (*Si*) establish a connection between the portal and the central veins. The sinusoids are lined by the so-called Kupffer cells (*Ku*), which are of a reticuloendothelial nature; i.e., the cells can perform phagocytic work. The hepatic cells (*Lr*) contain numerous mitochondria (*Mi*), stored glycogen (*Gl*), and small electron-dense bodies, most of which are located around the bile canaliculi (asterisks). The fine structure of the glycogen is described on page 12.

Magnification 3000×. Ep. UA.

*Bottom:*

The general architecture of the liver cell is more easily studied at higher magnification. The nucleus (*Nu*) occupies a large middle part of the cell and on all sides is surrounded by small Golgi areas (*Go*). Mitochondria (*Mi*) are abundant, are slightly elongated, and frequently are associated closely with lipid inclusions (*Li*) (see also page 13). Elements of the rough-surfaced endoplasmic reticulum (*Re*) are scattered throughout the cytoplasm. It should be kept in mind that one hepatic cell may carry on a variety of activities owing to its polyhedral shape, since the cell borders simultaneously on several sinusoids (*Si*) and bile canaliculi (*Bi* and asterisk). This explains, among other things, the wide distribution of Golgi areas (*Go*) and the occurrence of dense bodies—here collectively referred to as lysosomes (*Ly*)—in the neighborhood of a bile canaliculus.

Magnification 9000×. Ep. LH.

*References:* GENERAL 125, 136, 165, 215, 230, 235, 357, 687, 924, 929, 1063, 1231, 1232, 1384, 1542.
EXPERIMENTAL AND PATHOLOGICAL CONDITIONS 21, 23, 137, 299, 312, 313, 447, 475, 524, 526, 761, 845, 1028, 1115, 1174, 1233, 1237, 1257, 1258, 1325.

Page 70

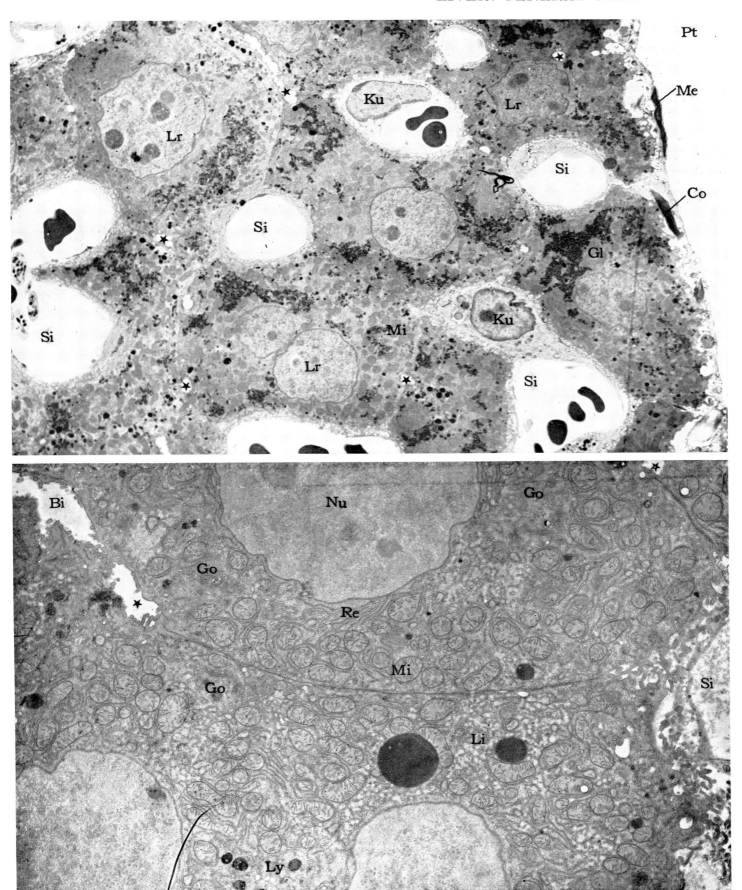

*Top:*

The cytoplasm of the liver cell is rich in ribosomes, most of which are attached to the endoplasmic reticulum (*Re*) near the nucleus (*Nu*). Small vacuoles or vesicles are present and could probably be termed smooth-surfaced endoplasmic reticulum, but most of these structures seem to belong to the Golgi complex. A variety of "dense bodies" occur in the liver cell. Some are termed microbodies (*Mb*) (cf. page 12); some are extremely dense and finely granular and probably correspond to lysosomes (*Ly*). Other granules contain finely divided particles, presumably ferritin (*Ft*), whereas still another type is located within the Golgi area (*Go*) and seems to be a Golgi vacuole filled with a slightly dense substance. These structures are all smaller than the mitochondria (*Mi*). It is too early to predict whether all the "dense granules" of the liver cell are derived from the same precursor structure, or whether they all represent individual cell organelles containing specific enzymes with assigned functions. The secretory surfaces of the cell exposed to the bile canaliculi (*Bi*) are provided with small microvilli. The plasma membranes (*Cm*) indicate the borderline of two adjacent hepatic cells. (For a detailed description of liver glycogen, see page 12.)

Hepatic cell. Magnification 16,000×. Ep. LH.

*Bottom:*

The liver sinusoid (*Si*) is lined by the thin endothelium of the Kupffer cell in which occur fenestrations (arrows) lacking the closing diaphragm of blood capillaries. The absorptive surface of the liver cell is differentiated into short microvilli (*Vi*), which occupy the space of Disse (*Di*) together with a network of delicate collagenous fibrils. Also, close to this surface are mitochondria (*Mi*), microbodies (*Mb*), and granules of the ferritin type (*Ft*). The main portion of the Kupffer cell harbors the nucleus (*Nu*), a few mitochondria (*Mi*), and elements of the rough-surfaced endoplasmic reticulum (*Re*). Near the surface appear small vesicles (*Pi*), presumably of micropinocytotic nature. Some Kupffer cells may contain granules (*Ly*) of varying sizes, possibly representing lysosomes (cf. page 13).

Sinusoid. Magnification 30,000×. Ep. LH.

*References:* HEPATIC CELL   25, 28, 80, 208, 216, 236, 238, 249, 338, 341, 466, 525, 584, 602, 666, 671, 865, 916, 1064, 1369, 1543.
SINUSOID   138, 150, 151, 206, 207, 379, 1024, 1247, 1254, 1265, 1476.
FRACTIONATION OF LIVER TISSUE   172, 897, 920, 923, 927, 997, 998.

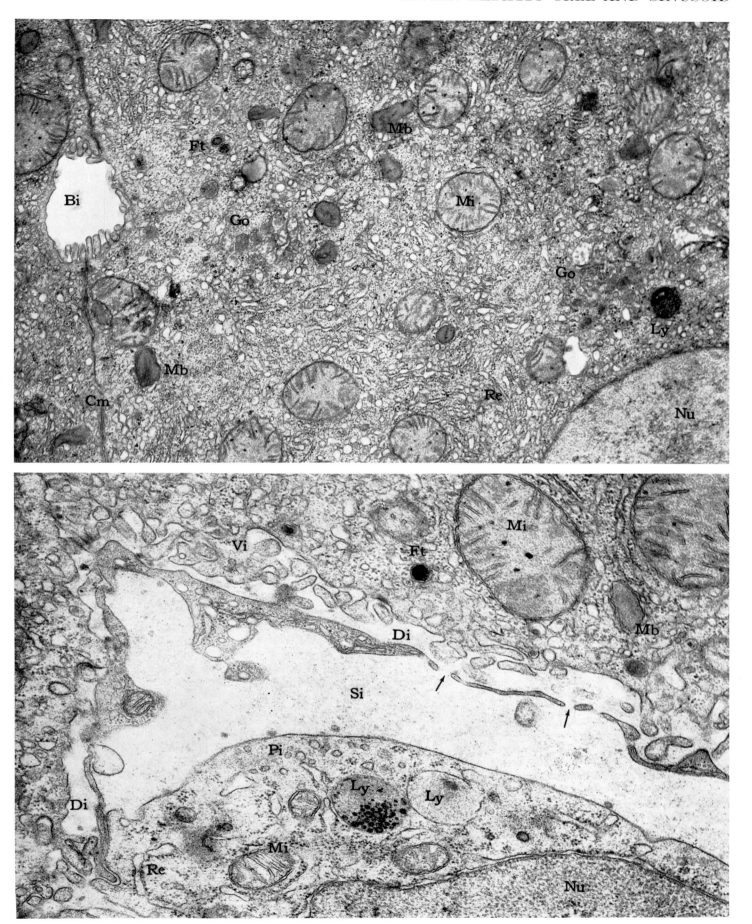

*Top:*    The gallbladder epithelium is composed of columnar cells with the nuclei ($Nu$) located near the basement membrane ($Bm$). Several folds ($Fo$) appear, some of which extend into mucosal diverticula. The luminal cell surface ($Lu$) is provided with numerous short microvilli ($Vi$). The majority of the small granules of the cytoplasm represent mitochondria ($Mi$), but some are of a different nature ($G$). Beneath the basement membrane ($Bm$) is the lamina propria ($Lp$), which is composed mainly of collagenous fibers and is traversed by numerous capillaries ($Ca$).

Magnification 2700×. Meth. Unstained.

*Bottom Left:*    Detail of the luminal part of a gallbladder epithelial cell. The microvilli ($Vi$) are short (for detail, compare with page 4). Adjoining cells are attached by terminal bars ($Tb$). The Golgi complex ($Go$) is small. Mitochondria ($Mi$) vary in size but cannot be mistaken for small granules ($G$), which have a single boundary membrane. It is believed that most of the granules represent absorbed substances, but a secretory process cannot be ruled out, since some granules are close to the Golgi area and structurally resemble small mucous granules in, for instance, the gastric surface cells or the cells of the uterine glands. Ribosomes ($Ri$) occur as well as occasional lysosomelike bodies ($Ly$).

Magnification 40,000×. Ep. LH.

*Bottom Right:*    The cytoplasm below the nucleus ($Nu$) displays a complex system of folds formed by lateral interdigitations of adjoining small cell processes, all lined by the cell membrane ($Cm$). The intercellular space ($Is$) occasionally appears to be dilated and seems to contain finely granular material. As in the intestinal mucosa, this may be a route of transportation for absorbed substances. The row of vesicles ($Rv$) is a frequent finding in cells with a high rate of fluid transportation and probably is a sign of high plasma membrane activity. Dense granules ($Ft$) occur, which resemble ferritin-containing bodies elsewhere in the biliary system. The basement membrane ($Bm$) is thin and structurally homogeneous and runs uninterruptedly beneath the epithelial cells.

Magnification 40,000×. Ep. LH.

*References:*   559, 1549.

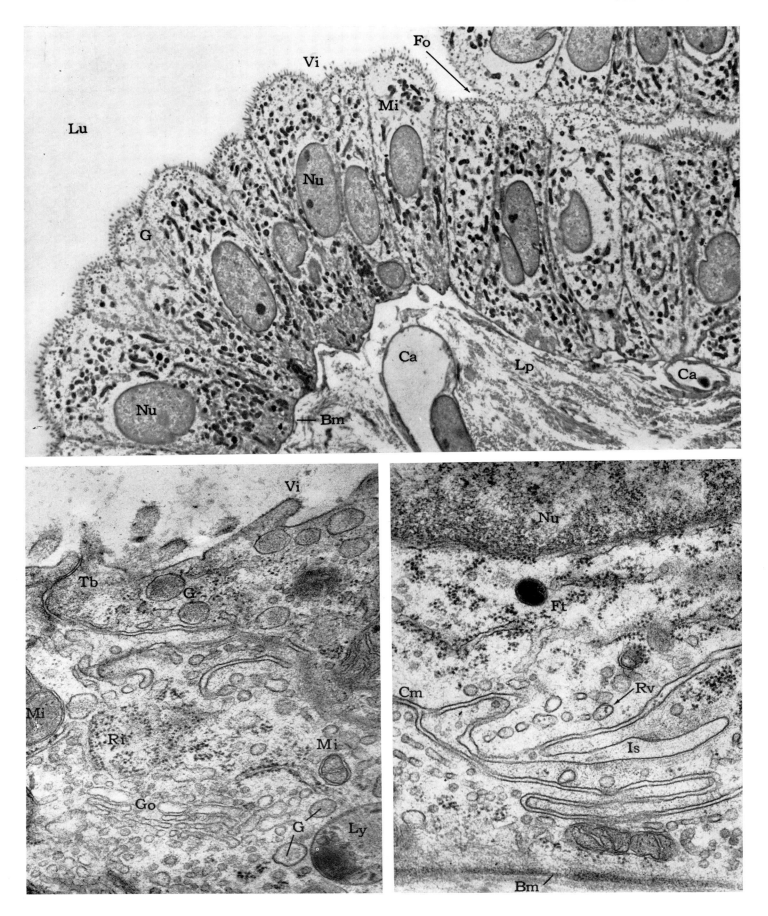

*Top:*    The exocrine portion of the pancreas is composed of pyramidal acinar cells (*Ac*) forming lobules, which are bound together by loose connective tissue rich in capillaries (*Ca*). The apices of several cells (1 to 4) converge toward a central lumen (*Lu*), filled with a secretory product of medium density. (A detailed description of this area is given on page 6). Small centroacinar cells (*Cac*) with irregularly shaped nuclei and sparse cytoplasm represent within the acini the beginning of the intralobular ducts. The acinar cell has a large spherical nucleus, and the basal two-thirds of the cell is characterized by a wealth of rough-surfaced endoplasmic reticulum (*Re*) in which occasional mitochondria (*Mi*) can be identified. Lysosomes are rare structures in these cells. The apical third of the cell is occupied by a large Golgi complex (*Go*) and numerous zymogenic granules (*G*) in various stages of maturation. (A detailed description of an acinar Golgi zone is given on page 8.)

Magnification 7300×. Ep. LH.

*Bottom:*    Enlargement of an area similar to the rectangle in the top picture. The cytoplasm of the acinar cell of the exocrine portion of the pancreas is the prototype for cells engaged in elaborating proteins to be used extracellularly, mostly a wide variety of enzymes. Its fine structure is, without exception, referred to as rough-surfaced endoplasmic reticulum. This consists of thin membranes (about 50A thick) studded on one side with rows of ribonucleoprotein particles (RNP or ribosomes) and limiting slightly irregular spaces or cisternae filled with a structureless substance of medium density. The ribosomes, which are attached to the membranes of the cisternae, are seen in grazing sections to be arranged in a rosetlike fashion (circle). The ribosomes have a mean diameter of about 150A. They also occur freely in the thin strands of cytoplasm between the cisternae. Across the field of view run two opposing cell membranes, each of which has an average thickness of about 70A and can easily be identified because of the dimension and the absence of attached ribosomes.

Magnification 53,000×. Ep. LH.

*References:*   148, 160, 219, 288, 298, 300, 304, 305, 472, 567, 568, 569, 571, 585, 647, 709a, 777, 901, 914, 988, 994, 1058, 1195, 1329, 1330, 1354b, 1354c, 1497, 1498, 1499, 1526, 1589.

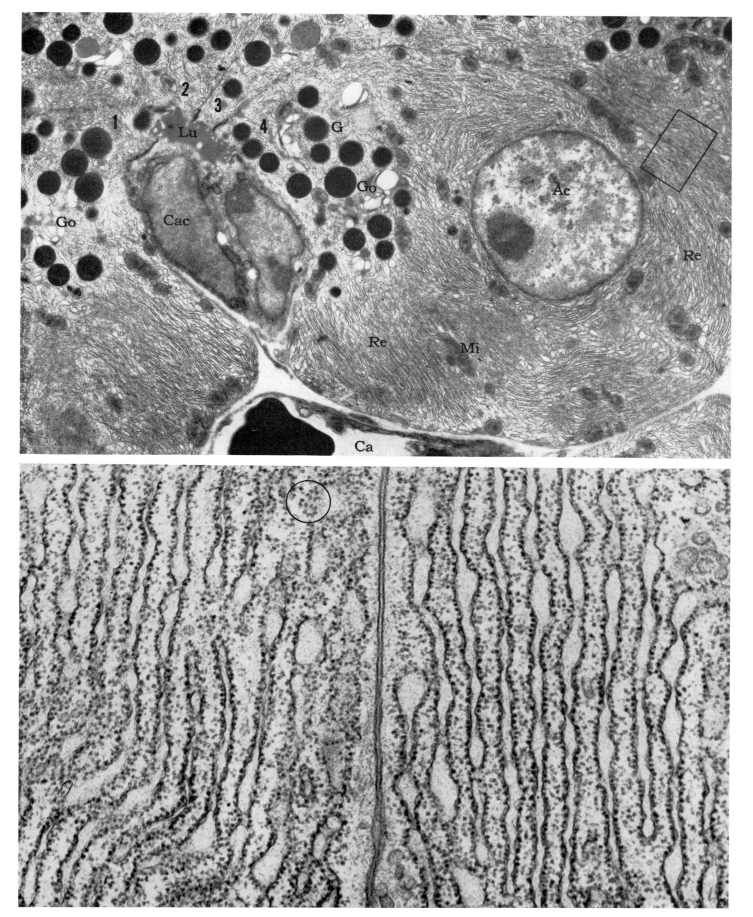

*Top:*   In this low-magnification electron micrograph of the cortex of an intestinal lymph node most of the cells are identified as lymphocytes of either a small (*Lyc*) or a large (*Ly*) size. The large ones have a big nucleus and more cytoplasm than the small cells. Cells with large oval nuclei and a light, elongated cytoplasm are considered to be reticular cells (*Rec*), which form a more or less continuous syncytium thoughout the lymph node. Occasional plasma cells (*Pl*) are present. Although the reticular cells may phagocytize material, true macrophages are considered to be cells with large chunks of dense material (*Mp*), which presumably have become detached from the reticular cell system. The absence of erythrocytes should be noticed.
Magnification 2600×. Ep. LH.

*Bottom Left:*   At somewhat higher magnification, it can be seen that the macrophages (*Mp*) contain dense granules of phagocytized material, which, as a structural unit, may be considered to represent lysosomes. The large lymphocytes (*Ly*) have a cytoplasm that is rich in ribosomes (*Ri*), mitochondria (*Mi*), and some profiles of rough-surfaced endoplasmic reticulum (*Re*). The small lymphocytes (*Lyc*) can be differentiated from the larger ones by their narrow cytoplasm.
Magnification 4000×. Ep. LA.

*Bottom Right:*   The wall of the cortical sinus of the intestinal lymph node is lined by endothelial cells (*Ed*) similar to those that are found in blood and lymph capillaries. However, contrary to these, they rest on a meshwork of fine reticular fibrils (*Ret*); a true continuous basement membrane is not present. In the lumen (*Lu*) of the cortical sinus is a small lymphocyte (*Lyc*). The nucleus is large; the scanty cytoplasm contains occasional mitochondria (*Mi*) and numerous ribosomes (*Ri*).
Magnification 28,000×. Ep. LA.

*References:*   182, 415, 425, 479, 529, 530, 531, 646, 784, 870, 933, 1086, 1137, 1370, 1391.

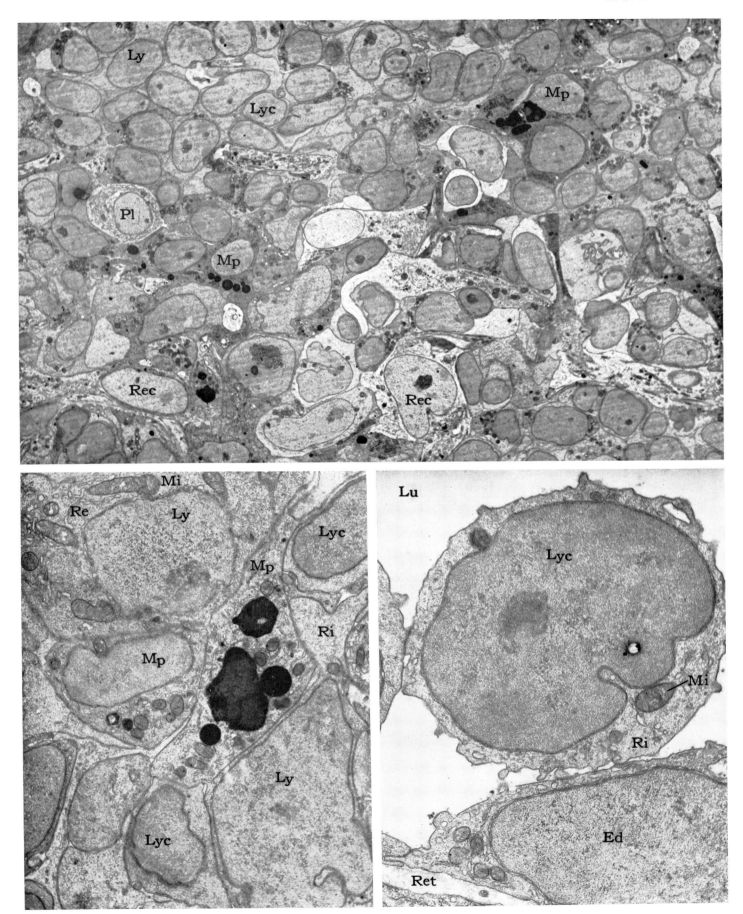

*Top:*

The spleen is covered with a capsule (*Caps*) composed of dense connective tissue. Trabeculae project in from the capsule and form, with a network of reticular cells (*Rec*) and fibers, a framework that is filled by splenic pulp. Terminal venous sinuses (*Si*) are lined by incomplete sheaths of reticular and endothelial cells. However, the problem concerning the "open" or "closed" circulation in the spleen is still not solved. The spleen of the mouse is an important myelopoietic organ and presents a picture much like that found in human bone marrow. The study of the fine structure of the spleen is just beginning, and an attempt will be made here to decipher only the cells that can be recognized easily. The reticular cells (*Rec*) and the macrophages (*Mp*) are similar to those of the lymph node. The megakaryocyte (*Meg*) is common in the mouse spleen (its fine details were discussed on page 2). Erythroblasts (*Eb*) in various stages of maturation (1 to 3) are characterized by their extremely dense cytoplasm, loss of the nucleus, and simultaneous decrease in size. Neutrophilic leukocytes (*Neu*) and small lymphocytes (*Lyc*) are easily identified, but to differentiate between a monocyte (*Mon*) and a myelocyte (*Myc*) is more difficult and requires higher magnification.

Magnification 2700×. Ep. LA.

*Bottom Left:*

The macrophage (*Mp*) contains an assortment of phagocytized material, including crystalloid bodies. The early erythroblast (*Eb*) has a cytoplasm in which the ribosomes (*Ri*) are stained more intensely than those of the small lymphocyte (*Lyc*). The cell undergoing mitosis (*Mit*) is of unknown origin. The intercellular spaces contain bundles of reticular fibrils (*Ret*).

Magnification 14,000×. Ep. LA.

*Bottom Right:*

A cross section of a sheathed artery reveals numerous smooth muscle cells (*So*) alternating with layers of basement membranes (*Bm*) in a jelly-roll fashion. The innermost layer consists of endothelial cells (*Ed*) lining the lumen of the vessel (asterisks), which is barely discernible because of the heavily contracted muscle cells that are richly provided with nerve endings (*Ne*).

Magnification 13,000×. Ep. LA.

*References:* 137, 196, 198, 336, 435, 572, 583, 696, 1390, 1392, 1502, 1503, 1504, 1505, 1506, 1507.

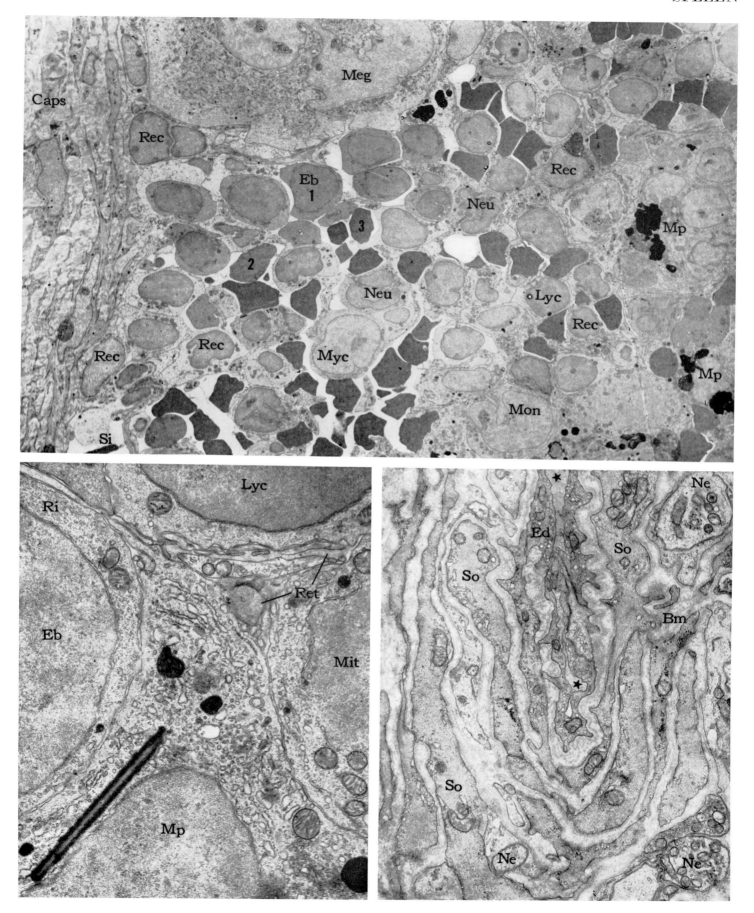

The epithelium of the human trachea (this illustration) is of a pseudostratified, ciliated columnar type. It rests on a basement, which is shown by the electron microscope to be composed of a thin, continuous basement membrane (*Bm*) and a thick layer of reticular and fine collagenous fibrils (*Ret*). Resting on this basement membrane is a layer of basal cells (*Ba*), which correspond structurally and functionally to the basal germinal layers of the epidermis, the cornea, and the esophagus. The superficial layer of the tracheal epithelium is composed of ciliated cells (*Cil*) and the mucus-producing goblet cells (*Gc*). Infrequently an odd cell type can be identified, which has been termed the brush cell (*X*).

Presumably both the ciliated and the mucous cells are derived from the basal cell layer, since cells of indifferent appearance (*Ia*) occur as an intermediate, incomplete layer, none of which can be said to represent either of the cell types mentioned. The ciliated cells (*Cil*) are provided with cilia (*C*) at the luminal surface (*Lu*), and the apical cytoplasm of the mucous cells (*Gc*) is to a varying degree filled with mucous granules, which can be seen to be discharged at the surface. (For a detailed study of the production of mucus, compare illustrations on page 67.) The indifferent cell (*X*) resembles most closely a ciliated cell except that microvilli are more abundant and cilia less abundant. It is believed that this cell is a basal cell that just has reached the surface of the epithelium as a replacement for ciliated cells lost in a sloughing-off process. The surface of the brush cell would then form cilia in order to replace the lost ciliated cell. Wide intercellular spaces (*Is*) occur. Some of these may be formed by cellular shrinkage, but most of the spaces are considered to represent intercellular pathways for the exchange of fluid and absorbed substances.

Human trachea. Magnification 2700×. Meth. Unstained.

*References:* 35, 217, 317, 368, 758, 759, 1147, 1149, 1153, 1162, 1163, 1165, 1377, 1437, 1545.

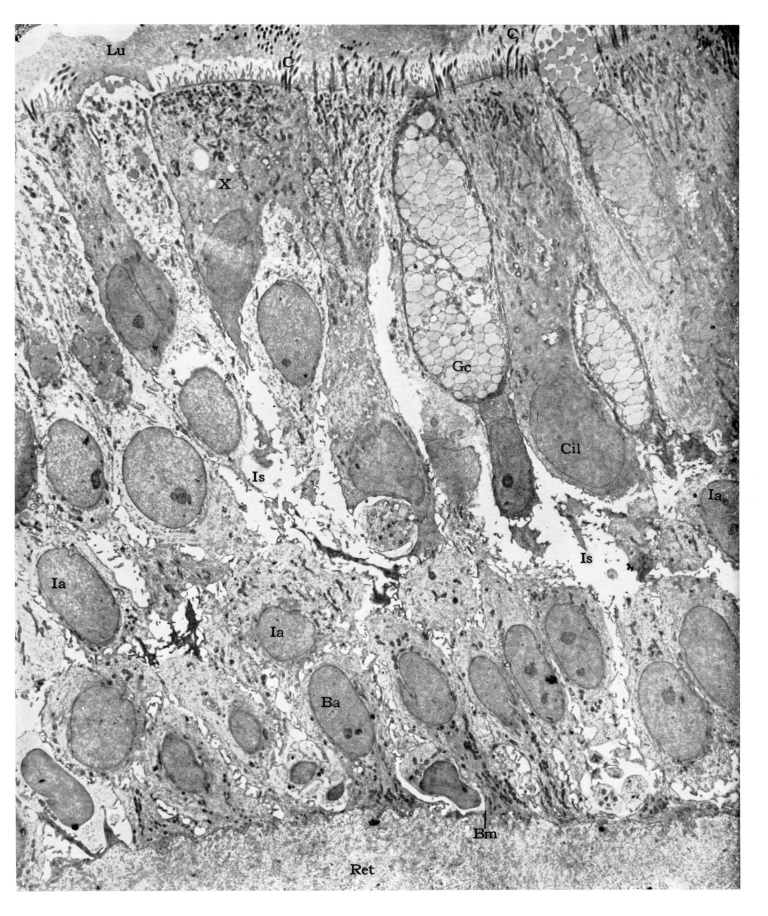

*Top:*     Detail of three ciliated cells and part of a goblet cell (*Gc*) of the human tracheal epithelium. The plasma membranes (*Cm*) of individual cells are attached to each other at the lumen by terminal bars (*Tb*). Each ciliated cell has about 250 cilia (*C*), each of which emanates from a basal corpuscle (*Bc*). The cilium, which tapers off toward the tip, is covered by the surface cell membrane and contains longitudinally arranged filaments, which arise within the basal corpuscle. Microvilli (*Vi*) between the bases of the cilia are short extensions of the surface. Aggregates of widely branched mitochondria (*Mi*) are in close proximity to the basal corpuscles (*Bc*). Short filamentous rootlets (*Fi*) extend downward from the basal corpuscle. (A detailed description of the cilium is found on page 4.)
Magnification 10,000×. Ep. LH.

*Bottom:*     Detail of two basal cells of the human tracheal epithelium. The nucleus (*Nu*) is large and is located in the center of the cell. Most of the cytoplasm is occupied by fine filaments (*Fi*), which are of the same size and general arrangement as similar structures in the basal layer of stratified squamous epithelia and are usually considered to be tonofilaments. The occurrence of tonofilaments in the basal cells of a pseudostratified columnar ciliated epithelium is not surprising and is an explanation for the fact that the tracheal epithelium under pathologic conditions quickly can become transformed into a stratified squamous epithelium. Numerous ribosomes (*Ri*) and mitochondria (*Mi*) occur together with occasional lysosomes (*Ly*). Slender cell processes project into the intercellular space (*Is*). The basement membrane proper (*Bm*) is thin, and the reticular fibrils (*Ret*) form an irregular network beneath. (For a close-up of the tonofilaments, see page 133.)
Magnification 16,000×. Ep  LH.

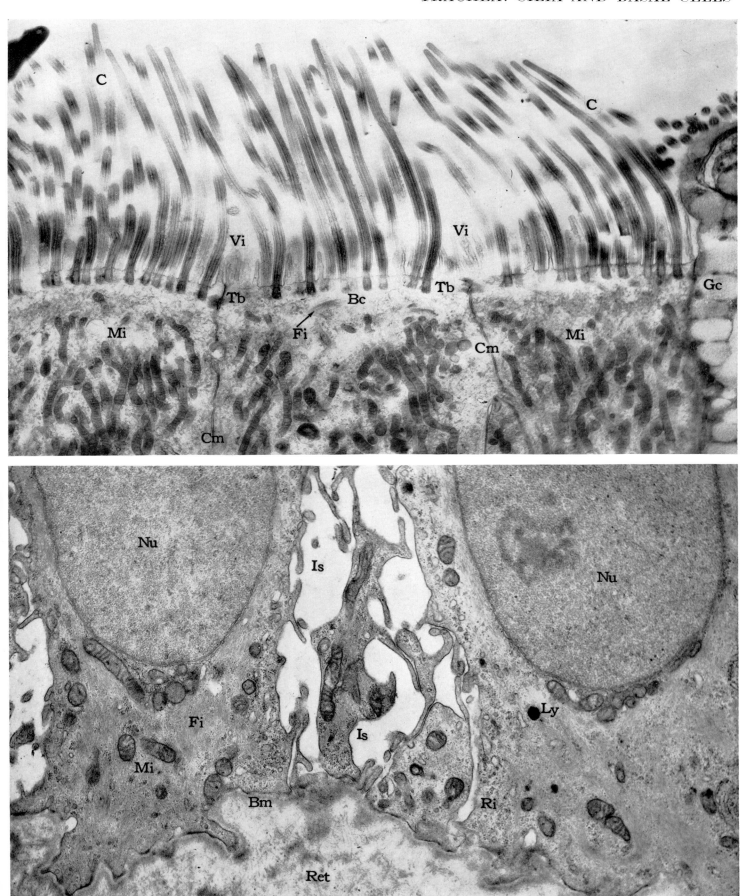

*Top:*    The terminal bronchioles of the lung of the mouse are lined with a low, simple columnar or cuboidal ciliated epithelium. The ciliated cell (*Cil*) has a small, basally located nucleus and a cytoplasm with few mitochondria. The cilia have the same fine structure as those of the trachea and extend into the bronchiolar lumen (*Lu*). The ciliated cells disappear gradually as the respiratory bronchioles are approached. The epithelium of the terminal bronchiole does not contain goblet cells, but the ciliated cells are interspersed with so-called Clara cells (*Cla*) of varying height. Their cytoplasm is rich in dense granules formerly considered to be secretory granules. However, they are mitochondria. The bronchiolar membrane forms longitudinal folds, which may result from contraction of occasional delicate smooth muscle cells (*Sm*), located between the epithelium and the connective tissue (*Co*). The folds are more or less permanent and may be a reserve for potential expansion of the terminal bronchiole during sudden rises in intrabronchiolar pressure.

Terminal bronchiole. Magnification 5000×. Ep. LA. UA.

*Bottom:*    Little is known about the function of the Clara cells. The luminal (*Lu*) parts of two cells are here shown at higher magnification with interposed cross-sectioned cilia (*Ci*) of a ciliated cell. The numerous spherical structures are mitochondria (*Mi*) having a peculiar ultrastructure with an almost complete absence of inner membranes. However, the triple-layered appearance of their outer membrane indicates their mitochondrial nature. The cytoplasm contains round and elongated profiles of the rough-surfaced endoplasmic reticulum (*Re*). Quite regularly, short profiles of the smooth-surfaced endoplasmic reticulum are wrapped around each mitochondrion in a most peculiar, multilayered fashion. Part of the nucleus (*Nu*) is seen in the lower right corner. The ultrastructure of the Clara cells indicates that the cells are engaged in processes that require large amounts of oxidative enzymes, possibly a secretion similar to that in the parietal cells of the gastric mucosa.

Clara cells. Magnification 16,000×. Ep. LH.

*References:*   655, 657, 658, 660, 1077, 1082, 1093, 1097, 1521.

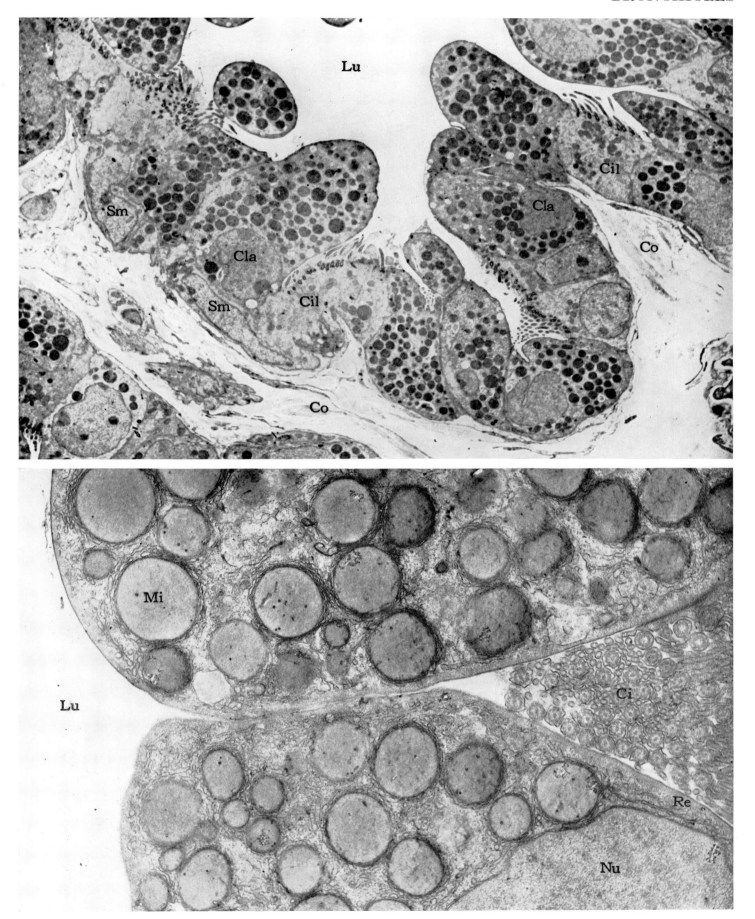

The lung is an organ in which the air and the blood capillaries establish an intimate interrelationship. The air sacs or alveoli (*Al*) are surrounded by a meshwork of anastomosing capillaries (*Ca*) filled with numerous erythrocytes (intensely dark-staining, irregular corpuscles). The wall between alveoli is usually referred to as an interalveolar septum. It is composed mainly of blood capillaries but also contains septal cells (*Se*), which seem to be a kind of fibroblast. The inside of the capillaries is lined by endothelial cells (*Ed*). The alveoli are lined by epithelial cells (*Ep*) mixed with occasional peculiar cells, the so-called "dust" cells (*Du*). The mouth of each alveolus (*Mo*) is surrounded by smooth muscle in man, whereas in mouse (this illustration) only reticular, elastic, and delicate collagenous fibers (*Co*) can be identified. Alveolar pores (*Ap*) establish a free communication between neighboring alveoli.

The visceral pleura borders on the pleural cavity (*Pc*) and is composed of thin, flattened mesothelial cells (*Me*) and a rich network of elastic and collagenous fibers (*Co*).

Magnifications 2000×. Ep. UA.

*References:* 43, 47, 144, 156, 187, 188, 278, 467, 492, 494, 554, 624, 625, 652, 653, 654, 656, 691, 707, 790, 792, 793, 798, 825, 1067, 1073, 1075, 1081, 1087, 1088, 1089, 1090, 1091, 1259, 1262, 1279, 1280, 1281, 1283, 1405, 1444, 1479, 1544, 1568.

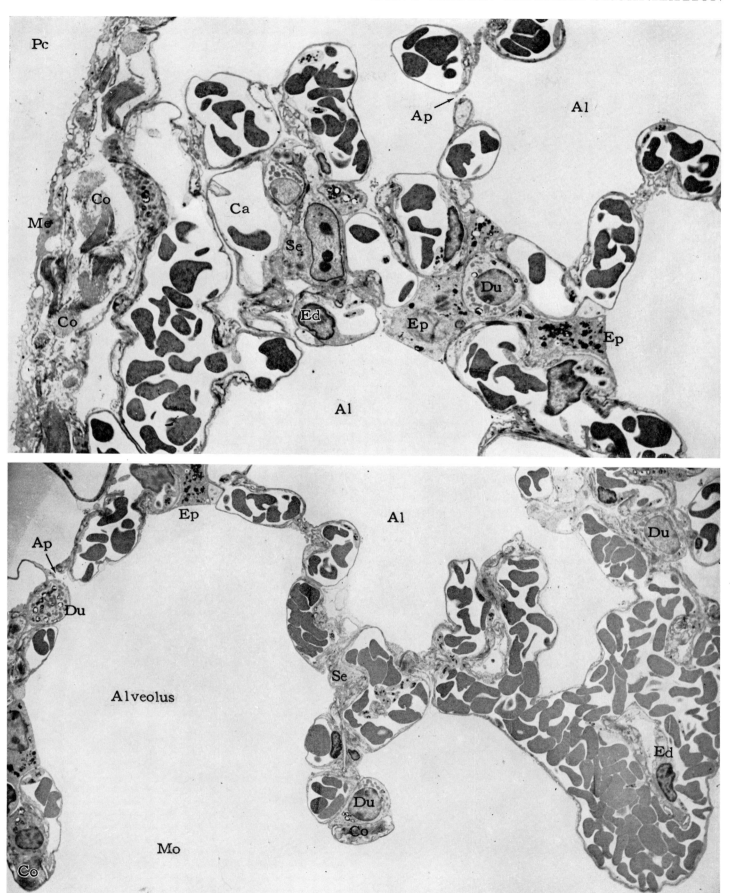

*Top:*     Detail of three cross-sectioned lung capillaries containing platelets (*Th*) and red blood cells (*Er*). The wall between the capillary lumen (*Ca*) and the alveolus (*Al*) is extremely thin and is composed of three layers: (1) The central part is represented by a basement membrane (*Bm*), which remains in direct connection with the collagen (*Co*) and the septal cells (*Se*). (2) The endothelial cell cytoplasm (*Ed*) forms the inner layer and contains numerous pinocytotic vesicles. (3) The thin epithelial cytoplasm (*Ep*) borders on the alveolus (*Al*) and contains occasional vesicles. A potential alveolar pore (*Ap*) can be identified between two of the capillaries. Although the endothelial cytoplasm is thin, it never shows any of the fenestrations so typical of thin capillary endothelium elsewhere in mammalian tissues.

Lung capillaries. Magnification 17,000×. Ep. LH.

*Bottom:*     Epithelial cells (*Ep*) with an identifiable nucleus are extremely rare and are usually located in small pockets of each alveolus (*Al*). The cytoplasm thins out into processes that extend along the interalveolar septa. The epithelial cells evidently have the potentiality of serving as macrophages, since varying numbers of dense bodies (*Ly*) with the characteristics of lysosomes can be encountered in the cytoplasm. The epithelial cell rests on a basement membrane, which in turn borders on septal cells (*Se*) and also rests directly on the septal collagenous fibers (*Co*). The capillary (*Ca*) at the left contains a granulocyte (*Gr*).

Alveolar epithelium. Magnification 22,000×. Ep. LH.

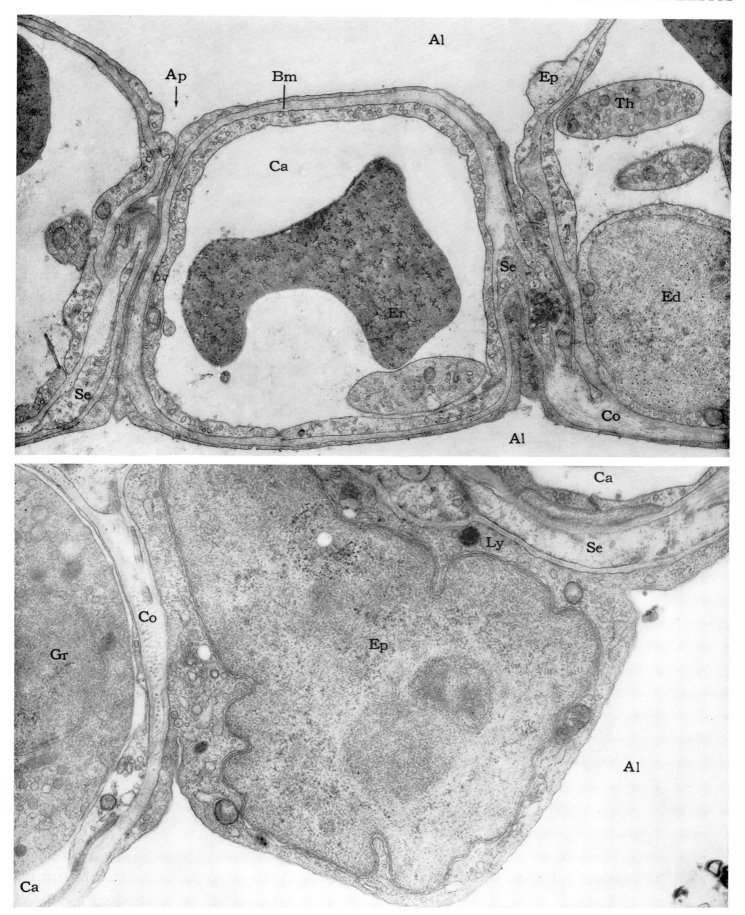

*Top:*    Detail of a so-called "dust" cell, which borders on the alveolar lumen (*Al*). The cytoplasm is rich in ribosomes (*Ri*), small vesicles (*Ve*), and scattered, short elements of the rough-surfaced endoplasmic reticulum (*Re*). The mitochondria (*Mi*) can be identified easily. The arrangement of their inner membranes is similar to what is seen in the mitochondria of the Clara cells in the terminal bronchioles (cf. page 87). The dust cells contain varying numbers of dense inclusion bodies (*Ib*), the nature of which is not fully understood. Some investigators claim that they are degenerating mitochondria. This does not seem likely, since small inclusion bodies can be identified that evidently represent an early stage of development. Later these bodies enlarge (1 to 4), and part of their content dissolves. The dust cell apparently is not an ordinary epithelial alveolar cell, since lateral cytoplasmic processes are never seen to extend over the basement membrane of the alveolar septum. On the contrary, the dust cell is always cuboidal and is wedged between true epithelial cells. It may be assumed that the dust cell is a variety of the bronchiolar Clara cell. The inclusion bodies do not look like lysosomes, although they may be formed from the products of degenerative changes in the cytoplasm of the dust cell.

Dust cell. Magnification 28,000×. Ep. LH.

*Bottom:*    Detail of a septal cell (*Se*). This cell is usually enclosed in sheaths of basement membranes (*Bm*) occurring centrally in the alveolar septum with epithelial (*Ep*) and endothelial (*Ed*) cells on either side. The cytoplasm contains numerous ribosomes (*Ri*), some small mitochondria (*Mi*), and a variable number of lipid droplets (*Li*). Its plasma membrane (*Cm*) borders on an intercellular space that is rich in fine collagenous fibrils (*Co*). The alveolus (*Al*) is at the top. It is believed that the septal cell is of connective tissue origin and has the capacity to lay down basement membrane material and collagen, similar to the mesangial cell of the glomerular capillaries of the kidney.

Septal cell. Magnification 37,000×. Ep. LH.

*References:*    ALVEOLAR CELLS    143, 171, 468, 469, 558, 626, 659, 661, 664, 669, 688, 791, 800, 941, 1072, 1083, 1085, 1095, 1252, 1260, 1261, 1278, 1282.
SEPTAL COMPONENTS    732, 789, 795, 1094.

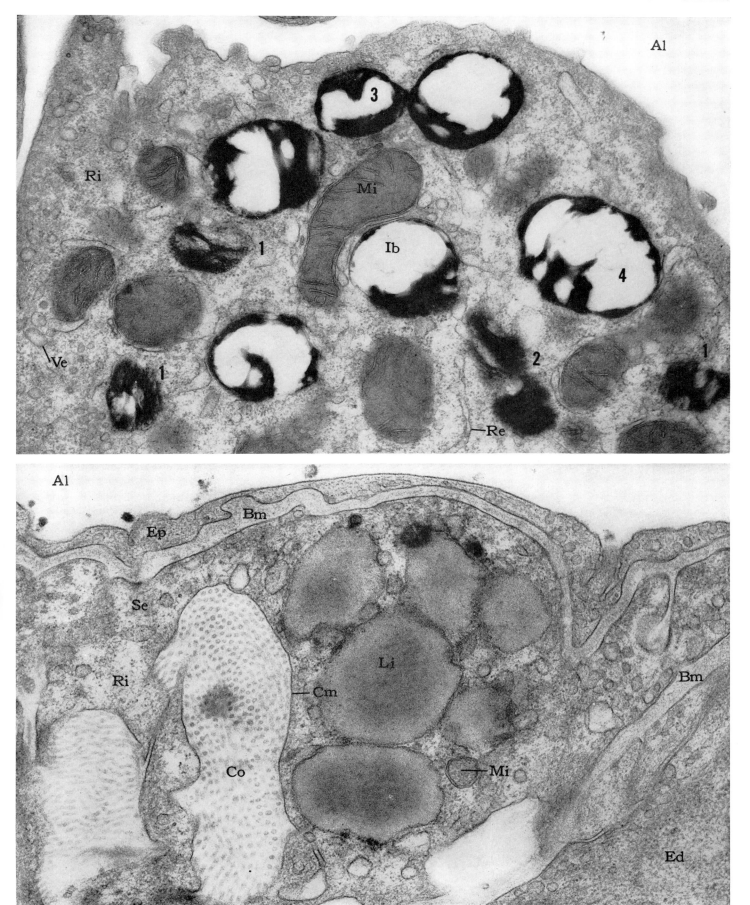

*Top:*  Part of a glomerulus of a nephron in the mouse kidney. The glomerulus is essentially a network of branching and possibly anastomosing capillaries (*Ca*), which are located in the urinary space of Bowman's capsule (*U*). The capillaries are lined by endothelial cells (*Ed*) and are covered by epithelial cells (*Ep*). Both cell types have an extensive flat cytoplasm except for the site of the nucleus. A thin basement membrane is interposed between these two cell layers. A third cell type, the mesangial (*Mc*) or intercapillary cell, occurs centrally within the capillary loops. One side of each capillary is always facing the mesangial cell, and the basement membrane of the capillary wall is thinned out and is often incomplete as it borders on the mesangial cell. The cytoplasm of the mesangial cell does not differ noticeably from that of the endothelial cell. However, there are extracellular spaces that contain fine reticular filaments, basement membranelike material (mesangial matrix), and, under certain pathologic conditions, collagenous fibrils. The origin and function of the mesangial cell is, therefore, reminiscent of the septal cell of lung tissue (cf. page 92).

Glomerular capillaries. Magnification 7000×. Ep. UA.

*Bottom:*  Detail of the glomerular capillaries (*Ca*). The endothelial cell (*Ed*) cytoplasm extends as a thin coating in which small fenestrations (*Fe*) can be seen in both cross-section and full face views. These fenestrations are bridged by a diaphragm as are capillaries elsewhere (cf. page 53). The basement membrane (*Bm*) of the capillary wall is a homogeneous structure, uninterrupted except for a few places where it borders on a mesangial cell. The epithelial cells (*Ep*) have a cytoplasm that extends over the capillaries in long, slender processes (*Fp*), frequently interdigitating with other similar processes. The urinary space (*U*) of the capsule of Bowman is connected with the lumen of the proximal tubule of the nephron.

Glomerular filtration membrane. Magnification 15,000×. Ep. UA.

*References:*  GENERAL  77, 78, 346, 347, 510, 511, 513, 712, 716, 743, 895, 896, 954, 972, 973, 975, 976, 978, 1078, 1136, 1161, 1175, 1176, 1211, 1249, 1400, 1422, 1550.

FILTRATION MEMBRANE  349, 350, 351, 354, 512, 641, 714, 715, 717, 1146, 1158, 1338.

MESANGIUM  67, 68, 352, 616, 742, 745, 746, 974, 1079, 1556.

VASCULAR POLE  96, 126, 127, 543, 553, 744, 955, 956, 1156, 1421.

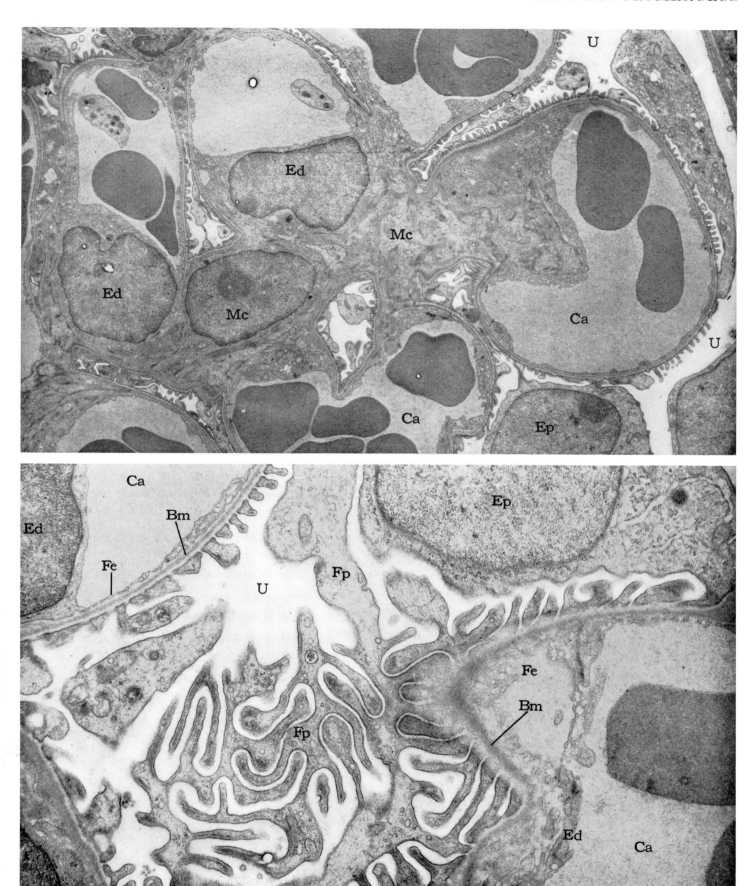

*Top:*

The proximal segments of the tubular nephron in cross section (this illustration) contain seemingly cuboidal cells with round nuclei ($Nu$), but the actual lateral cell borders are difficult to see at a low magnification. This is explained by the shape of the basal cell part, which has a complex appearance owing to infoldings of the cell membrane. Cytoplasmic processes of adjacent cells interdigitate with these folds, and this obscures the site of the true lateral cell border. The tubule is surrounded by a thin basement membrane ($Bm$) and a rich capillary network ($Ca$). Most of the dense spherical structures in the cell are mitochondria ($Mi$). The luminal ($Lu$) cell surface has a multitude of long slender processes, usually referred to as microvilli or brush border ($Bb$).

Proximal segment. Magnification 3000×. Meth. Unstained.

*Bottom:*

The structure of the distal segment of the nephron varies, depending on the location. In the thick ascending limb (this illustration), the cells are of a low columnar type with the nucleus ($Nu$) placed apically. Most of the mitochondria ($Mi$) are elongated and are arranged side by side with the long axis perpendicular to the basement membrane ($Bm$). The apex of the cell contains a few round mitochondria and a multitude of tiny vesicles, and the luminal ($Lu$) surface of the cell is provided with short and relatively coarse microvilli ($Vi$). Capillaries ($Ca$) around the distal segment are shared with proximal segments ($Px$) of neighboring nephrons.

Distal segment. Magnification 3000×. Meth. Unstained.

*References:*  11, 15, 26, 48, 147, 152, 179, 218, 279, 316, 754, 755, 756, 833, 844, 922, 1040, 1046, 1135, 1151, 1152, 1154, 1155 1157, 1160, 1201, 1250, 1328, 1422.

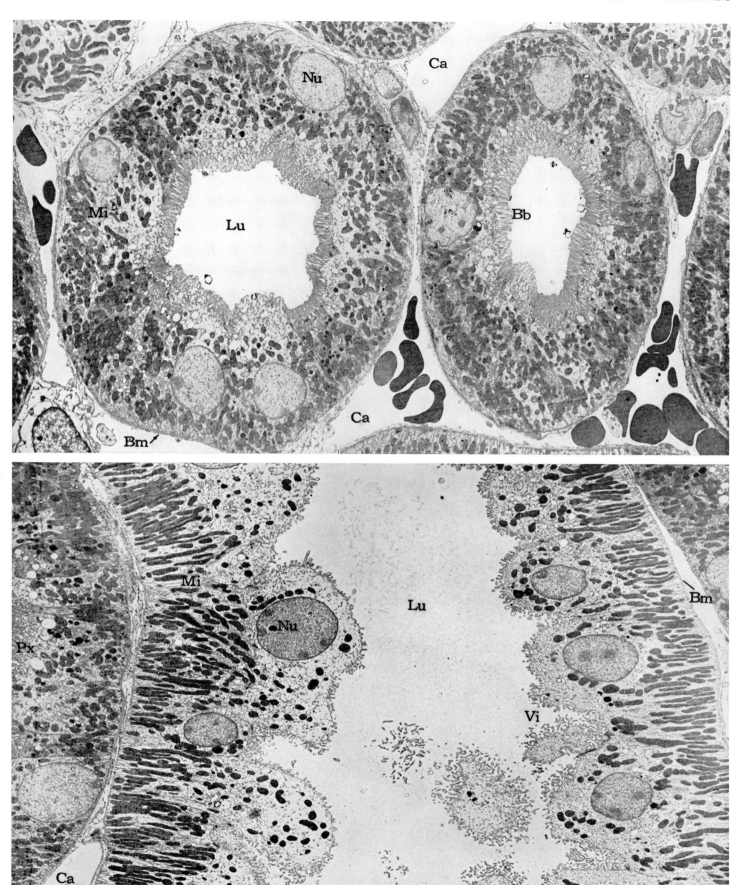

*Top and*
*Bottom Left:*

Details of proximal segment cells. The brush border zone (*Bb*) is composed of thin villi, which emerge from the cell surface. Tubular invaginations (*Tu*) occur frequently between the bases of the villi. It is believed that the tubules become pinched off from their contact with the surface membrane as part of a micropinocytotic phenomenon. The tubules then presumably enlarge to become vacuolar (*Va*) structures. Whether the vacuoles transform into lysosomes (*Ly*) is not clear, but cytoplasmic bodies (*X*) with the appearance of forms intermediate between large vacuoles (*Va*) and lysosomes (*Ly*) are frequently found. Ribosomes (*Ri*) and mitochondria (*Mi*) occur in great abundance, whereas elements of the rough-surfaced endoplasmic reticulum (*Re*) are scanty.

The basal part of a cell within the proximal segment shows a multitude of plasma membrane (*Cm*) infoldings near the basement membrane (*Bm*). Most of the resulting cytoplasmic compartments (*Cc*) emanate from the same cell, but some are derived from the adjacent cell. The compartments may contain mitochondria (*Mi*) and medium-sized vesicles (*Ve*), but the rows of small vesicles (*Rv*) also seen have been interpreted as the result of a formation or breakdown of plasma membranes.

Proximal segment. Magnifications: *Top* 25,000×; *Bottom* 30,000×. Ep. LH.

*Top and*
*Bottom Right:*

Detail of distal segment cells. The apical cytoplasm above the nucleus (*Nu*) is pervaded by numerous vesicles (*Ve*) of fairly uniform size. Most are spherical but a few are compressed slightly. They are bounded by a single thin membrane, the cytoplasmic aspect of which is studded by small granules with a diameter about one-third that of a ribosome (*Ri*). It has been assumed that the vesicles represent the structural evidence of secretion or fluid transportation. The microvilli (*Vi*) at the surface are small and coarse. The rough-surfaced endoplasmic reticulum (*Re*) is not prominent in these cells.

The base of the cells of the distal segment is highly clefted by deep infoldings of the plasma membrane (*Cm*). Some of the cytoplasmic compartments (*Cc*) are extremely narrow, whereas others are wide enough to lodge the extremely long mitochondria (*Mi*). Special attention should be paid to the close relationship between the outer mitochondrial membrane and the plasma membrane seeming to favor an enzymatic cooperation between these two structures. The basement membrane (*Bm*) of the distal segment does not show any peculiar fine structural details but is usually thinner than in the proximal segment of the nephron.

Distal segment. Magnifications: *Top* 20,000×; *Bottom* 35,000×. Ep. LH.

*References:* 112, 113, 455, 747, 748, 859, 861, 874, 875, 1042, 1071, 1134, 1145, 1148, 1210, 1234, 1246, 1253, 1266, 1355, 1399, 1424, 1442, 1499, 1575.

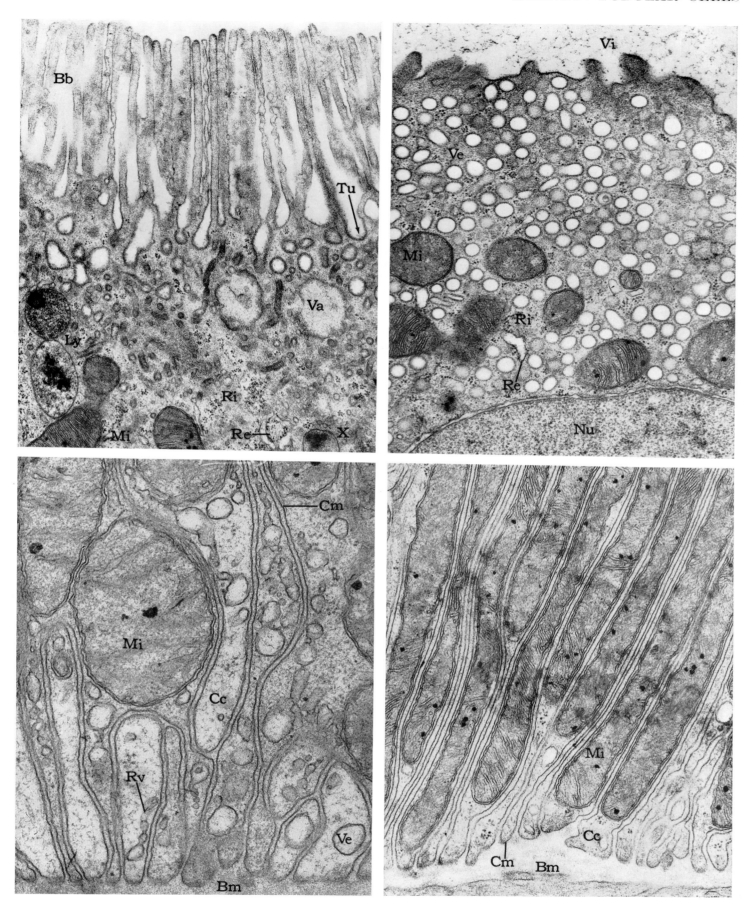

*Top:*    The cells of the thin segment (*Ts*) of the nephron can be studied most advantageously in the renal papilla. They are of a squamous type and therefore resemble endothelial cells (*Ed*) of the nearby capillaries (*Ca*) when one examines them with the ordinary light microscope. However, the resolving power of the electron microscope shows that the cells of the thin segment (*Ts*) have a peculiar scalloped appearance (arrows) when the tubule is cross-sectioned. This pattern results because the squamous cells have long cytoplasmic processes that spread out along the basement membrane (*Bm*) of the tubule and alternate with similar, interposed processes from adjacent cells. The capillary endothelium (*Ed*), furthermore, is thinner yet than the cytoplasm of the thin segmental cells, and there is usually a slight staining by the blood plasma in contrast to the clear urinary space of the tubular lumen (*Ts*).

Thin segment. Magnification 4000×. Meth. Unstained.

*Bottom:*    The large collecting tubules (*Ct*) or the ducts of Bellini are lined by columnar cells and stand out clearly against the squamous epithelium of the thin segment (*Ts*). The cells of the ducts of Bellini have a cytoplasm of medium density with few mitochondria (*Mi*) and basally located lipid droplets (*Li*). A few coarse protrusions characterize the luminal surface. The part of the cell that faces the basement membrane (*Bm*) has a relatively flat surface, but the lateral sides of the cell are highly irregular, and this makes it easy to locate the cell boundaries (*Cm*). The nucleus (*Nu*) is located in the basal half of the cell.

Collecting tubule. Magnification 2000×. Ep. UA.

*References:*   757, 760, 788, 860, 1041, 1408, 1423.

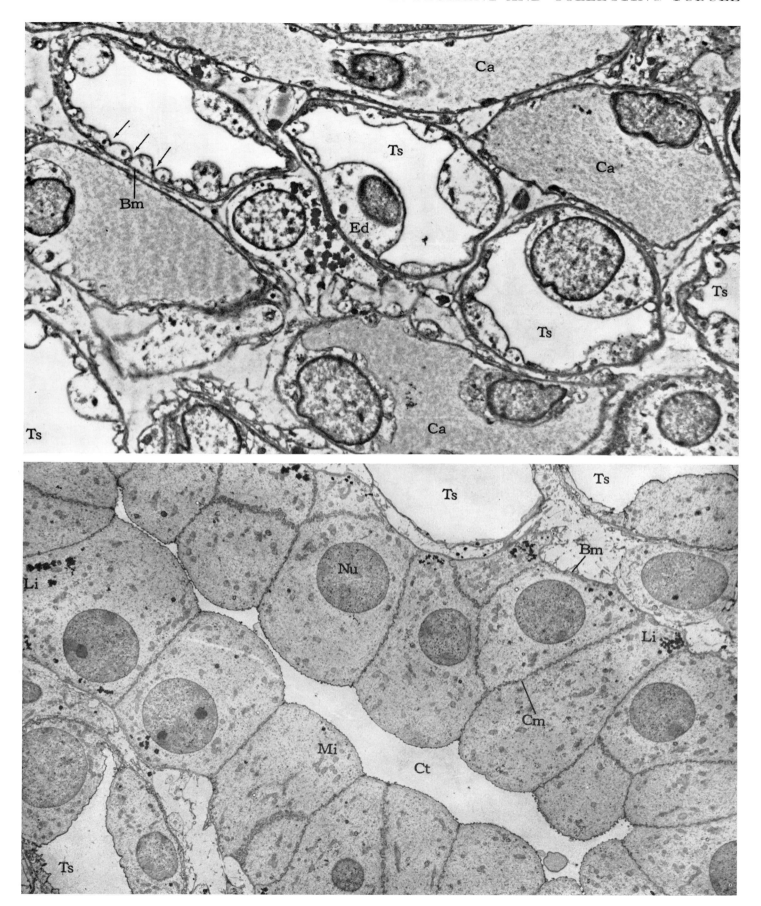

*Top:*    The epithelium of the urinary bladder is of the transitional epithelial type. There are mainly two kinds of cells: the basal cell (*Ba*) and the superficial squamous cell (*Sq*). The basal cells are cuboidal and are arranged in layers of which the most basally located rests on a thin basement membrane (*Bm*). The superficial squamous cells form a single layer near the lumen (*Lu*) of the urinary bladder. The appearance of the transitional epithelium varies according to the degree to which the bladder is filled. In the empty bladder of the mouse (this illustration), the basal cells form two layers, whereas in man five to six layers may occur. The superficial squamous cells are large and extend over several basal cells. The lamina propria (cf. page 16) is of the areolar connective tissue type and contains numerous capillaries (*Ca*).

Urinary bladder epithelium. Magnification 8000×. Ep. LH.

*Bottom Left:*    Detail of the luminal part (*Lu*) of a superficial squamous cell. The nucleus (*Nu*) is large, and the nuclear envelope displays a large number of bridged fenestrations (*Fe*). The cytoplasm contains a fair number of mitochondria (*Mi*), some ribosomes and short filaments (*Fi*), and an abundance of vesicular components—some spherical (*Ve*) and others of an oblong, fusiform type (*Cy*). The latter are specific for the cells of the transitional epithelium and so far have not been identified in any other cell of the mammalian body. It has been suggested that they are dissolved crystals. The origin and function of these structures are unknown, but they seem to migrate toward the luminal (*Lu*) cell surface, which is provided with short microvilli (*Vi*). Numerous electron-dense bodies of the lysosome type occur frequently in this cell (*Ly*, top picture).

Superficial cell. Magnification 27,000×. Ep. LH.

*Bottom Right:*    Detail of a basal cell. The cytoplasm is richer in ribosomes (*Ri*) than the superficial cell, and local areas of rough-surfaced endoplasmic reticulum (*Re*) are often seen to acquire a whirl-like, concentric arrangement. This type of structure is often called paranucleolar body. A small number of vesicles (*Ve*) and elongated vacuoles (*Cy*) also occur in the basal cells. The nucleus (*Nu*) is smaller and denser than the nucleus of the superficial cell.

Basal cell. Magnification 16,000×. Ep. LH.

*References:* 175, 977, 1035, 1464.

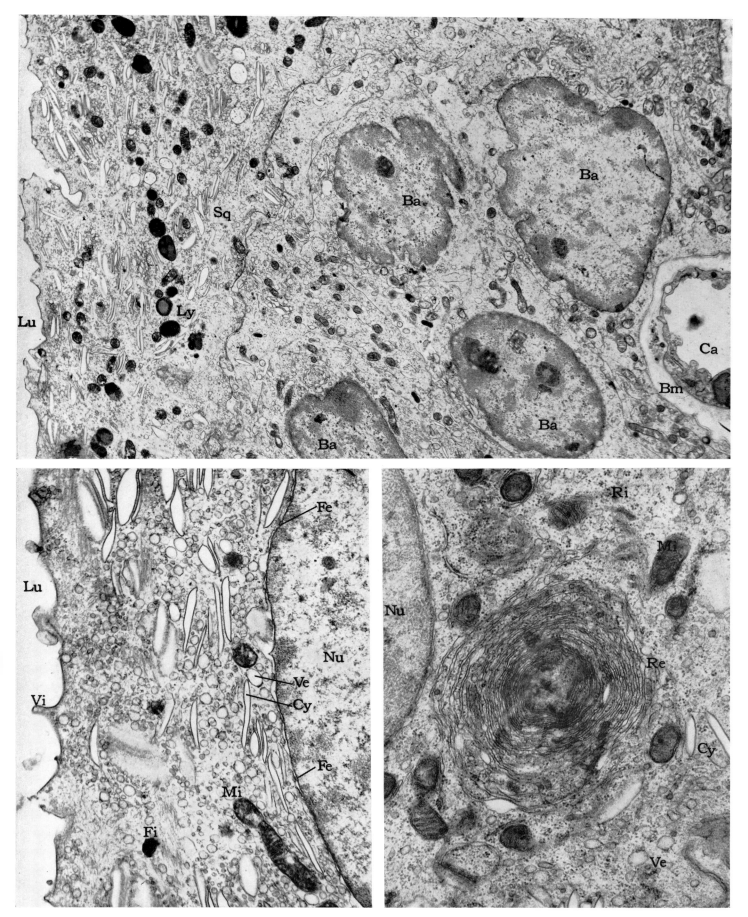

*Top:*

The wall of a convoluted seminiferous tubule of the testis consists of a complex stratified epithelium resting on a thin basement membrane (*Bm*). Within the epithelium occurs a continuous growth of cells, a process termed spermatogenesis, involving growth as well as a series of cellular cleavages. Basally located are the spermatogonia (*Sg*), which are not shown in their full extent in this illustration. Primary and secondary spermatocytes cannot be identified in this tubule. Most of the basally located cells are early spermatids (*Sp*) developing shortly after each of two secondary spermatocytes has given rise to two spermatids. In the early spermatids, the nuclei are rich in chromatin, and a complete cell separation has not as yet occurred (arrows). In the late spermatids (*S*), a process of maturation occurs known as spermiogenesis (final stages of spermatogenesis) and entailing drastic changes in the nucleus, the Golgi complex, and the centrosome. Cells with supporting and possibly endocrine functions extend from the basement membrane (*Bm*) to the tubular lumen (*Lu*). These are the Sertoli cells (*Sc*), which harbor the spermatids as they mature into spermatozoa, of which heads (*He*) and tails (*Ta*) can be identified.

Tubular epithelium. Magnification 2200×. Ep. LA.

*Bottom:*

Detail of the basal portion of a Sertoli cell (*Sc*) and presumably some secondary spermatocytes (*SII*). The Sertoli cell cytoplasm contains a Golgi zone (*Go*) as well as numerous mitochondria (*Mi*) and lipid inclusions (*Li*). The cell rests on a thin basement membrane (*Bm*), which in turn is surrounded by flattened fibroblasts (*Fib*) and reticular fibrils, forming the outer capsule or tunica propria. It is believed that the cells actually are secondary spermatocytes, since they have only a narrow cytoplasm with few mitochondria, a small Golgi complex (*Go*), and nuclei rich in chromatin and indications of threadlike chromosomes (arrows). The cell division has not as yet been completed, since there is a free connection (arrows) between the cells. Centrioles (*Ce*) are present in both the Sertoli cell and in one of the spermatocytes.

Spermatocytes. Magnification 8000×. Ep. LH.

Page 104

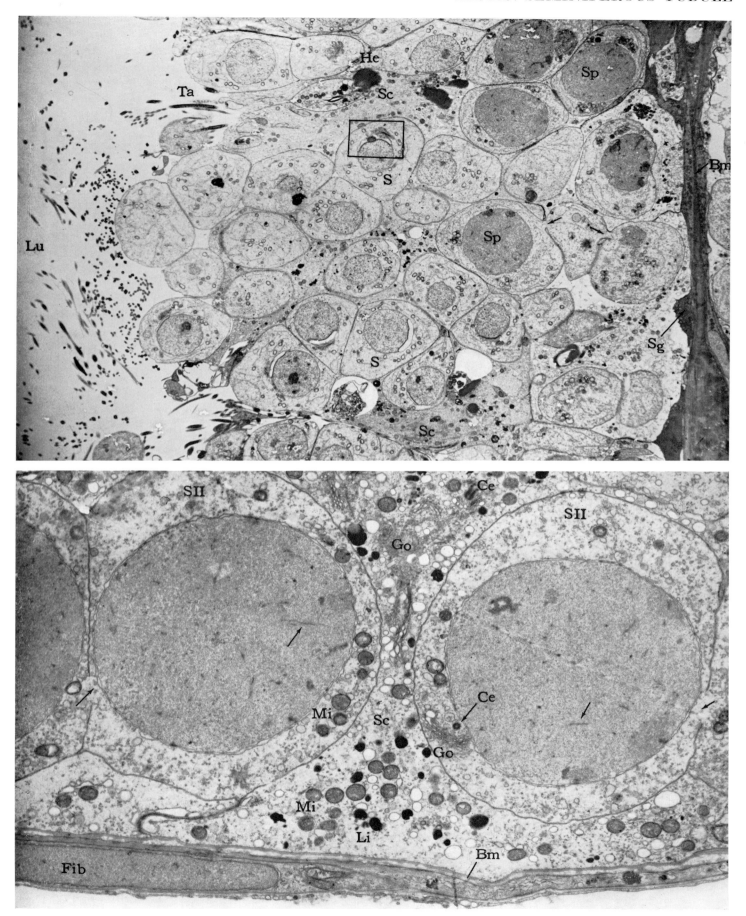

*Top Left:*    Detail of a spermatid, corresponding to the boxed-in area on the previous page. This illustrates the early development of the head cap of the spermatozoon. Within the Golgi complex (*Go*) is elaborated a proacrosomal granule (*Pag*), which also appears within an enlarged part of the Golgi membranes. The membrane unit is moved and settles on top of the spermatid nucleus (*Nu*), where it is referred to as an acrosomal vesicle (*Ab*) containing the acrosomal granule (*Ag*). Mitochondria (*Mi*) are widely scattered within the spermatid, the border of which is indicated by its cell membrane (*Cm*).

Spermatid. Golgi complex. Magnification 18,000×. Ep. LH.

*Top Right:*    Next in the maturation of the spermatid, the acrosomal vesicle is entirely filled by a substance similar to the early acrosomal granule; the vesicle covers the top of the nucleus (*Nu*) and is also drawn out into a frontal tip. The entire structural complex is now referred to as the head cap (*Hc*). Transient structures—the filaments of the manchette (*Man*) or the caudal tube—are identified at the lower circumference of the head cap. Mitochondria (*Mi*) and vesicular components of the smooth-surfaced endoplasmic reticulum (*Sm*) occur in the cytoplasm of the spermatid.

Spermatid. Head cap. Magnification 20,000×. Ep. LH.

*Bottom Left:*    While the head cap is being formed, the two centrioles move to the opposite part of the nucleus, where they are identified as the proximal (*Cp*) and distal (*Cd*) centrioles. The central longitudinal filaments (*Lf*), which later form the center of the sperm tail, grow from the distal centriole. A row of vesicles (asterisks) line up along the filaments, indicating the formation of the tail plasma membrane. The mitochondria (*Mi*) have internal clear spaces, which arise from a separation of individual components of the inner mitochondrial membranes.

Spermatid. Centrioles. Magnification 38,000×. Ep. LH.

*Bottom Right:*    Upon reaching a close contact with the nucleus (*Nu*), the two centrioles and a newly formed structure, the end knob (*Ek*), indent the nuclear membrane. The origin of the end knob or the connecting piece is not known, but its segmented structure forms the beginning of the coarse, peripheral, longitudinal filaments (*Lf*). The cell membrane of the sperm tail is evident at this stage and the proximal two vesicles (asterisks) remain. At the edge of the end knob appears a dense structure, the end ring (*End*). A few filaments (*Fi*) of the caudal tube are still present in the cytoplasm of the maturing spermatid.

Spermatid. Tail. Magnification 30,000×. Ep. LH.

*References:* 18, 94, 132, 133, 189, 190, 191, 365, 366, 439, 609, 680, 681, 690, 709, 877, 935, 936, 938, 1374, 1480, 1570, 1583.

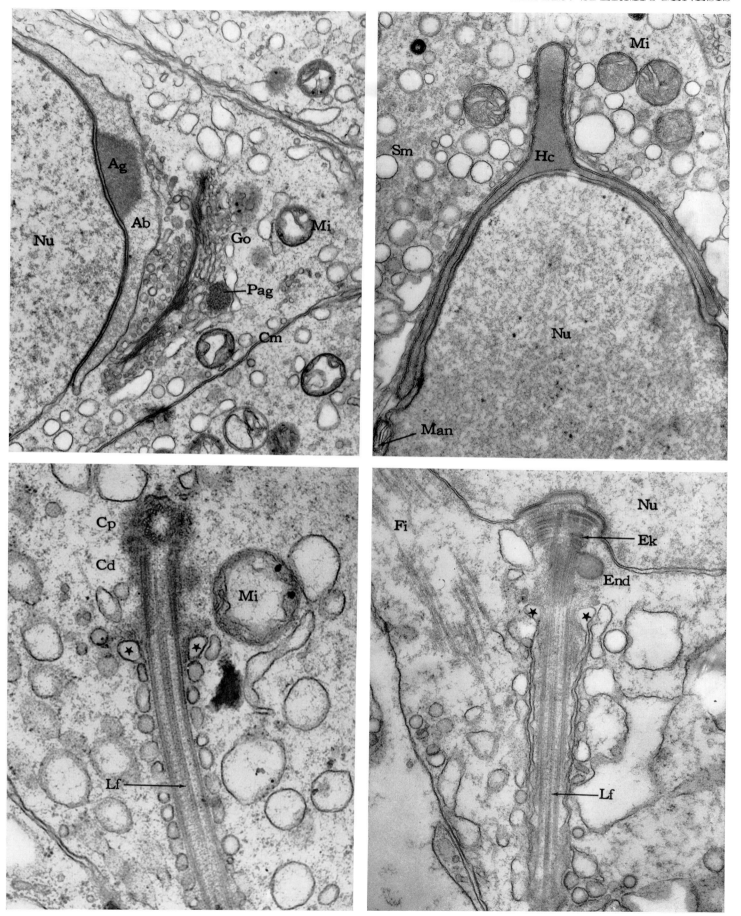

*Top Left:* In the mature spermatozoon, the head cap (*Hc*) is narrowed down to a thin coating of the nucleus. The head of the sperm (*He*) is marked by the extreme condensation of the chromatin of the nucleus in which only occasional light areas are seen. There is now a firm relationship between the end knob (*Ek*) and the peripheral axial filaments of the tail (*Pf*), and the midpiece of the sperm is characterized by the mitochondrial (*Mi*) sheath wrapped around the axial filaments. The entire structural complex is enveloped by the cell membrane (*Cm*). The proximal (*Cp*) and distal (*Cd*) centrioles may still be identified, the latter in direct connection with the central axial filaments (*Cf*).

Head and middle piece. Magnification 28,000×. Ep. LA.

*Top Right:* The length of the middle piece varies with the species but is always marked by the mitochondrial sheath. This is not a continuous spiral of one mitochondrion, but rather several mitochondria with end-to-end connections (*Ec*). The border between the middle piece and the principal piece is marked by a dense end-ring (*End*). The axial filaments of the principal piece are surrounded by a fibrous sheath (*Fs*).

Middle and principal pieces. Magnification 24,000×. Ep. LA.

*Bottom:* The details of the axial filaments and the fibrous sheath of the principal piece (2) are more easily understood by studying cross sections of the tail in which the terminal piece of the tail (3) can also be identified. The fibrous sheath has two longitudinal columns (*Lb*) connected by transversely arranged, circumferential ribs (*Rs*). The central axial filaments (*Cf*) are arranged in pairs with nine pairs located peripherally and one in the center. This arrangement (nine, plus two in the center) is identical to that of a cilium. There are nine coarse, peripheral axial filaments (*Pf*) in the middle piece of the tail, but they gradually taper off in the principal piece (2) and disappear in the terminal piece of the tail (3). The function of the axial filaments is to generate waves by the tail.

Tails, cross sections. Magnification 71,000×. Ep. UA.

*References:* 3, 8, 89, 104, 199, 200, 201, 203, 360, 733, 939, 942, 1277, 1407, 1414.

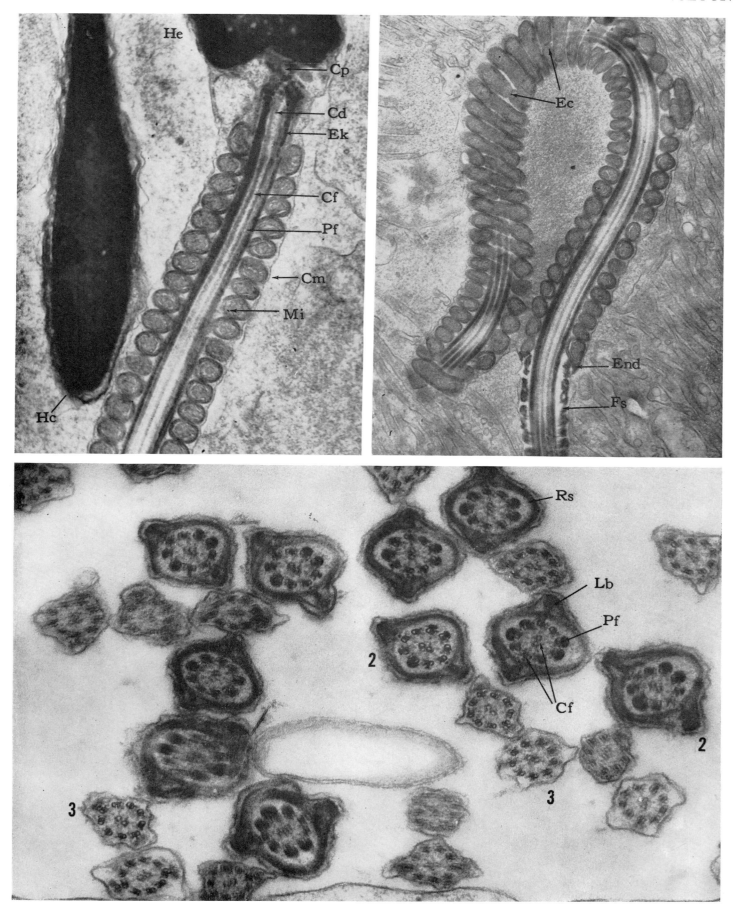

*Top:*  The ductuli efferentes of man are lined by an epithelium that contains both columnar and cuboidal cells with oval nuclei (*Nu*). The cells rest on a thin basement membrane (*Bm*), which forms the borderline against the surrounding connective tissue with its fibroblasts (*Fib*) and collagenous fibrils (*Co*). Because of the occurrence of low cuboidal cells alternating with tall columnar cells, cryptlike formations appear along the ductuli efferentes. The luminal surface (*Lu*) of both cell types can be provided with either brush border extensions (*Bb*) or cilia (*C*), and the crypts, therefore, may not be considered to represent intraepithelial glands, as has been suggested. The cells contain fair numbers of mitochondria (*Mi*) and lysosomes (*Ly*). The latter structures have been considered to be pigment granules. Small basal cells (*Ba*) occur infrequently and may possibly form a layer of undifferentiated cells for replacement of sloughed-off surface cells.

Ductuli efferentes. Human specimen. Magnification 3200×. Meth. Unstained.

*Bottom:*  The epithelium of the ductus epididymis in the mouse is of a columnar type with a layer of small basal polyhedral cells (*Ba*). Both the columnar cells and the basal cells reach the basement membrane (*Bm*) of the duct, which is surrounded by a circularly arranged layer of thin smooth muscle cells, not clearly seen in this low-magnification illustration. A rich network of capillaries (*Ca*) surrounds the tubules. The nucleus (*Nu*) of the columnar cell is located near the base. The entire cytoplasm is pervaded by short and usually dilated cisternae of the rough-surfaced endoplasmic reticulum (*Re*), except for areas dominated by the Golgi complex (*Go*). Granules (*G*) possibly of a secretory nature occur frequently as well as mitochondria (*Mi*) and lysosomes (*Ly*). The cells taper off toward the lumen (*Lu*) of the duct where they are attached to each other by terminal bars (*Tb*). The surface is differentiated into specialized structures, the so-called stereocilia (*Stc*). (A detailed description of stereocilia is found on page 4.) These are long, nonmotile extensions. Small tubular indentations of the surface membrane occur between their bases as in the cells of the proximal segment of the nephron (cf. page 99). Numerous spermatozoa are present in the lumen (*Lu*) of the duct.

Ductus epididymis. Magnification 4000×. Ep. UA.

*References:*  DUCTULI EFFERENTES  731.
DUCTUS EPIDIDYMIS  225, 610.

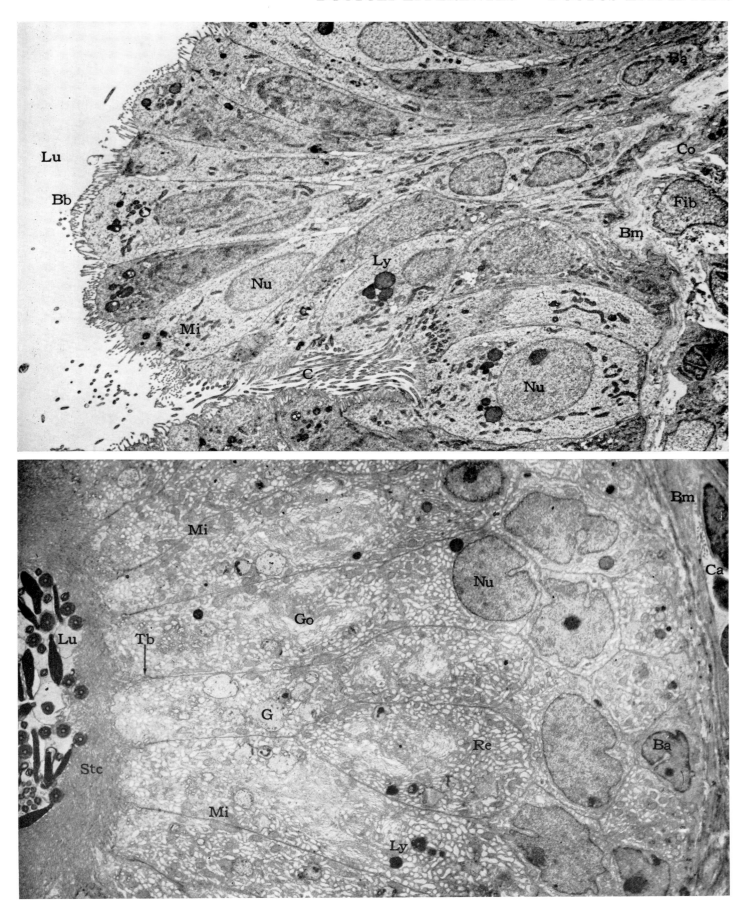

*Top:* The function of the vesicular gland of the mouse (this illustration) is not directly comparable to that in man, since in the mouse there also exists a coagulating gland. A mixture of the secretions of both glands seems to be necessary in the mouse in order that there be optimal action on the sperm. However, basically, the structures of the vesicular epithelium of the mouse and man do not differ considerably. The mucosa is thrown into many fine, intricate folds and consists of a single layer of tall columnar cells, which are somewhat lower when the lumen (*Lu*) is distended by secretion. A few small basal cells (*Ba*) are seen between the bases of the columnar cells. They seem to be undifferentiated cells with the potentiality of developing into secretory cells. The lamina propria (*Lp*) contains a thick capillary network.
Magnification 2400×. Ep. UA.

*Bottom:* The ultrastructure of the epithelial cell of the seminal vesicle clearly indicates that this is a typical secretory cell. The entire cell is filled with rough-surfaced endoplasmic reticulum (*Re*) with elongated and interconnected cisternae (*Ci*). The well-developed Golgi complex (*Go*) is located at the apical portion of the nucleus (*Nu*). As in other secretory cells, the Golgi membranes and vacuoles represent the sites where the secretory products first appear. The secretory granule (*G*) does not fill the entire Golgi vacuole and is usually eccentrically located within the vacuole with a halolike appearance. The granules migrate toward the lumen where the secretion is stored in great quantities. Microvilli (*Vi*) project into the lumen. Mitochondria (*Mi*) and lysosomelike granules (*Ly*) are infrequent organelles in these cells. Capillaries (*Ca*) occur frequently beneath the vesicular epithelium.
Magnification 8300×. Ep. UA.

*References:* 106, 242, 432.

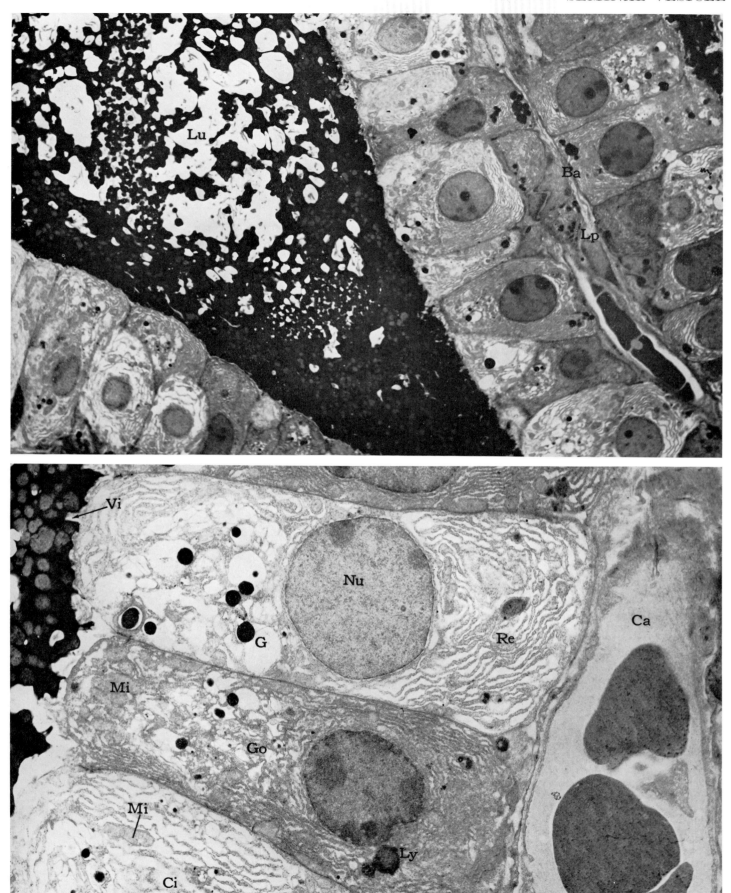

*Top:*     The free surface of the cortex of the ovary, which bulges into the peritoneal cavity (*Lu*), is covered by a layer of cuboidal cells, the germinal epithelium (*Ge*), beneath which a thin layer of dense fibrous connective tissue forms the tunica albuginea (*Tal*) containing capillaries (*Ca*). The primary follicles (*Pr*) are seen immediately beneath the tunica albuginea, while those of more advanced development are more deeply located. The germinal epithelium serves as the origin of primary oocytes (*Oo*) during fetal life in man, whereas in the mouse (this illustration) a continued production of ova by the germinal epithelium has been demonstrated to occur during maturity.

Magnification 2000×. Ep. Unstained.

*Bottom Left:*     Detail of the apex of a cell from the germinal epithelium. The nucleus (*Nu*) is lobulated and occupies a large part of the cell. The cytoplasm is rich in mitochondria (*Mi*) and ribosomes (*Ri*). A well-developed Golgi region (*Go*) exists, but only a few elements of the rough-surfaced endoplasmic reticulum (*Re*) can be identified. Into the peritoneal cavity (*Lu*) project numerous microvilli (*Vi*).

Magnification 15,000×. Ep. LH.

*Bottom Right:*     The bases of the germinal cells rest on a thin basement membrane (*Bm*) separating the germinal cell layer from the tunica albuginea, which in turn is composed of fibroblasts (*Fib*). Again, it should be noticed how large the nuclei (*Nu*) are within the germinal cells. The basal cytoplasm contains mitochondria (*Mi*) and large lipid inclusions (*Li*).

Magnification 15,000×. Ep. LH.

Page 114

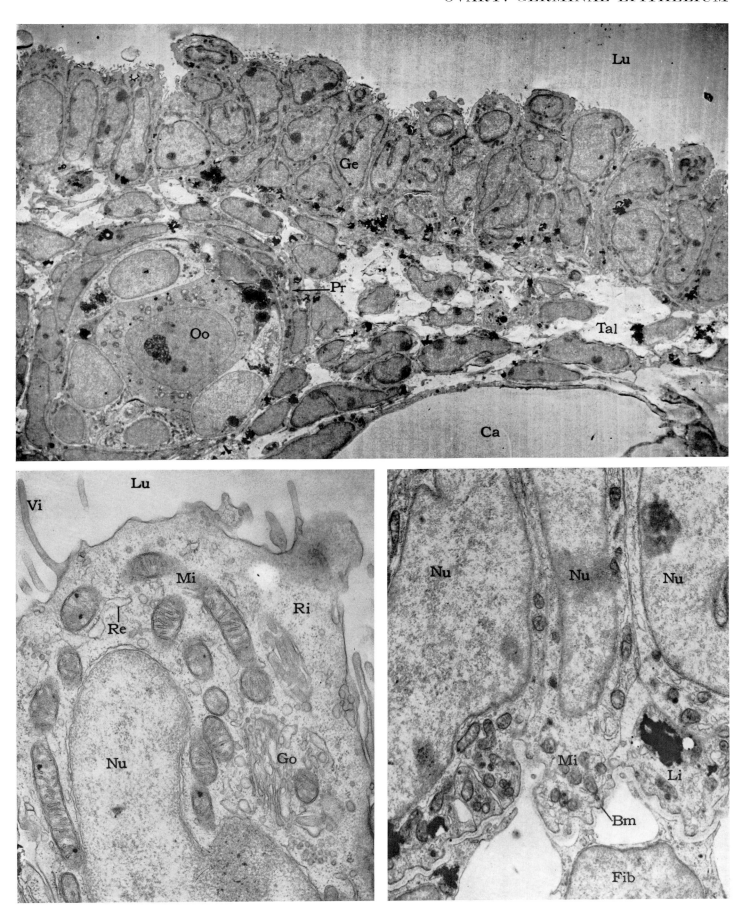

*Top:*
The young oocyte (*Oo*) is comparatively small, the centrally located nucleus occupying a large part of the cell. The cytoplasm contains spherical mitochondria (*Mi*), small and widely scattered Golgi areas (*Go*), conglomerates of small vesicles and multivesicular bodies (*Mv*), and occasional short dense filamentous structures (*Fi*). Flat follicular cells (*Fc*) are wrapped around the oocyte, and a well-defined basement membrane (*Bm*) surrounds the primary follicle. Adjacent cells (*TL*) are theca lutein cells of a corpus luteum of ovulation.

Magnification 9000×. Ep. LH.

*Bottom:*
Detail of a primary oocyte (*Oo*) and the surrounding follicular cell (*Fc*). The various structures of the oocyte may now be studied more closely. Both the oocyte and the follicle cell are bordered by a plasma membrane (*Cm*), and thin cytoplasmic strands (*Cs*) of other follicle cells may be interposed. The nucleus of the oocyte (*Oo Nu*) is bordered by a triple-layered membrane in which fenestrations (*Fe*) can be identified, all closed by a thin, single-layered membrane. The same structural features characterize the nuclei of the follicle cells (*Fc Nu*). The cytoplasm of the oocyte is rich in ribosomes (*Ri*) but poor in rough-surfaced endoplasmic reticulum (*Re*). Vesicular components are abundant, some indicating the proximity of a Golgi complex (*Go*) and others associated with and enclosed in multivesicular bodies (*Mv*). Mitochondria (*Mi*) have a clear, outer, triple-layered membrane, but the inner membranes are usually located eccentrically and are arranged in different directions at different portions of a mitochondrion. This arrangement seems to be peculiar to all mitochondria of the growing oocyte and cannot be seen in the follicular cells (*Mi*). Occasional lysosomes (*Ly*) occur as well as dense filamentous structures (*Fi*) of unknown nature and function.

Magnification 28,000×. Ep. LH.

*References:* 13, 14, 88, 124, 174, 438, 685, 686, 1030, 1104, 1371, 1382, 1475, 1529, 5131.

Page 116

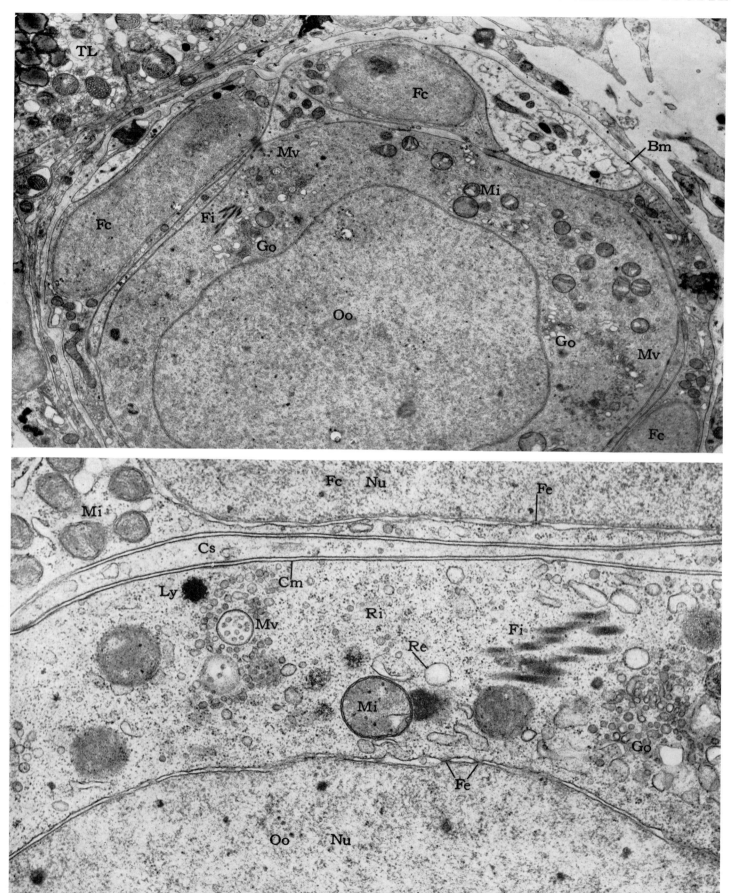

Several important structural changes occur as the primary follicle is transformed into a secondary follicle (this illustration). The oocyte itself enlarges, mostly owing to an increase of the cytoplasm but also, to some degree, of the nucleus (*Nu*). The nucleolus (*No*) assumes a definite shape and structure and does not have the threadlike appearance of the early oocyte nucleolus, which indicated preparation for nuclear cleavages (cf. page 114). (A detailed description of the secondary oocyte nucleolus is given on page 14.) A so-called yolk nucleolus (*Yn*) appears, consisting of closely arranged mitochondria. The multivesicular bodies (*Mv*) increase in size and number, and other vesicular components, possibly elements of the smooth-surfaced endoplasmic reticulum, emerge in a sheathlike fashion, in a section assuming the appearance of rows of vesicles (*Rv*). The oocyte plasma membrane (*Cm*) differentiates into microvilli, and a homogeneous substance of medium density is laid down around the oocyte to form the zona pellucida (*Zp*).

Simultaneously the flat follicular cells are transformed into columnar cells and arrange themselves into several layers. The differentiation of the follicular cells has not been completed in this illustration, but the cells nearest the basement membrane (*Bm*) will gradually form the membrana granulosa (*Mg*), whereas those closest to the zona pellucida (*Zp*) will be arranged to establish the so-called corona radiata (*Cor*). Small intercellular spaces also become evident as a first indication of a follicular antrum (*An*). The zona pellucida is traversed by numerous, thin, protoplasmic extensions, of which some emerge from the oocyte surface (*Cm*) and some from the cells of the corona radiata (*Cor*). In the lower right corner are precursors of the cells that form the theca interna (*Ti*).

Magnification 2900×. Ep. UA.

*References:* 173, 493, 848, 907, 1056, 1372, 1383, 1441, 1474.

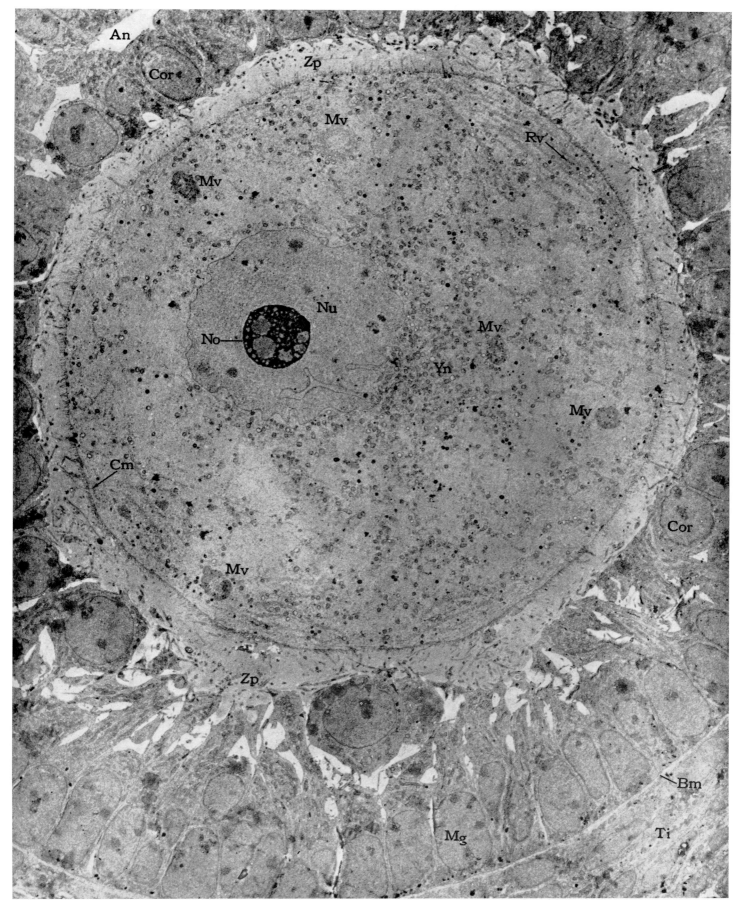

*Top Left:*     Detail of a secondary follicle presented to facilitate the understanding of the inter-relationship of the oocyte (*Oo*), plasma membrane (*Cm*), zona pellucida (*Zp*), and cells of the corona radiata (*Cor*). The coarse protrusions (*Pu*) of the corona radiata cells quite regularly reach the surface of the oocyte (*Cm*), whereas the microvilli (*Vi*) of the oocyte reach only about halfway across the zona pellucida. Some of the oocyte organelles can be studied more closely at this magnification. Golgi areas (*Go*) and mitochondria (*Mi*) are evident. The aggregations of large spherical structures are believed to represent smooth-surfaced endoplasmic reticulum (*Sm*).

Secondary oocyte. Magnification 16,000×. Ep. LA.

*Top Right:*     In the secondary oocyte cytoplasm one can also identify lipid inclusions (*Li*), lysosomes having a pleomorphic appearance (*Ly*), and mitochondria (*Mi*). The vacuoles of the smooth-surfaced endoplasmic reticulum are either distributed at random (*Sm*) or arranged in rows (*Rv*). The Golgi complex (*Go*) is small but can be readily recognized and separated without difficulty from the multivesicular bodies (*Mv*).

Secondary oocyte. Magnification 16,000×. Ep. LA.

*Bottom:*     Further structural changes occur as the oocyte and follicle grow and as maturation approaches. The surface villi of the oocyte (*Oo*) decrease in height, and the protrusions of the corona radiata cells (*Cor*) almost disappear, leaving the zona pellucida (*Zp*) relatively free. The follicular cells that border on the antrum (*An*) seem to be loosely arranged and are usually referred to as the cumulus oophorus (*Cum*).

Cumulus oophorus. Magnification 3500×. Ep. LA.

*References:*   202, 416, 633, 890, 961, 963, 1373, 1473, 1532, 1561, 1573.

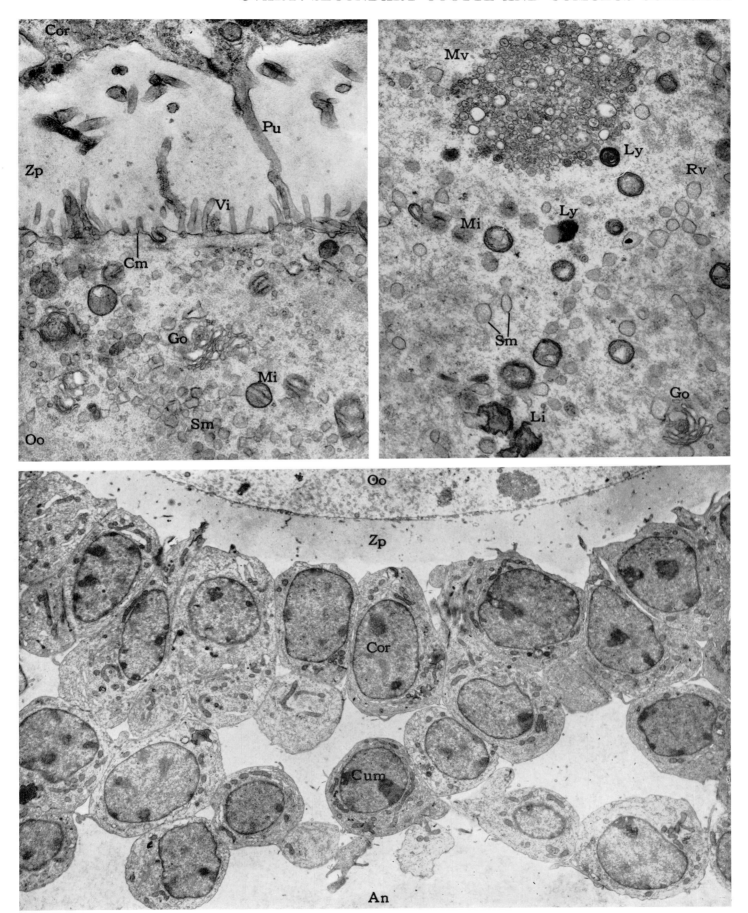

In the mouse, several corpora lutea of ovulation appear simultaneously and can be identified easily. Two types of cells occur, of which one is derived from the membrana granulosa, being composed of follicular cells and located inside the basement membrane of the ovarian follicle. Cells of this type are usually referred to as granulosa lutein cells. The second cell type originates from the theca interna cells, which are separated from the cells of the membrana granulosa by the basement membrane of the follicle. In the corpus luteum, this type of cell is called a theca lutein cell.

*Top:*

This figure illustrates details of *granulosa lutein cells*. The cells are fairly large and are polyhedral with a relatively dense cytoplasm. The nucleus ($Nu$) is large, and centrioles ($Ce$) are often observed. The Golgi complexes ($Go$) are scattered among an abundance of ribosomes ($Ri$) and numerous elements of the smooth-surfaced endoplasmic reticulum ($Sm$). The mitochondria are fairly numerous and of variable shape. Lipid granules ($Li$) occur but are not particularly abundant.

Granulosa lutein cell. Magnification 20,000×. Ep. LA.

*Bottom:*

The *theca lutein cells* are smaller than the granulosa lutein cells and are extremely abundant in the mouse ovary in which a precursor or close relative of these cells seems to correspond to the interstitial or stroma cell of the human ovary. The nuclei ($Nu$) are small. The cytoplasm contains numerous ribosomes ($Ri$) and aggregates of glycogen particles ($Gl$) but few representatives of the smooth-surfaced endoplasmic reticulum ($Sm$). The mitochondria ($Mi$) are large, are invariably spherical, and have a peculiar inner structure (described in detail on page 10). Lipid granules ($Li$) occur in great abundance with variable shape, size, and electron denisty.

Theca lutein cell. Magnification 21,000×. Ep. LH.

*References:* 314, 315, 771, 1560.

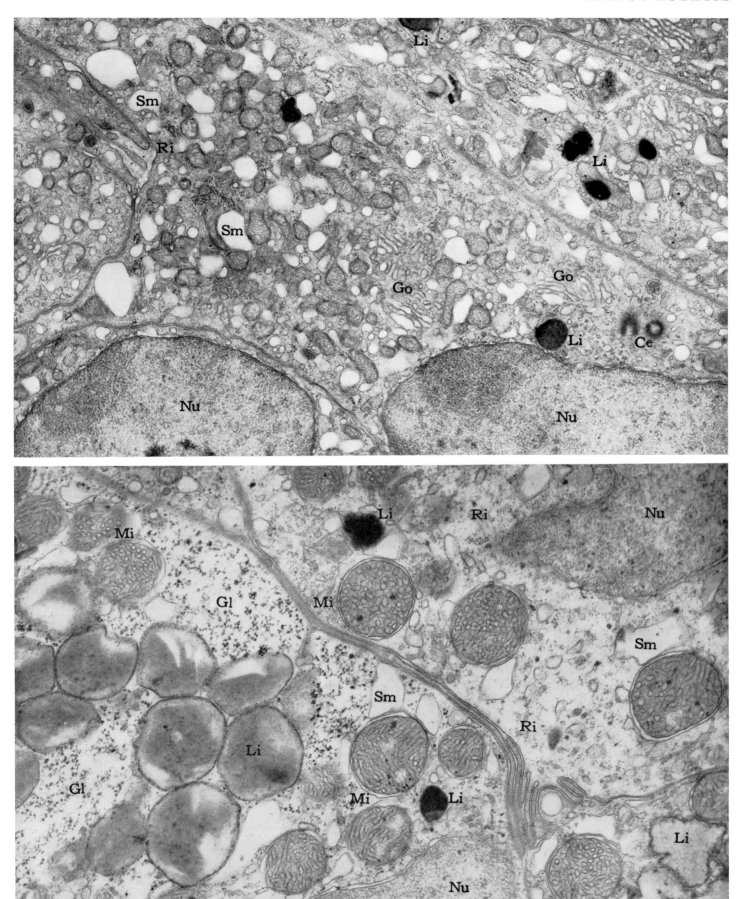

*Top:*     The epithelium of the oviduct (fallopian tube) consists of a single layer of columnar cells. There are two types of cells—ciliated and nonciliated or secretory cells. Only the secretory type of cell is shown in this illustration. The nuclei ($Nu$) are centrally located, and the cytoplasm above is filled with varying numbers of secretory granules ($G$). Fine microvilli project into the lumen ($Lu$). Fair numbers of mitochondria and lysosomes occur in the cytoplasm, which to a great extent is occupied by rough-surfaced endoplasmic reticulum as in most secretory cells. A thin basement membrane ($Bm$) separates the epithelium from the lamina propria ($Lp$); the latter is rich in capillaries ($Ca$).

Magnification 3500×. Ep. UA.

*Bottom:*     Several secretory cells and parts of a ciliated cell are seen in this detail of the fallopian tube epithelium. The cross-sectioned cilia ($Ci$) have the ordinary fine structural composition. A few basal corpuscles ($Bc$) are also cross sectioned, and here the spread of the rootlets ($Ro$) and the absence of the central filaments should be noted. The Golgi complex ($Go$) of the nonciliated cell is fairly large, and the apex of the cell is occupied by numerous secretory granules ($G$). The microvilli ($Vi$) are numerous and quite slender. The structure of the epithelium of the oviduct varies according to the estrus cycle and the ratio of ciliated to nonciliated cells changes. Moreover, the nonciliated cells undergo cyclic changes during activation of secretion. The illustrations presented here are selected from an animal in mid-estrus, and the secretory cells consequently have become quite active. The true nature of the secretion of the nonciliated cells is not entirely clear, but judging from the fine structure of the secretory granules, it is most likely a mucous secretion.

Magnification 17,000×. Ep. LA.

*References:* 86, 87, 97, 98, 418, 551, 552, 565, 945, 946, 962, 1429, 1430.

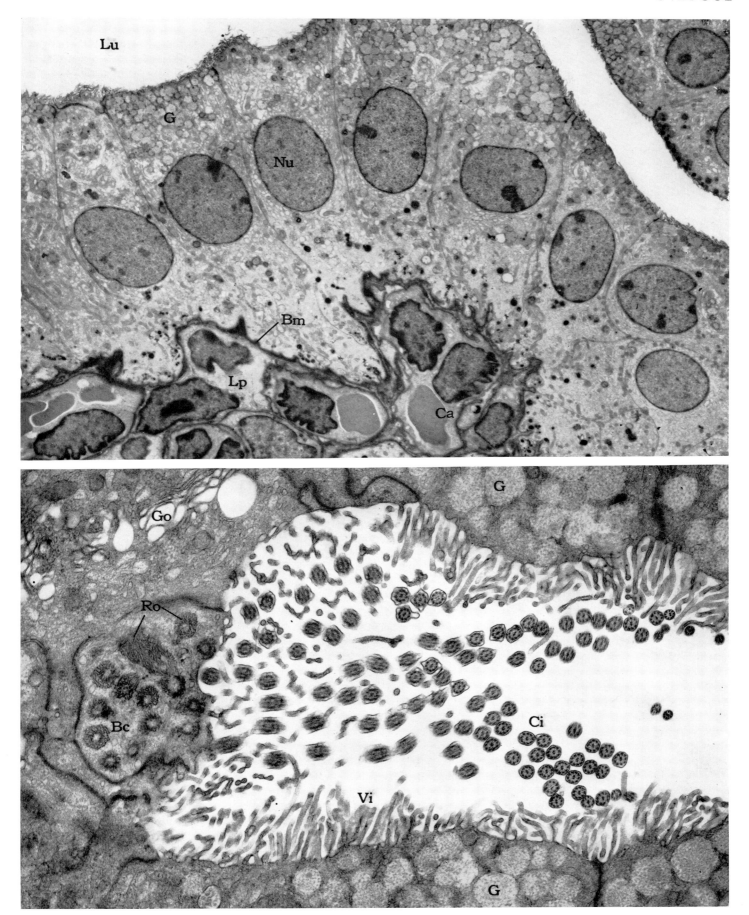

*Top:*  Projecting down from the lumen of the uterus of the mouse are simple branched tubular glands, several of which are shown here in cross and longitudinal sections with a centrally located lumen (asterisks). The glands are lined with a low columnar epithelium surrounded by a thin basement membrane, which borders on a lamina propria ($Lp$) containing numerous polyhedral fibroblasts. Most of the epithelial cells are quite narrow with a large, centrally placed nucleus, but cells of a more cuboidal shape are interspersed. The cells are in a secretory phase with numerous dense granules accumulating toward the lumen of the gland in which a secretion of medium density is present.

Uterine glands. Magnification 2100×. Ep. UA.

*Bottom Left:*  Detail of the luminal ($Lu$) cell surface of an epithelial cell of a uterine gland. The cytoplasm is rich in secretory granules ($G$), which display all gradations of density. Whether the granules represent a mucous or a serous secretion cannot be established solely on the basis of fine structure but they most closely resemble the zymogen granules of the exocrine part of the pancreas. There is a certain similarity, however, to the specific mucous granules of the surface cells of the gastric mucosa. The microvilli ($Vi$) are short and have a distinct, furry, extraneous coating. Mitochondria ($Mi$) are few in number, as are the profiles of the rough-surfaced endoplasmic reticulum ($Re$). Ribosomes ($Ri$) are abundant. A cross-sectioned centriole ($Ce$) can be identified.

Apex of epithelial cell. Magnification 15,000×. Ep. LH.

*Bottom Right:*  The rough-surfaced endoplasmic reticulum ($Re$) is abundant beneath the nucleus ($Nu$), and the cytoplasm contains numerous ribosomes ($Ri$). The cisternae ($Ci$) are quite irregular in shape and communicate freely with one another and with the perinuclear space. Mitochondria ($Mi$) are unusually scarce, but large accumulations of lipid droplets ($Li$) occur near the basement membrane ($Bm$). In summary, this is a cell that seems to have an excretory function, judging by the presence of the apical granules, as well as a possible endocrine function, judging by the numerous basal lipid droplets.

Base of epithelial cell. Magnification 16,000×. Ep. LH.

*References:*  99, 663, 736, 737, 908, 909, 910, 947, 948, 949, 950, 951, 952, 953, 1381, 1450, 1516, 1519.

Page 126

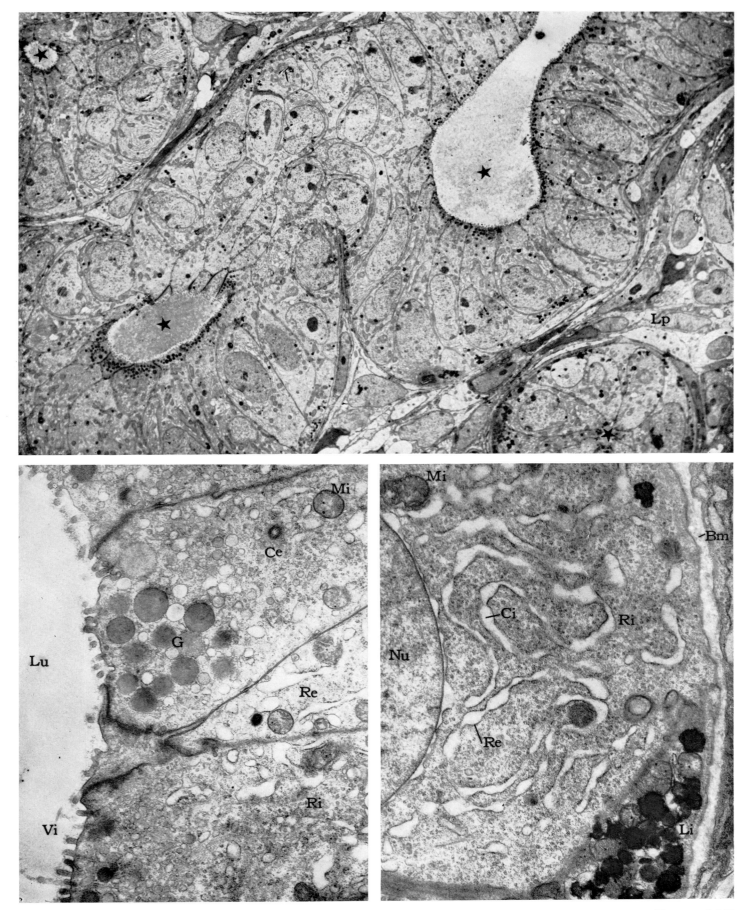

*Top:*

The mammary gland is a typical branched tubular gland with rather straight secretory tubules. In the resting state, the gland contains few tubules but has an abundance of intra-lobular areolar tissue. The connective tissue in the active lactating gland is scarce and in this illustration is represented by a few mast cells (*Ma*) but an abundance of small capillaries (*Ca*).

The secretory cells forming the tubules are cuboidal or low columnar with a nucleus (*Nu*) located basally. The lumen contains secretory products that can be classified into two groups: large lipid granules (milk fat) and small dense granules (milk protein).

Active mammary gland. Magnification 2000×. Ep. LA.

*Bottom.*

The cells have an ultrastructure that clearly indicates their excretory nature. The rough-surfaced endoplasmic reticulum (*Re*) and the free ribosomes are abundant and contribute to the great density of the cell. The Golgi complex (*Go*) is large, and mitochondria (*Mi*) are scattered throughout the cytoplasm. The small protein granules first appear within membrane-bound vacuoles in the Golgi area. One vacuole may contain several small protein granules. The vacuoles move toward the apex of the cell where the vacuolar membrane joins with the luminal plasma membrane before a discharge of the protein granules occurs into the tubular lumen. The origin of the large fat granules is not clear. These granules do not form within the Golgi area but appear anywhere in the cell and gradually increase to the size of the nucleus (*Nu*). The large granule is also bound by a membrane, which remains as the granule is discharged.

Myoepithelial cells (*My*) participate in narrowing the tubular lumen by contraction.

Magnification 8000×. Ep. LA.

*References:* MAMMARY GLAND   40, 41, 42, 44, 506, 591, 592, 703, 704, 709a, 735, 1389, 1511, 1512, 1513.
MAST CELL   500, 579, 1203, 1363.

Page 128

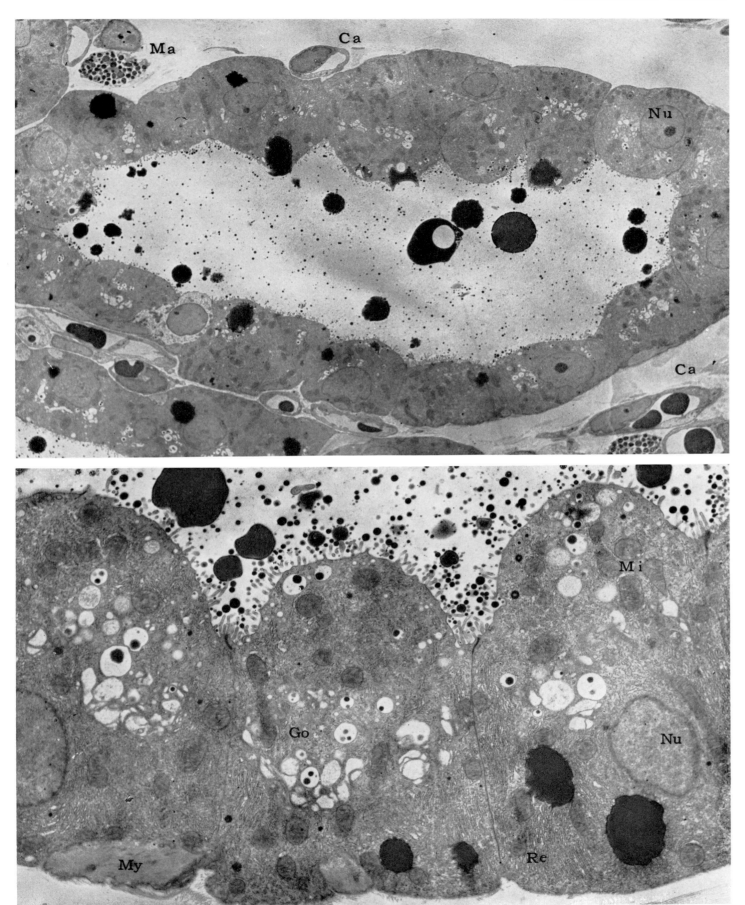

*Top:*　　　Cross section of a free villus in the human full-term placenta. The surface of the villus is covered with a continuous layer, the syncytial trophoblast (*Cyn*), which is a true syncytium with numerous nuclei and without intervening cell membranes. The surface of the syncytial trophoblast has a multitude of microvilli (*Vi*). Most of the dense, multishaped structures in the cytoplasm are secretory granules. The cytotrophoblasts (*Cyt*) or Langhans cells with a lighter cytoplasm do not form a continuous layer but rest on a thin basement membrane, which separates the trophoblasts from the connective tissue core of the villus. The fetal capillaries (*Ca*) with endothelial cells (*Ed*) occupy part of this core, in which occur numerous collagenous fibrils (*Co*) and macrophages (*Ho*) (also referred to as Hofbauer cells). Numerous erythrocytes (*Er*) are seen in the fetal capillaries, but none is present in the maternal blood space (*Mt*) in this illustration.

　　　Human placenta. Free villus. Cross section. Magnification 2100×. Meth. Unstained.

*Bottom Left:*　　　Detail of the free surface of a syncytial trophoblast (*Cyn*) in the human placenta at the third month of pregnancy. Between the bases of the microvilli (*Vi*) are tubular indentations (arrows) that lead into large, irregular intracellular spaces (asterisk). They are evidently engaged in a micropinocytotic activity. A small Golgi complex (*Go*) may elaborate dense granules (*G*) of varying size, which supposedly are the structural evidence for a secretory activity. The cytoplasm is rich in vesicular components of the smooth-surfaced endoplasmic reticulum (*Sm*) and free ribosomes. Lipid inclusions (*Li*) and mitochondria (*Mi*) occur frequently.

　　　Human placenta. Syncytial trophoblast. Magnification 19,000×. Ep. LH.

*Bottom Right:*　　　Detail of two cytotrophoblasts (*Cyt*) resting on the basement membrane (*Bm*) with an intervening thin strand of a syncytial trophoblast (*Cyn*) provided with numerous microvilli projecting into the intercellular space (*Is*). Small desmosomes (*Ds*) hold the cells together. The Langhans cell also has a small Golgi complex (*Go*), and the cytoplasm is rich in ribosomes (*Ri*) and rough-surfaced endoplasmic reticulum (*Re*). Mitochondria (*Mi*) occur, but the smooth-surfaced endoplasmic reticulum of the cytotrophoblast is lacking.

　　　Human placenta. Cytotrophoblast. Magnification 18,000×. Ep. LH.

*References:*　45, 59, 101, 102, 251, 254, 549, 550, 705, 738, 1169, 1256, 1416, 1460, 1533, 1534.

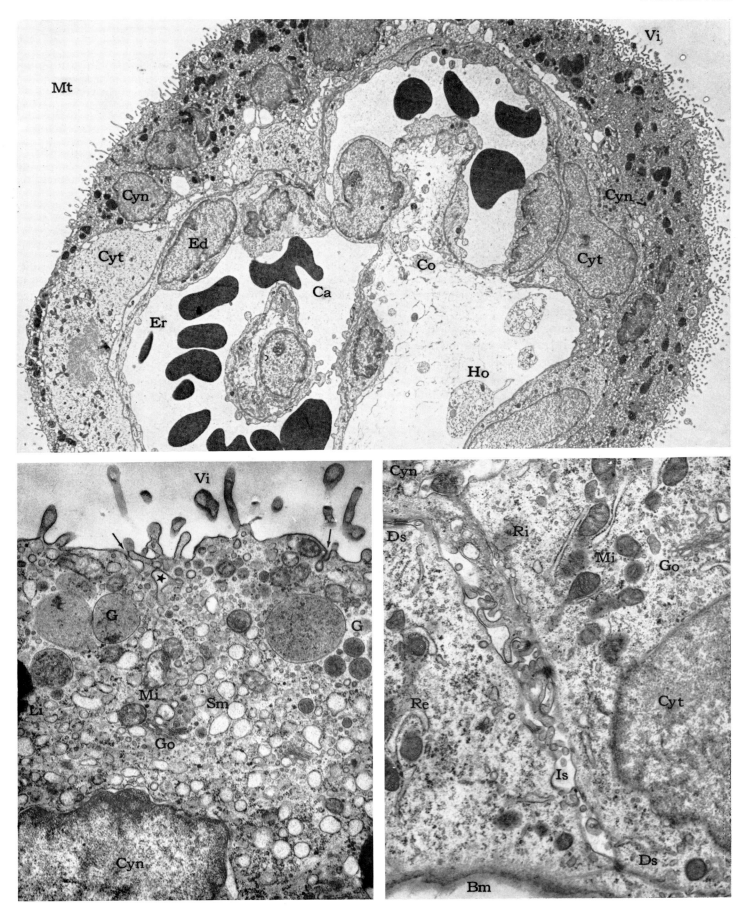

Epidermis is one of a few tissues in the mammalian body that are extremely difficult to preserve adequately using current techniques in electron microscopy. This is most probably explained by the slow penetration rate of osmium tetroxide owing to a tough keratinized surface and a dense collagenous dermis, which on two sides hinder the fixative in reaching the basal cell layers of the epidermis. The difficulties in properly illustrating the ultrastructure of the skin have been circumvented by selecting newborn mouse skin for the survey picture (top), the basal layer of human trachea to elucidate the tonofilaments (bottom left), and the surface layers of the mouse esophagus, which is fully keratinized in this species (bottom right), to describe the structure of soft keratin.

*Top:*

On a thin basement membrane (*Bm*) rest the cells of the stratum germinativum (*Germ*). The most basally located cells are small, and the nucleus (*Nu*) occupies a major part of the cell. The cytoplasm is dense. As the cells migrate upward, they enlarge and stretch out parallel to the surface, and because of this fewer nuclei seem to be present. The cytoplasm clears up and coarse fibrils appear. In the epidermis of young animals, a few small intercellular spaces (*Is*) are seen, whereas in the germinal layer of mature epidermis, abundant intercellular spaces open up. In the stratum granulosum (*Gran*), the cells become even more elongated and the nuclei, rare. The cytoplasm clears up more, fibrils crisscross the cell, and also at this moment small keratohyalin granules (*Ke*) appear, which increase in size near the surface cell layers. The cells are held together by numerous desmosomes (*Des*).

Epidermis. Newborn mouse. Magnification 4800×. Ep. UA.

*Bottom Left:*

In the basal cells, most of the density of the cytoplasm is explained by an abundance of ribosomes (*Ri*) and tonofilaments (*To*). The tonofilaments are loosely arranged and have an irregular course throughout the cell, whereas they occur in bundles in the stratum granulosum, here giving rise to the tonofibrils seen with the light microscope. The tonofilaments converge on (or originate from) desmosomes (*Des*), which are specializations of the cell membrane (*Cm*) by which the cells are attached to each other across the intercellular space (*Is*). A few mitochondria (*Mi*) and lysosomes (*Ly*) can be seen in the basal layers of the epidermis.

Basal cell. Human trachea. Magnification 35,000×. Ep. LA.

*Bottom Right:*

The stratum corneum (*Corn*) is the most superficial part of the epidermis. It consists of several layers of cells that are extremely flat and fully keratinized. Between the uppermost cell layer of the stratum granulosum (*Gran*) and the stratum corneum (*Corn*) exists an ill-defined layer that usually is referred to as the stratum lucidum (*Luc*).

The following events occur as the cells move from the granulated to the cornified layers: The cell membrane (*Cm*) changes from a thin, 70A-thick structure to a dense, approximately 100A-thick membrane. The desmosomes (*Des*) become faint and remain only as a dense intercellular substance. The keratohyalin granules disappear, and the tonofilaments simultaneously become coarser, more irregular, but also more closely arranged. Cell constituents like the mitochondria (*Mi*) and the nucleus become trapped and ultimately obscured. It is as though the entire cell became condensed, now fully occupied by keratin (*Ker*). Near the surface of the skin, the intercellular spaces (*Is*) again loosen up, presumably as a step toward desquamation.

Stratum corneum. Mouse esophagus. Magnification 66,000×. Meth. UA.

*References:* GENERAL 37, 116, 117, 118, 119, 120, 121, 122, 134, 162, 167, 170, 185, 392, 421, 443, 488, 556, 580, 606, 608, 612, 728, 753, 830, 831, 840, 841, 880, 957, 958, 966, 970, 1037, 1038, 1057, 1106, 1108, 1109, 1168, 1313, 1314, 1315, 1317, 1510, 1590. BASEMENT MEMBRANE 205, 1036, 1251, 1312, 1509. MELANOCYTE 169, 184, 280.

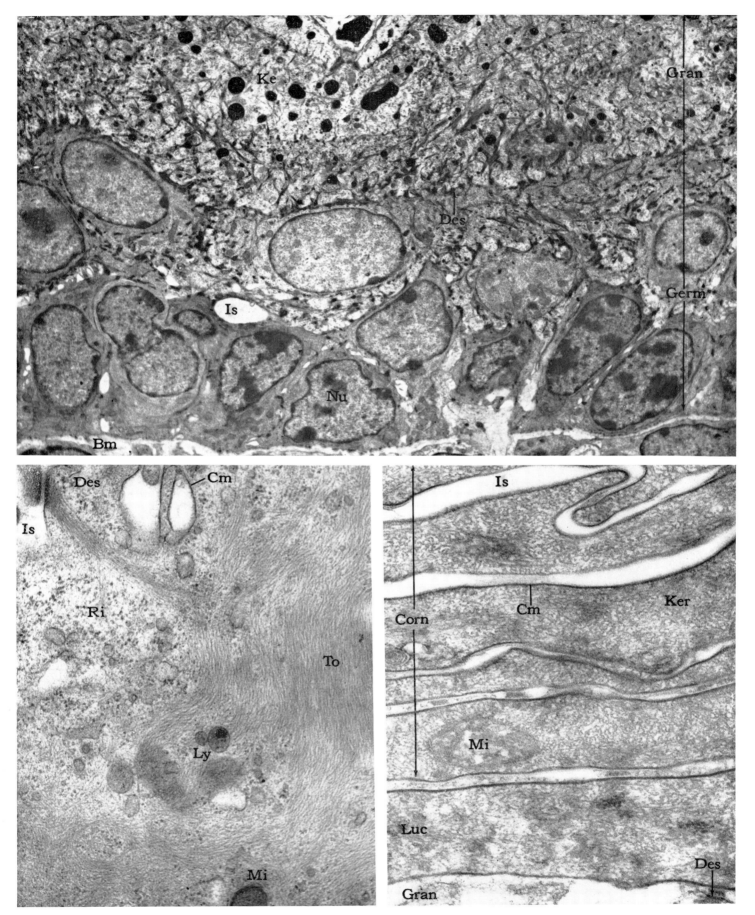

In a cross section of the follicle of the growing hair of the white mouse, one can conveniently study the various layers that participate in the early formation of the hair. (1) The connective tissue sheath is incomplete in this illustration, but some fine collagenous fibrils (*Co*) and the nucleus of a fibroblast are evident adjacent to a thin basement membrane (*Bm*), which sometimes is thick and is referred to as the glossy or vitreous membrane. (2) Next there is a rather broad layer of epithelial cells, which constitute the external root sheath. These cells do not become keratinized. Their nuclei (*Nu*) are comparatively large, and the cytoplasm contains scattered mitochondria (*Mi*) as well as broad areas that are rich in glycogen (*Gl*).

(3) Internal to the epithelial cells of the external root sheath is a narrow, dense cuff of keratinized cells. These are the cells of Henle's layer, and parts of seven cells can be identified. The cells undergo a type of keratinization, the end products of which are referred to as *soft keratin*. In this process is involved an interaction of ribosomes, tonofilaments, and trichohyalin granules. As the keratinization proceeds, structures such as mitochondria and nuclei (*Nu*) gradually die and disappear or become obscured by the process.

(4) Deep to the layer of Henle is Huxley's layer. These cells are not yet keratinized but eventually undergo soft keratinization. Numerous trichohyalin granules (*Tr*) are present in these cells. The largest ones are irregular; the smallest are spherical. (5) The layer deep to this is the cuticle of the inner root sheath. The cells contain a large nucleus (*Nu*) and numerous, small, spherical trichohyalin granules. This layer also undergoes soft keratinization.

(6) The cuticle of the hair cortex is seen next and appears to contain intensely opaque, small bodies. These cells undergo a type of keratinization that is different from the soft or hard type of keratinization. The product has been referred to as *amorphous keratin*. Probably the cell constituents that participate are ribosomes and small, irregular, opaque bodies that structurally do not resemble trichohyalin granules. These cells acquire a scalelike appearance as they become keratinized and develop an imbricated arrangement with a free blunt edge as they reach maturation.

(7) The cortex of the hair is deep to the hair cuticle. The cytoplasm of the cells contains a large number of spherical structures—cross-sectioned tonofibrils. No pigment granules are present since this hair is from an albino mouse. The cells of the hair cortex eventually contain *hard keratin*, in the production of which ribosomes and tonofilaments participate but not trichohyalin granules. (8) The nucleus in the center may indicate the location of a medullary cell of the hair. Ordinarily these cells do not become keratinized.

Hair follicle. White mouse. Magnification 8000×. Meth. UA.

*References:*   22, 50, 51, 82, 83, 84, 85, 95, 166, 393, 842, 1168, 1204, 1205, 1206, 1207, 1208.

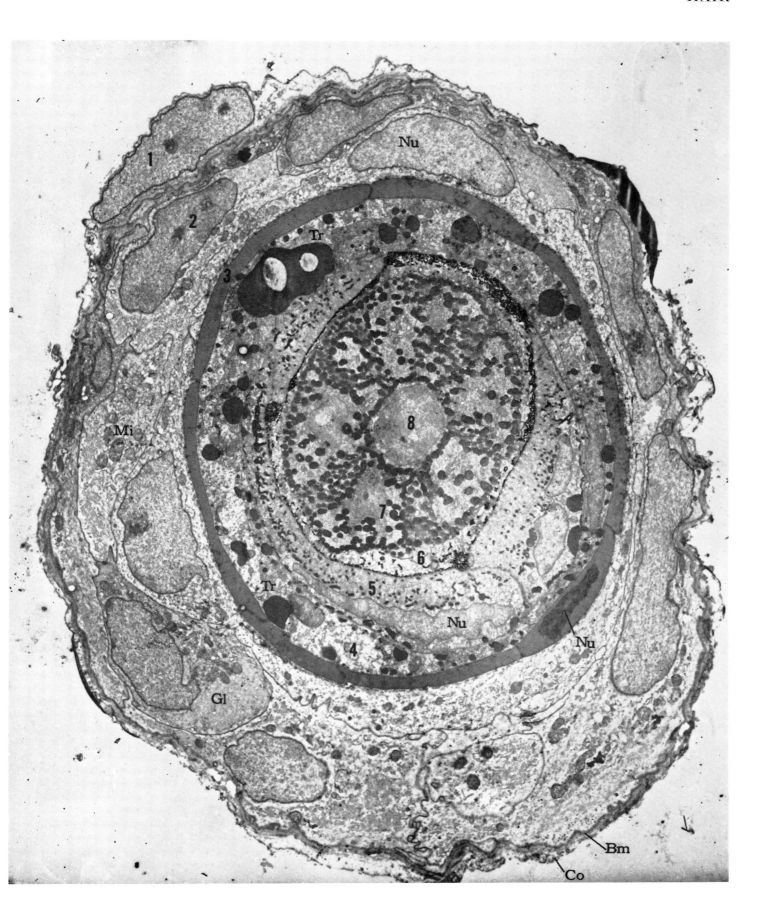

The thyroid gland is composed of numerous spherical follicles, which do not seem to be interconnected. A rich capillary network (*Ca*) surrounds the follicles, and some of the smallest capillaries sometimes assume an intercellular location within the epithelial wall of the follicle. Numerous arterioles (*Ar*) supply the gland with blood, and they have the appearance, in cross section, of follicles but normally contain a rich supply of erythrocytes (*Er*). The center of the follicles is occupied by colloid (*Col*), which varies greatly in density from one follicle to the other. The follicular cell is slightly cylindrical, cuboidal, or flat, depending on its functional state and on the repletion of the follicle. In the cuboidal cell, the nucleus (*Nu*) is located centrally.

The cytoplasm is rich in rough-surfaced endoplasmic reticulum with a great variation in the distention of the cisternae (*Ci*). This can be most advantageously studied in tangential sections (*TG*) of the follicular wall. The cisternae are filled with a substance of medium density, and it is generally believed that the precursor of the hormone is elaborated by the endoplasmic reticulum. However, it is not generally accepted that the assortment of dense granules (*G*), which appear anywhere in the cytoplasm, actually represents secretion granules. Granules are observed with varying grades of density suggestive of intergrades between dark round granules and large, less dense granules. In addition to the large granules, small granules and vesicles containing substances of varying density are found in a specific layer immediately beneath the luminal cell surface. A well-developed Golgi complex exists, usually located between the nucleus and the follicular cell surface, and mitochondria (*Mi*) are abundant. Tiny microvilli (*Vi*) project into the colloid (*Col*), and the entire follicle is surrounded by a thin basement membrane (*Bm*). As for the function of the follicular cell, it remains to be established how the colloid is formed and discharged and which pathway the hormone, probably located within the colloid, follows when it is transported across the follicular epithelium to the capillaries (*Ca*).

Magnification 3700×. Ep. UA.

*References:* 252, 296, 297, 301, 302, 303, 378, 431, 566, 623, 709a, 817, 818, 879, 917, 1103, 1216, 1394, 1395, 1396, 1397, 1398, 1465, 1466, 1468, 1536, 1537, 1576.

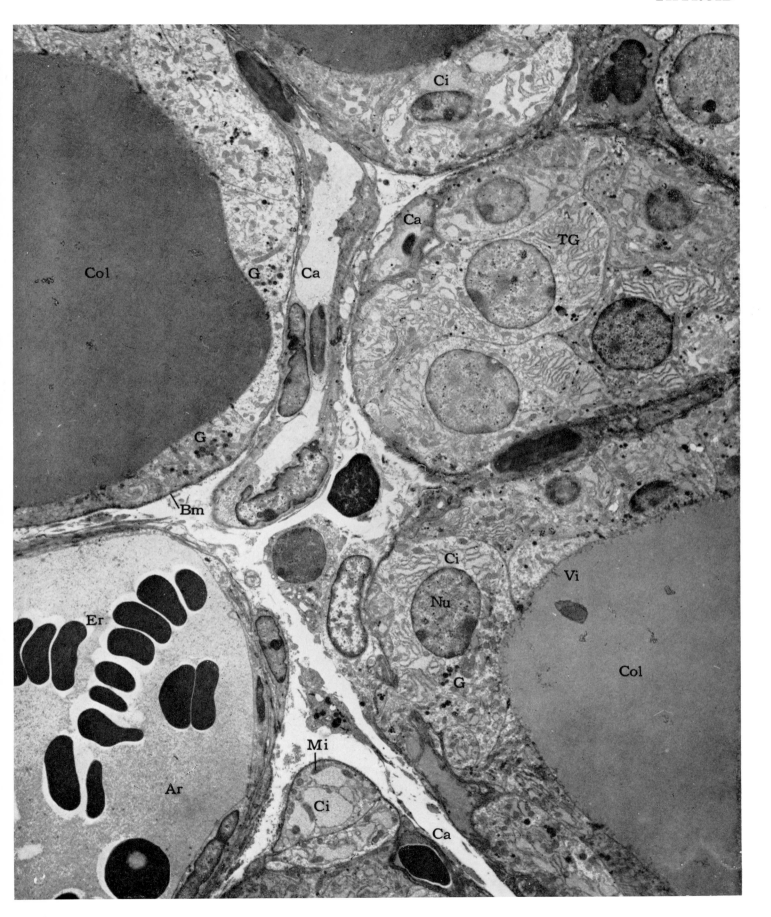

*Top:*   Parathyroid gland of 52-year-old woman with no clinical evidence of hyperparathyroidism. The specimen was removed during surgery performed for a nontoxic nodular goiter.

The parathyroid gland consists of irregular cords of polyhedral cells traversed by many small capillaries ($Ca$) and a connective tissue rich in collagen ($Co$), fibroblasts ($Fib$), and mast cells ($H$). The cells of this gland are small, and the nuclei, therefore, seem numerous and close together. The most frequent cell type is the chief cell. The majority of the chief cells have a dense cytoplasm ($CD$), but some have a rather pale cytoplasm ($CP$). Still another variety of the chief cell has an almost clear cytoplasm ($CC$), some of which is aggregated in the upper left corner of this illustration. A rare type of cell with an enormous concentration of granules is usually called oxyphil cell ($Ox$).

Magnification 1000×. Ep. UA.

*Bottom Left:*   Detail of a pale chief cell from the same human parathyroid, showing part of the nucleus ($Nu$) and a capillary ($Ca$) in the connective tissue ($Co$). A thin basement membrane ($Bm$) surrounds the cell cords. The cytoplasm contains sacs of rough-surfaced endoplasmic reticulum ($Re$), free ribosomes ($Ri$), mitochondria ($Mi$), and a small Golgi complex ($Go$). The area of the cell that appears pale in the top picture is in this illustration occupied by glycogen granules ($Gl$), since lead acetate stains it, whereas uranyl acetate (top picture) does not. Thus, the clearer the cytoplasm in ordinary histological specimens, the richer the cell's content of glycogen. Small dense granules reminiscent of secretory granules ($G$) in other endocrine cells occur infrequently in narrow cytoplasmic protrusions near the basement membrane ($Bm$).

Magnification 11,000×. Ep. LA.

*Bottom Right:*   Detail of an oxyphil cell in the same human parathyroid, showing parts of chief cells ($CD$). The nucleus ($Nu$) is spherical and is located in the center of the cell. The cytoplasm is filled with densely packed mitochondria ($Mi$), between which are scattered groups of ribosomes ($Ri$). Secretory granules cannot be identified, and the granules that have been described in light microscopy all represent mitochondria. At the ultrastructural level, there seems to be no ground for the assumption that oxyphil cells are derived from chief cells, since intermediate stages have not been observed.

Magnification 11,000×. Ep. LA.

*References:*   239, 734, 773, 774, 904, 1102, 1230, 1438, 1467.

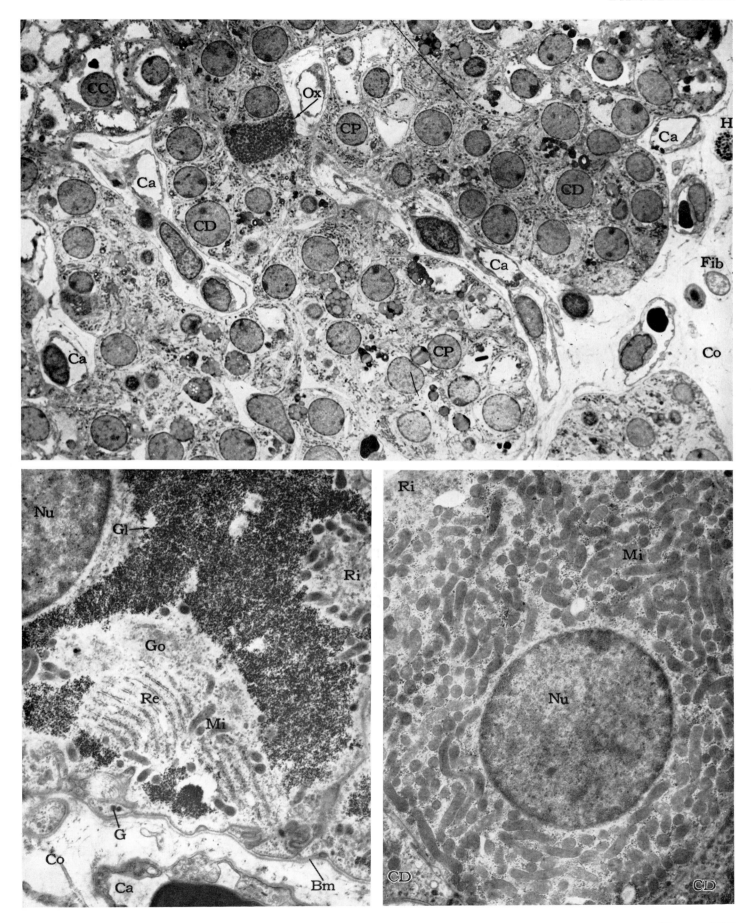

*Top:*  The adrenal gland is surrounded by a dense connective tissue capsule (*Caps*), which contains numerous arterioles and capillaries (*Ca*). The cells of the adrenal cortex are gathered in zones, of which the outermost is called the zona glomerulosa (*Glomer*) followed by the zona fasciculata (*Fascic*) and the zona reticularis (not shown), which borders on the adrenal medulla. Because one zone merges gradually into the next, it is difficult to see definite demarcation lines. The cells of the zona glomerulosa are of a columnar shape and are arranged in archlike groups, whereas the cells of the fasciculata are polyhedral and are arranged in more or less definite radial columns or cords (*Cord*). Capillaries (*Ca*) form a rich network throughout the cortex. The nuclei of the glomerulosa cells are usually large and have a light nucleoplasm, whereas those of the fasciculata, especially in the neighborhood of the reticularis, are small and are characterized by a dense nucleoplasm (*Da*). Occasionally these cells contain two nuclei (asterisk). Most cells of the cortex contain numerous lipid droplets, which are not easy to preserve perfectly. This is particularly true in the cells of the inner fasciculata and often contributes to a foamy appearance of the cytoplasm.

Magnification 2000×. Ep. LA.

*Bottom Left:*  The cells of the zona glomerulosa, located next to the capsule (*Cu*) of the adrenal gland, have a definite columnar shape, a large oval nucleus (*Nu*), and a sparse cytoplasm containing numerous mitochondria (*Mi*) and lipid droplets (*Li*). The cells converge toward some of the capillaries (*Ca*) from which they are separated by the thin basement membrane (*Bm*) that surrounds groups of cells.

Magnification 4000×. Ep. LA.

*Bottom Right:*  Detail of an area roughly corresponding to the rectangle indicated in the previous picture. Each cell is bordered by the plasma membrane (*Cm*). The cytoplasm contains an abundance of ribosomes (*Ri*) and tubular or vesicular elements of the smooth-surfaced endoplasmic reticulum (*Sm*). The mitochondria (*Mi*) are spherical or slightly oval with the fine structure typical of most endocrine cells. The lipid granules (*Li*) of the zona glomerulosa are usually well preserved and have irregular outlines.

Magnification 46,000×. Ep. LH.

*References:*  27, 63, 64, 149, 209, 210, 211, 273, 335, 430, 769, 770, 772, 803, 873, 1225, 1226, 1248, 1445, 1567, 1585, 1587, 1588.

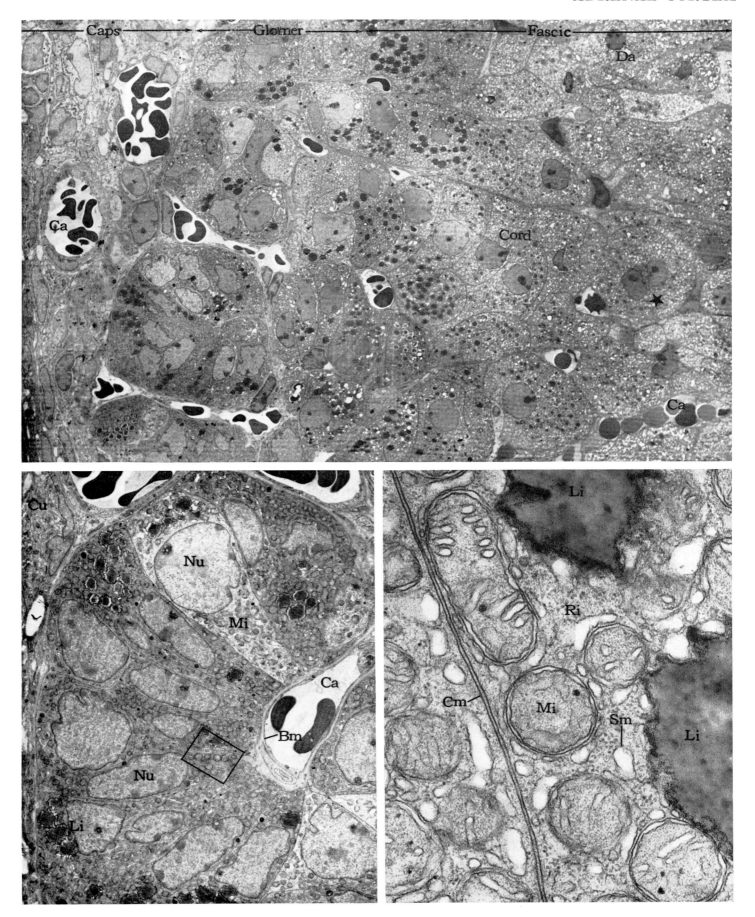

*Top:*

The islets of Langerhans are aggregations of irregular masses of pale cells with endocrine function, scattered between the exocrine acinar cells of the pancreas. The cells contain a large number of granules, and it is mainly because of a certain variation in the density, shape, and ultrastructure of these granules that different cell types can be distinguished with some degree of accuracy. Even in a low magnification electron micrograph it is difficult to distinguish the cell types, and differentiation can only be based on the knowledge of their fine structure at higher magnifications. The alpha cell (*A*) is relatively large and contains an abundance of spherical, highly electron-dense granules. The beta cell (*B*) is smaller and occurs more frequently than the alpha cell. It contains many irregular granules of medium density together with a small number of lysosomes and aggregations of ferritin particles. The latter types of cell organelles show up with high electron density and may easily be confused with alpha cell granules at low magnifications. The delta cell (*D*) is small, with a pale cytoplasm seemingly lacking granules at low magnifications. Thin capillaries (*Ca*) form a network throughout the islet.

Cat pancreas. Magnification 3600×. Ep. LH.

*Bottom:*

The alpha cell cytoplasm (*A*) displays areas rich in rough-surfaced endoplasmic reticulum (*Re*) as well as an overall high concentration of ribosomes (*Ri*). The mitochondria (*Mi*) are relatively large but scarce. Near the Golgi complex (*Go*) is frequently seen a centrosome (*Ce*). The secretory granules (*G*) have an intensely stained core and a loosely fitting membranous envelope. The alpha cell granules arise within the vesicles and membranes of the Golgi complex. Dense granules of varying shape (*Ft*), provided with tightly fitting membranes, represent aggregations of ferritin particles (cf. page 13, top left). The ultrastructure of the beta cell (*B*) does not differ considerably from that of the alpha cell. It does contain a greater amount of rough-surfaced endoplasmic reticulum (not shown). The secretory granules (*G*) are quite different, however, in man, cat, dog, and bat. Here they display a central prismatic, crystalline structure (best seen in upper left corner), which is encased in a less dense homogeneous material. The entire structure is surrounded by a thin membrane. It seems that the beta cell granules are elaborated by the cisternae of the rough-surfaced endoplasmic reticulum. The delta cell (*D*) is structurally quite similar to the alpha cell with the exception that the secretory granules (*G*) are less dense. Lysosomes (*Ly*) are frequently present in both the beta and delta cells. Unmyelinated nerves (*Ne*) are commonly seen to contact the plasma membrane of either cell type (asterisk). Both the alpha and beta granules are believed to become discharged into the connective tissue space (*Co*) across the basement membrane (*Bm*). It seems that the granules become dissolved here and subsequently diffuse into the thin capillary (*Ca*).

The alpha cells probably secrete glucagon, whereas the beta cells are said to produce insulin or its precursor. The role of the delta cell is unknown. It has been suggested that it represents an aged or degenerated alpha cell.

Cat pancreas. Magnification 16,000×. Ep. LH.

*References:* 65, 66, 389, 433, 709a, 720, 721, 722, 723, 724, 725, 726, 727, 902, 903, 1393, 1525, 1527, 1528.

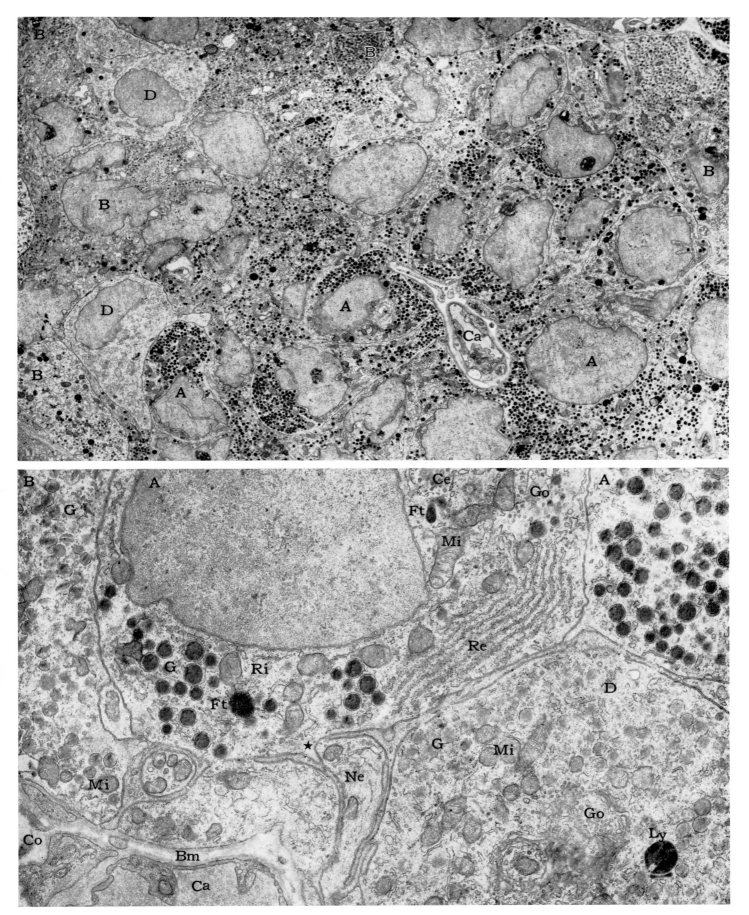

*Top:*  The epithelium covering the anterior part of the cornea is of the same nonkeratinizing stratified squamous type that is found in the esophagus. In the mouse the basal layer of low columnar cells (*Ba*) rests on a thin basement membrane (*Bm*), whereas in man this layer is thicker and is referred to as Bowman's membrane. Toward the surface of the epithelium, the cells gradually change from columnar to polyhedral (*Pol*) or wing cells, and to flat, surface cells (*Su*). The nuclei (*Nu*) of the basal cells are extremely dense but gradually become clearer in cells located closer to the surface. The same is true for the density of the cytoplasm. The opposite is true, however, for the plasma membranes. These have a wavy course and are thin and difficult to discern in the basal layer, but increase in thickness and become straight near the surface. Because of this, it is easy to see the cell borders, even at low magnification.

Magnification 2200×. Ep. UA.

*Bottom Left:*  Two areas have been selected to demonstrate the details of a nonkeratinized stratified squamous epithelium. (For details of other areas containing a similar epithelium, consult page 56, the esophagus.) This figure illustrates the base of a basal cell on the thin basement membrane (*Bm*) and corresponds to the lower rectangle in the top picture. The extreme density of the cytoplasm of these cells is explained by the large numbers of ribosomes (*Ri*) and tonofilaments (*To*). Only a few mitochondria can be detected. The lateral plasma membrane (*Cm*) is thin and is provided with small desmosomes (*Des*). The basal plasma membrane (*Cm*) contains numerous, regularly spaced densities, which, upon close examination, turn out to represent half-desmosomes (*Dm*); that is, the counterpart of a paired desmosome is missing. The nuclear membrane (*Nu*) is obscured by the dense accumulation of ribosomes.

Basal cells. Magnification 27,500×. Ep. UA.

*Bottom Right:*  Detail of an area corresponding to the upper rectangle in the upper picture. The light cytoplasm of the surface cells is explained by a paucity of ribosomes (*Ri*) and tonofilaments (*To*), permitting the mitochondria (*Mi*) to stand out clearly. The plasma membranes (*Cm*) have increased in thickness as with those of keratinized cells, but keratinization does not occur because keratohyalin granules are absent in the cells of the corneal epithelium. During preparation for the process of desquamation, the small desmosomes (*Des*) loosen up and the intercellular space (*Is*) becomes wide.

Surface cells. Magnification 27,500×. Ep. UA.

Page 144

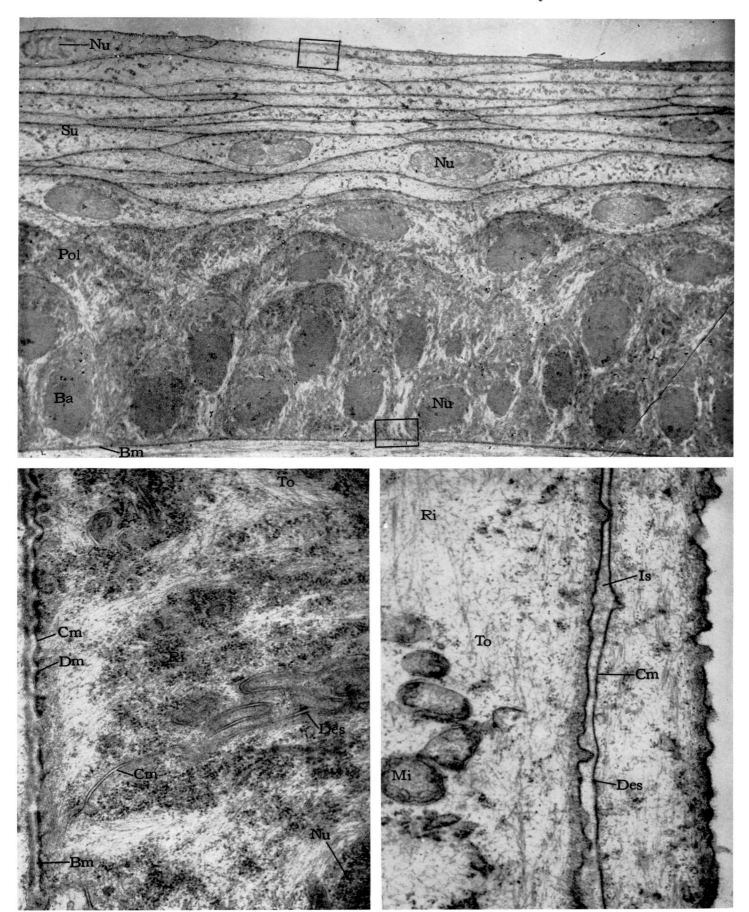

*Top:*    Deep to the stratified squamous epithelium of the external surface of the cornea is the stroma or substantia propria (*SP*), the posterior elastic membrane or Descemet's membrane (*DM*), and the corneal mesenchymal epithelium (*Mep*), often referred to as endothelium, which borders on the anterior chamber of the eye (*Ach*). The substantia propria (*SP*) is composed of layers of collagenous fibrils intermingled with long, slender stroma cells, most of which represent fibroblasts (*Fib*), although occasional Schwann cells (*Sch*) occur in conjunction with thin unmyelinated nerves. The membrane of Descemet (*DM*) is thicker than the anterior basement membrane or Bowman's membrane (cf. page 145) in the mouse, whereas in man, Bowman's membrane is thinner than Descemet's membrane. The cells of the mesenchymal epithelium (*Mep*) are flat and interdigitate with each other in an overlapping fashion.

Magnification 3900×. Ep. LH.

*Bottom Left:*    Detail of the substantia propria. The nucleus of the fibroblast (*Fib*) occupies a major part of the cell depth. The cytoplasmic inclusions are more sparse than is normally the case in fibroblasts elsewhere (cf. page 17). There is a predominance of ribosomes, and the profiles of the rough-surfaced endoplasmic reticulum are short in the mature cornea. The long and thin cytoplasmic processes frequently make contact with those of adjacent cells in the same plane. The collagen occurs in layers, within each of which the fibrils run parallel to each other. The collagenous fibrils in one lamella form essentially right angles with those in adjacent layers; the result is that the fibrils are cut across (*Cr*) as well as lengthwise (*Le*). The fibril diameter averages 200A, which is less than the corresponding figure recorded in the sclera of the eye (cf. page 17). The characteristic collagen period is not easily resolved in the stroma of the cornea but averages 650A.

Corneal stroma. Magnification 18,500×. Ep. LH.

*Bottom Right:*    Detail of the membrane of Descemet (*DM*) and the corneal mesenchymal epithelium (*Mep*) with the anterior chamber of the eye at the extreme right. *Descemet's membrane* is characterized by an amorphous substance similar to the zona pellucida of the ovum or the capsule of the lens, and this puts it into the category of basement membranes. However, cross striations (*Cr*) of coarse bands and filaments occur interconnected by thin filaments. This degree of organization is higher in some species, for instance, the cow and the chick, whereas in other species, like the mouse, rat, and man, it is not so pronounced. Because of the filaments observed and the results obtained from x-ray diffraction examination, it has been suggested that the membrane of Descemet be placed in the collagen class of proteins rather than being classified as a basement membrane with elastic properties.

The cells of the *corneal mesenchymal epithelium* are of a squamous type with elongated nuclei (*Mep*). The cells interdigitate and overlap at the surface toward the anterior chamber of the eye, where the intercellular attachment is assured by a terminal bar (between asterisks). Desmosomes are not present, but specialized areas of the plasma membrane (*Cm*) occur where the intercellular space is decreased locally. The mitochondria (*Mi*) are small and spherical. They have concentrically arranged inner membranes in both mouse and man. There is an abundance of ribosomes (*Ri*) and some short profiles of the rough-surfaced endoplasmic reticulum (*Re*). Pinocytotic vesicles occur (not shown) in these cells, and the presence of both cell membrane invaginations and vesicles suggests that the hydration of the cornea is actively regulated by the cells of the corneal mesenchymal epithelium.

Descemet's membrane and corneal mesenchymal epithelium. Magnification 26,000×. Ep. LH.

*References:*   81, 276, 376, 634, 635, 636, 637, 638, 639, 640, 676, 678, 679, 834, 1050, 1236, 1287, 1288, 1291, 1292, 1301, 1310, 1522.

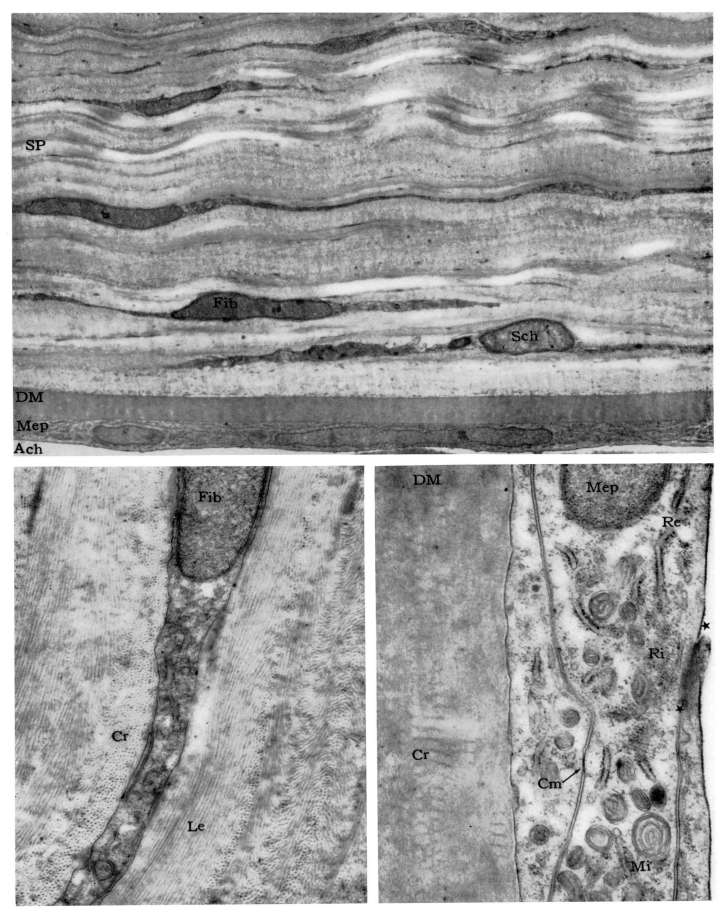

*Top:*    Meridional section of the iris, with the anterior (*Ach*) and posterior chambers (*Pch*) of the eye on either side of the iris. The margin of the iris, connected with the ciliary body (*Cb*), is called the ciliary margin (*Cim*). At the angle of the iris (*Ai*) is seen a portion of the uveal framework (*Uf*), which is in open connection with the trabecular spaces of Fontana and possibly also with the nearby canal of Schlemm. The iris has a central, loose stroma (*St*) composed of fibroblasts, collagen, nerves, and occasional pigmented cells. Numerous small arterioles and capillaries (*Ca*) are present, most of which are arranged concentrically around the pupil. Toward the anterior chamber (*Ach*) the iris is covered with a continuous layer of extremely long and flat cells, the anterior pigmented epithelium (*AP*). The posterior surface is covered with a double layer of cells, the posterior pigmented epithelium (*Pep*). The inner layer (*Il*) is thin near the ciliary margin (*Cim*) and the cell nuclei are far apart, whereas the cells of the outer layer (*Ol*) are cuboidal and the nuclei close. The shape of the cells gradually changes toward the pupillary margin of the iris. The cells of the outer layer flatten out, and the cells of the inner layer increase in thickness and become less squamous.

Magnification 2100×. Meth. Unstained.

*Bottom Left:*    The posterior pigmented epithelium of the iris is a direct continuation of the ciliary portion of the retina. It contains two layers of cells, the inner (*Il*) and the outer layer (*Ol*). The posterior pigmented epithelium is surrounded by a thin continuous basement membrane (*Bm*), which on one side borders on the posterior chamber of the eye (*Pch*) and on the other side establishes a wavy and complex borderline toward the collagenous fibrils (*Co*) of the iridial stroma. The two cell layers are held together by desmosomes (*Tb*) in similarity with the cells of the ciliary portion of the retina (cf. page 149). Like those cells, the overall cytoplasmic density of the superficial layer is greater than that of the deep layer, mostly because of a denser accumulation of ribosomes. The mitochondria (*Mi*) are spherical and dense in both cell types, but the pigment granules (*Pg*) are larger in the cells of the inner layer. The interior of the pigment granule is lamellar. In the white mouse (this illustration) the lamellae are loosely arranged, whereas they are extremely densely packed in the pigments of the brown mouse.

Posterior pigmented epithelium. Magnification 14,000×. Ep. LH.

*Bottom Right:*    The iris diminishes in thickness toward the pupillary margin (*Pup*), here partly shown in a meridional section through the circular sphincter muscle of the pupil. The anterior pigmented epithelium (*AP*) is, as with the posterior pigmented epithelium, encased in a thin, continuous basement membrane (*Bm*), which borders on the anterior chamber of the eye (*Ach*). The anterior pigmented epithelium terminates shortly before the pupillary margin (at *Bm* arrow), but the basement membrane itself continues uninterrupted, enveloping the sphincter muscle. The smooth muscle cells (*So*) of the sphincter have a small diameter. The cytoplasm is occupied mainly by the contractile elements (small, dense dots) intermingled with some mitochondria. Like smooth muscle cells elsewhere, cytoplasmic processes establish a lateral cell contact (asterisks).

Sphincter of the pupil. Magnification 21,000×. Ep. LH.

*References:* 449, 450, 599, 695, 762, 1433, 1434, 1435, 1461.

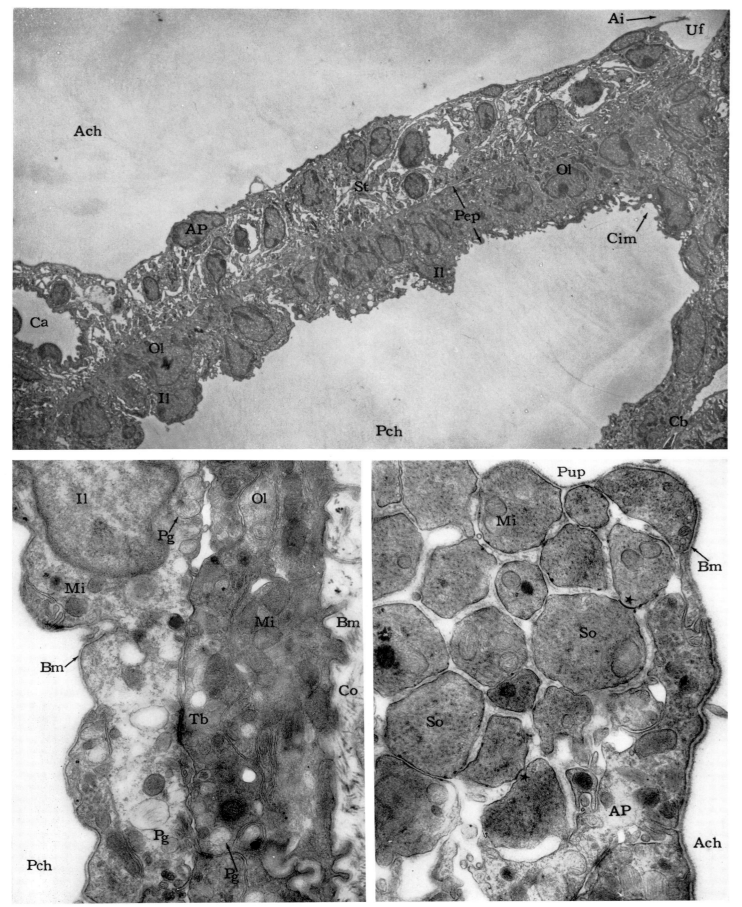

*Top:*
Meridional section of two ciliary processes, each of which projects into the posterior chamber of the eye (*Pch*). The stroma (*St*) of the ciliary process is covered by the ciliary epithelium, which consists of a double layer of epithelial cells, the inner nonpigmented layer (*Il*) and the outer pigmented layer (*Ol*). The stroma contains numerous capillaries (*Ca*), most of which are marked by the red blood cells (intensely black,) and a delicate connective tissue. The cells of the inner nonpigmented epithelium (*Il*) are of a low columnar or cuboidal shape with the deep recesses of the posterior chamber of the eye between them (arrows). The cells of the outer pigmented epithelium (*Ol*) are cuboidal or flat, and the cytoplasm has an overall greater density than that of the inner layer cells.

Ciliary processes. White mouse. Magnification 2600×. Meth. Unstained.

*Bottom Left:*
INNER NONPIGMENTED EPITHELIUM. Detail of an area similar to the left rectangle in the top picture. The nuclei (*Nu*) are large in the cells of the inner nonpigmented epithelium. The cytoplasm displays a fair number of ribosomes (*Ri*). The mitochondria (*Mi*) are few and have a spherical shape. The cells are separated from the posterior chamber of the eye (*Pch*) by the internal limiting membrane (*Ilm*), which in the mouse and rabbit is represented by a thin basement membrane but in man consists of a broad meshwork of fibrils and basement membrane-like material. The plasma membrane, which faces the posterior chamber, is elaborately infolded, reminiscent of the tubular cells of the nephron (cf. page 99, bottom). The lateral surfaces of the cells also show interdigitations, which seem to be more prominent in some species (rabbit) than in others (mouse, man). Desmosomes (*Des*) hold the cells together. The deep recesses (arrow) are utilized for the anchorage of the zonular fibers (not shown).

Ciliary process. White mouse. Magnification 16,000×. Ep. LH.

*Bottom Right:*
OUTER PIGMENTED EPITHELIUM. Detail of an area similar to the right rectangle in the top picture. The nucleus (*Nu*) occupies a major part of the cell. The cytoplasm is dense because of an abundance of ribosomes (*Ri*) and spherical or slightly elongated mitochondria (*Mi*). Pigment granules (*Pg*) are few in the white mouse and have a pale interior. The margin of the outer epithelium (*Ol*) is rather straight and is provided with a large number of desmosomes (*Des*) where it borders on the inner epithelium (*Il*). The external limiting membrane (*Elm*) is formed by a thin basement membrane, which often is thrown into elaborate folds and in man becomes quite thick. Toward the external limiting membrane the cell membrane of the outer pigmented epithelium has a folded appearance, and lateral interdigitations of cells occur also. The capillaries (*Ca*) of the stroma (*St*) with their thin endothelium are closely applied at this region.

It is commonly accepted that the major portion of the aqueous humor is secreted by the ciliary epithelium. The cells of the inner nonpigmented layer have been said to offer the most likely structural evidence for this process because of their resemblance to other cells noted for their water transport. However, it seems likely that both layers of the ciliary epithelium participate in the secretion, since both cell types display the structural basis for transport of fluid and the outer pigmented layer is in close apposition to the capillary network of the ciliary processes.

Ciliary process. White mouse. Magnification 16,000×. Ep. LH.

*References:*   593, 594, 595, 597, 598, 600, 1018, 1019, 1020, 1535.

Page 150

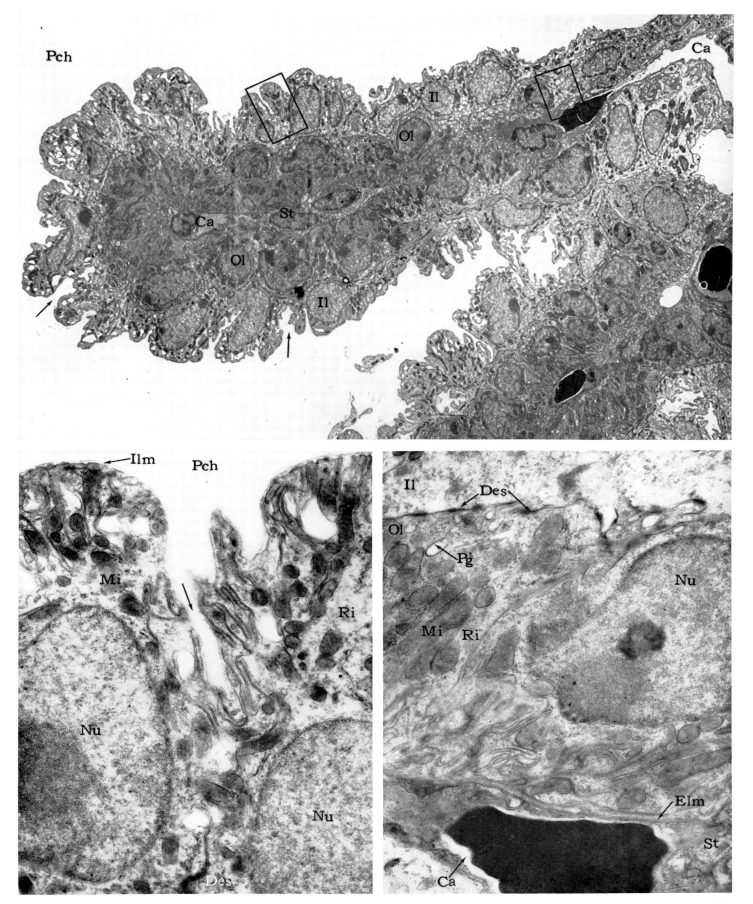

*Top Left and Right:*

The crystalline lens is here shown at low magnification, sectioned in the horizontal plane near the equator. The lens is surrounded by a capsule (*Cu*) with a fine structure reminiscent of the zona pellucida of the ovary (cf. page 119). The homogeneous appearance indicates the similarity to a basement membrane. The lens consists mainly of long slender cells, the lens fibers. The fibers are arranged quite regularly and in parallel, although within one area the fibers may be oriented differently from those of an adjacent area. The borderline between the areas is referred to as the lens suture (*sut*) and shows an interdigitated arrangement of the fibers that are sectioned longitudinally (*length*) and those that are sectioned across (*cross*). The lens fibers are hexagonal in shape. The anterior surface of the lens is covered by a simple cuboidal epithelium (*Ep*), which is missing at the posterior lens surface of the mature species. Near the equator of the lens (this illustration) the epithelial cells are no longer cuboidal but stretch out and become long and cylindrical in the process of transformation into lens fibers. This transformation involves a loss or extinction of the nucleus as well as mitochondria, rough-surfaced endoplasmic reticulum, and ribosomes—structures originally present in the surface epithelium. As the transformation progresses, an amorphous substance becomes predominant, and the cells are gradually transformed into lens fibers in the sequence indicated (2 to 4).

Magnification 2500×. Ep. UA.

*Bottom Left:*

Detail of three lens fibers corresponding to the areas 3 and 4 in the top picture. The lens develops from the ectoderm, and it may be expected therefore that the changes that take place during the transformation of the lenticular cells could be compared with the keratinization of cells of ectodermal origin. In fact, the process is reminiscent of the formation of hard keratin in the hair cortex. When most cell organelles are obscured by the accumulated amorphous substance, the delicate plasma membrane of individual cells (arrows) seem to fuse and form one single, coarse membrane (asterisk).

Magnification 34,000×. Ep. UA.

*Bottom Right:*

Detail of three lens fibers from the central mass of the lens, the so-called nucleus of the lens. This area is not shown in the top picture, but is located approximately 50 microns to the right of the cross-sectioned lens fibers. The amorphous or finely granular substance predominates also in these cells, but the cell borders are now characterized by one single, dense membrane, joined on either side by an electron-translucent layer. This is identical with the cell relationship of the fully keratinized cells of the hair cortex. It may therefore be concluded that the lens fibers represent a specialized cornified epithelium of the hard keratin type with the exception that the keratinization occurs without the appearance of the keratin filaments present in the hard keratin of the hair or the coarse granules of the amorphous keratin of the hair cuticle. It is obvious that the functional demands on the lens fibers are different from those on the cortical cells of hair, and it is therefore to be expected that the cornification of the lens fibers will be different.

Magnification 41,000×. Ep. UA.

*References:* 30, 192, 395, 615, 1101, 1142, 1301, 1469, 1470, 1471, 1472.

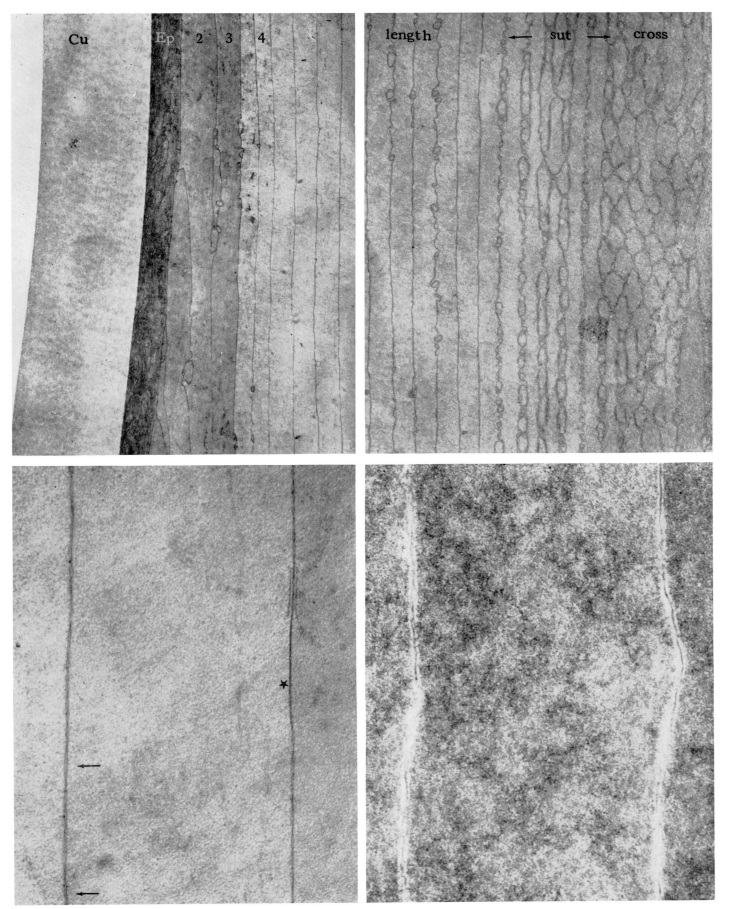

# RETINA

*Left:*   The structural elements of the retina form ten layers, which from without inward are:

1. THE PIGMENT EPITHELIUM LAYER.   The cells are low cuboidal with round nuclei and numerous thin, pigment-containing processes, extending down between the free ends of the outer segment of rods.

2. THE LAYER OF RODS AND CONES.   The cones are missing in the retina of the mouse. The rods can be subdivided into two structurally different parts: *The outer segment* of rods consists of numerous, densely packed disks, which supposedly are composed of double layers of lipid molecules sandwiched between very thin layers of proteins or proteins and carbohydrates. *The inner segment* of rods contains a varying number of mitochondria and small cytoplasmic vesicles. The two segments are interconnected by a thin stalk with centrally located filaments arranged in a pattern reminiscent of a cilium.

3. THE EXTERNAL LIMITING MEMBRANE.   This membrane is derived from dense terminal bars located at one level in the borders of the photoreceptor cells.

4. THE OUTER NUCLEAR LAYER.   These are the nuclei of the photoreceptor cells. Presumably because of space limitation, these nuclei are arranged in different layers. The body of the receptor cell is extremely narrow and can be seen mainly as thin, dense, fibrillar structures between the nuclei. The light areas stem from the cytoplasm of Müller cells.

5. THE OUTER PLEXIFORM LAYER.   In this layer, synaptic connections occur between the photoreceptor cells and the bipolar cells.

6. THE INNER NUCLEAR LAYER.   The majority of the nuclei, presumably those with a light nucleoplasm, belong to the bipolar cells. The dense oval nuclei are located within the Müller cells.

7. THE INNER PLEXIFORM LAYER.   The highly branched, proximal ends of the bipolar cells and the numerous dendrites of the ganglion cells form synaptic junctions within this layer.

8. THE GANGLION CELL LAYER.   The nucleus of the ganglion cell is fairly large and the cytoplasm is light. The bases of dense Müller cells are interposed. These cells most likely have a supporting function within the retina. They terminate at the level of the outer limiting membrane.

9. THE NERVE FIBER LAYER.   Although not shown here in its full extension, this layer contains the axons of the ganglion cells that form the majority of the fibers of the optic nerve.

10. THE INTERNAL LIMITING MEMBRANE.   A thin basement membrane (not shown).

Magnification 1600×. Ep. LH.

*Top Right:*   Detail of the outer limiting membrane, showing parts of several neuroreceptor nuclei (*Nu*) located within the outer nuclear layer. Cytoplasmic extensions of adjacent receptor cells (*Ph*) can be seen to contain both vesicular (*Ve*) and neurofilamentous (*Fi*) components. At least one receptor cell is clearly seen to extend beyond the outer limiting membrane. This "membrane" is formed by terminal bars (asterisks) of its own cell membrane and those of adjacent Müller cells (*Mr*) and other receptor cells. The continuation of the receptor cell is thus more properly referred to as an inner segment of a retinal rod (*It*).

Outer limiting membrane. Magnification 16,000×. Ep. LH.

*Bottom Right:*   Detail of the outer plexiform layer, showing synaptic connections (1 to 3) between receptor cells (*Ph*) and the neurons of the layer of the bipolar cells (*Bp*). The terminal branchlets (*Bp*) of the bipolar dendrites end in an invagination of the plasma membrane of the dense synaptic end of the photoreceptor cell (*Ph*). In the center are located two large vacuoles (*Va*), and the dendritic branchlets of the bipolar cell establish contact with both the vacuoles and the receptor cell membrane. The density of the synaptic end is explained by the presence of numerous small synaptic vesicles, a peculiar, ribbon-shaped structure (*Rb*), and mitochondria (*Mi*).

Outer plexiform layer. Magnification 16,000×. Ep. LH.

*References:*   193, 194, 195, 256, 259, 265, 271, 272, 277, 285, 294, 373, 374, 375, 385, 396, 729, 730, 739, 740, 741, 785, 820, 866, 881, 894, 1119, 1300, 1339, 1342, 1343, 1347, 1349, 1350, 1412, 1431, 1432, 1436, 1463, 1552, 1554, 1555, 1557, 1558, 1559, 1562, 1563.

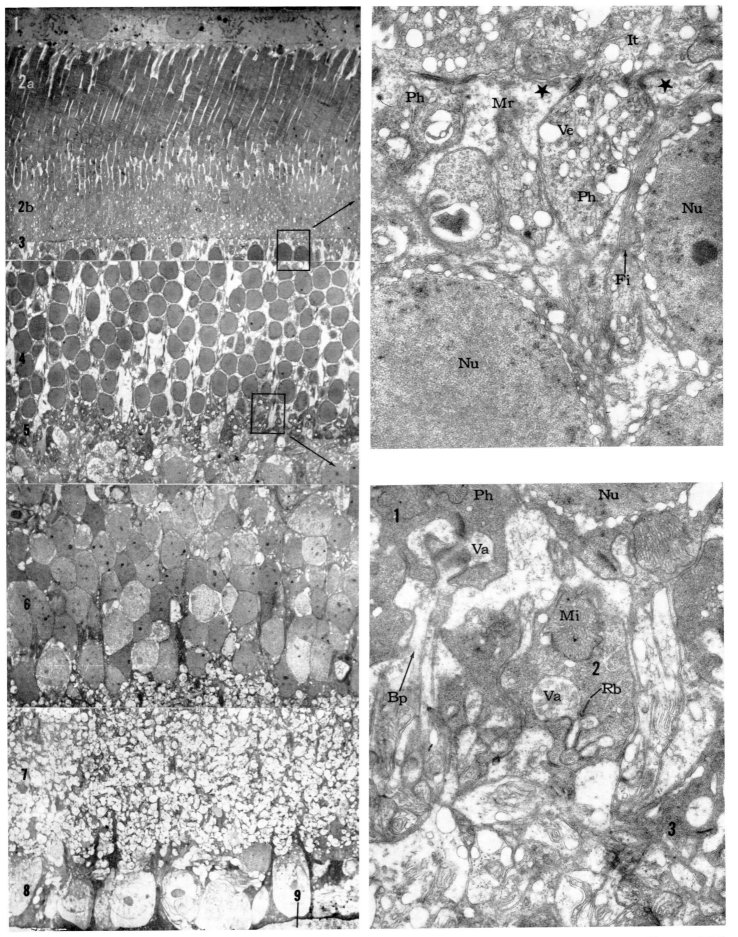

# ORGAN OF CORTI: GENERAL ORGANIZATION

*Top Left*
*and Right:*

The organ of Corti is located in the cochlea of the inner ear and consists of a highly differentiated neuroepithelium. It rests on the basilar membrane (*Bas*), which separates the endolymphatic space of the cochlear duct or the scala media (*Coc*) from the scala tympani (*Tymp*). Two sets of receptor cells form the functionally most important structure of the organ of Corti. These are the outer (*Oh*) and inner (*Ih*) hair cells. The outer hair cells (*Oh*) are most abundant and have an elongated shape, whereas the inner hair cells (*Ih*) are fewer, shorter, and wider. The dendrites of the bipolar ganglionic cells of the cochlear nerve (*Cne*) emerge from the connective tissue within the tympanic lip (*Tyl*), and fine nerve fibers (*Ne*) travel to both sets of hair cells, here making a synaptic contact with the basal end of the hair cell (rectangle). The delicate receptor cells are lodged within a complex system of supporting cells. The base of the outer hair cell (*Oh*) rests on the cup-shaped body of the outer phalangeal or Deiters' cell (*Oph*). Deiters' cells originate at the basilar membrane (*Bas*), and each continues as a slender cell process through the space between the outer hair cells, terminating with a specialized region, the phalanx (*Ax*), at the surface of the epithelium. The inner hair cells (*Ih*) are more completely surrounded by the inner phalangeal cells (*Iph*). Cells with a light cytoplasm, the border cells (*Bo*), form a transition of the neuroepithelium toward the internal spiral sulcus (*Isc*).

The outer (*Op*) and inner (*Ip*) pillar cells contain intracellular filaments with cytoskeletal function. Both types of pillar cells are club-shaped (*He*) at the epithelial surface. Between the pillar cells is located the inner tunnel, or tunnel of Corti (*Tc*), and between the outer pillar cell (*Op*) and the first row of outer hair cells (*Oh*) is the space of Nuel (*Nue*).

Guinea pig cochlea. Magnification: Left 1050×. Right 950×. Ep. UA.

*Bottom Left:*

OUTER WALL OF COCHLEA. Between the scala vestibuli (*Vest*) and the cochlear duct (*Coc*) is Reissner's membrane (*R*) or the vestibular membrane. It separates the perilymphatic (*Vest*) and endolymphatic (*Coc*) systems. The outer wall of the cochlear duct is covered by a low stratified columnar epithelium (*Ep*), which contains pigment (intensely dense granules). The epithelium forms the main part of the stria vascularis (*Stv*). The cells display numerous plasma membrane infoldings and mitochondria similar to the cells of the proximal segment of the nephron (cf. page 99, bottom). It is assumed that the endolymph is secreted by these cells. Beneath the epithelium is a wide network of connective tissue (*Co*) containing numerous capillaries (*Ca*).

Guinea pig cochlea. Magnification 3000×. Ep. LH.

*Bottom Right:*

BASILAR MEMBRANE: ZONA ARCUATA. The part of the basilar membrane (*Bas*) that extends from the foramina nervosa to the base of the outer pillar cells is called the zona arcuata. The inner pillar cell (*Ip*) rests on the basilar membrane. Fine unmyelinated nerves (*Ne*), which are the peripheral branches of the bipolar ganglionic cells, penetrate the cytoplasm of the pillar cell and traverse the tunnel of Corti (*Tc*) on their way to the outer hair cells. The basilar membrane (*Bas*) consists of coarse, interconnected basilar fibers (*Fi*) or auditory strings, which are arranged radially. Each fiber is composed of an irregular mass of fine collagenous filaments. The filaments are embedded in a homogeneous substance, which becomes evident on one side as a thick basement membrane (*Bm*). Toward the scala tympani (*Tymp*) the basilar membrane is lined by the cells of the tympanic covering layer (*Tcl*). These cells have long slender processes and form an irregular network in which the vas spirale (*Vs*) is located.

Guinea pig cochlea. Magnification 4000×. Ep. LH.

References: 318, 319, 320, 321, 325, 326, 327, 329, 330, 331, 333, 334, 426, 427, 428, 429, 628, 629, 630, 631, 632, 689, 1356, 1357, 1358, 1359, 1360, 1361, 1367, 1378, 1379, 1514, 1515.

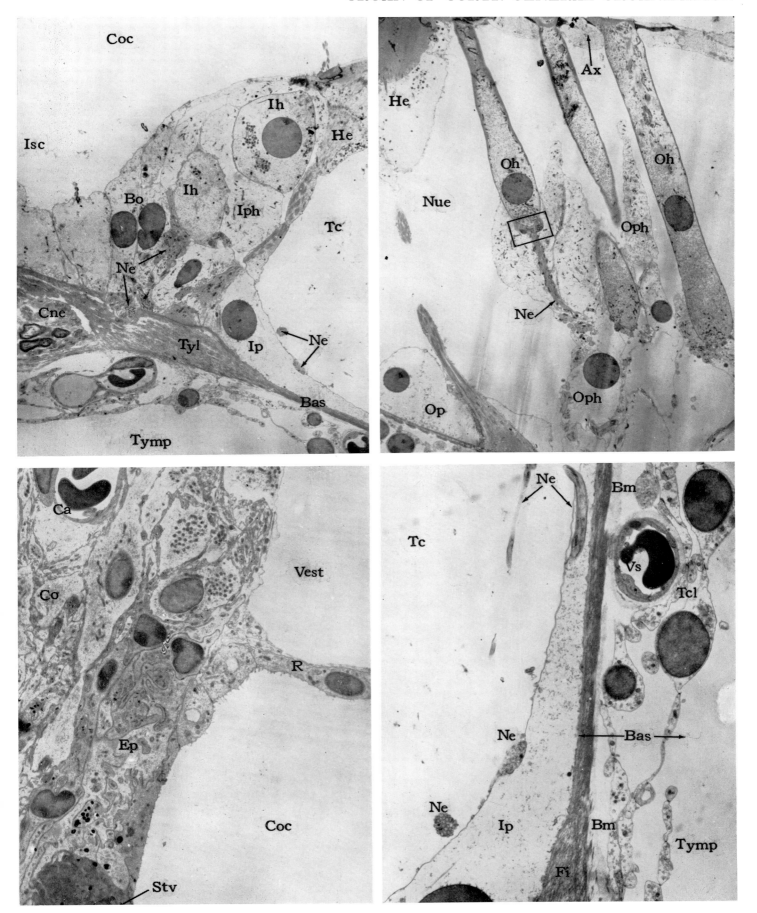

# ORGAN OF CORTI: RETICULAR MEMBRANE AND HAIR CELL

*Top:*    RETICULAR MEMBRANE.    The reticular membrane is formed by the surfaces of the inner (*Ip*) and outer (*Op*) pillar cells, as well as by the phalanges of the outer phalangeal cells (not shown). The head of the inner pillar cell (*IpHe*) has a rectangular head plate (*Hp*), which covers the outer pillar cell (*Op*) and contacts the cuticle (*Cut*) of the first row of outer hair cells (*Oh*). The head contains a dense, homogeneous structure, which is traversed by thin filaments with an average thickness of about 200A. The filaments become richly aggregated in the head plate (*Hp*) of the inner pillar cell. The head of the outer pillar cells (*OpHe*) similarly displays a dense homogeneous structure and filaments (*Fi*). From the head of the outer pillar cell a laminar phalangeal process (*Pp*) proceeds in an eccentric direction, passing through the outer hair cells of the first series (*Oh*), narrowing considerably, and finally broadening toward its contact with the second series of outer hair cells (far right). Part of the tunnel of Corti (*Tc*) is identified between the outer and inner pillar cells, and Nuel's space (*Nue*) between the outer pillar cell and the outer hair cell.

Guinea pig cochlea. Magnification 4700×. Ep. LH.

*Bottom Left:*    HAIR CELL SURFACE.    Beneath the thin surface membrane of the outer hair cell is a thick cuticle (*Cut*) with a homogeneous, dense structure. The auditory hairs (*Ha*) display a central axial fibril, which extends as a root (*Ro*) into the cuticle. A terminal bar (*Tb*) connects the hair cell to adjacent phalanges of the Deiters' cells and the inner phalangeal cells. Layers of discontinuous membranes (*Lm*) are located inside the plasma membrane within the supra-nuclear part of the outer hair cell to a depth of about 1 micron (compare with top picture). Immediately below the cuticle (*Cut*) several rounded bodies (*Hb*) occur in close proximity with mitochondria (*Mi*). The bodies correspond to the Hensen bodies of light microscopy. Each body is composed of concentric membranous layers, which show a close resemblance to the lamellar layers (*Lm*) beneath the plasma membrane. The Hensen bodies resemble the structure of the Golgi complex in some cells. The cytoplasm also contains a multitude of ribosomes (*Ri*) and some granules (*Ly*), which structurally resemble lysosomes.

Guinea pig cochlea. Magnification 16,000×. Ep. LH.

*Bottom Right:*    RECEPTONEURAL JUNCTION.    This is an enlargement of the receptoneural junction of an outer hair cell in the first row, as is indicated by a rectangle in the top right picture on page 157. The infranuclear region of the outer hair cell (*Oh*) is occupied by numerous mitochondria (*Mi*). They correspond to the granules that collectively are referred to as the Retzius body of the light microscope. The basal surface of the outer hair cell does not show the multilayered discontinuous membranes present beneath the plasma membrane of the supranuclear region. The cytoplasm of the hair cell contains scattered small vesicles and ribosomes. The nerve endings about the base of the hair cell are classified into two main groups, although additional kinds occasionally can be identified. The nerve endings are club-shaped swellings of the thin unmyelinated nerves, here approaching from the right, and surrounded by the cytoplasm of the Deiters' cells (*Oph*). The numbers of both types of nerve endings (*E1* and *E2*) are approximately equal, although a certain variation can be noted in relation to different hair cells in different cochlear turns. The type E1 nerve ending is smaller than the type E2; it contains relatively few synaptic vesicles and mitochondria, whereas the type E2 nerve ending displays an abundance of these cell organelles. The nerve endings adhere closely to the thin plasma membrane of the hair cell with a narrow intervening synaptic cleft. Inside the plasma membrane of the hair cell is found an accessory membrane pair (not clearly resolved in this illustration) in relation to the type E2 nerve ending, which is absent in connection with the type E1 ending. It has been assumed that the type E1 ending is engaged in afferent nerve impulses whereas some of the type E2 endings are efferent in nature.

Guinea pig cochlea. Magnification 21,000×. Ep. LH.

Page 158

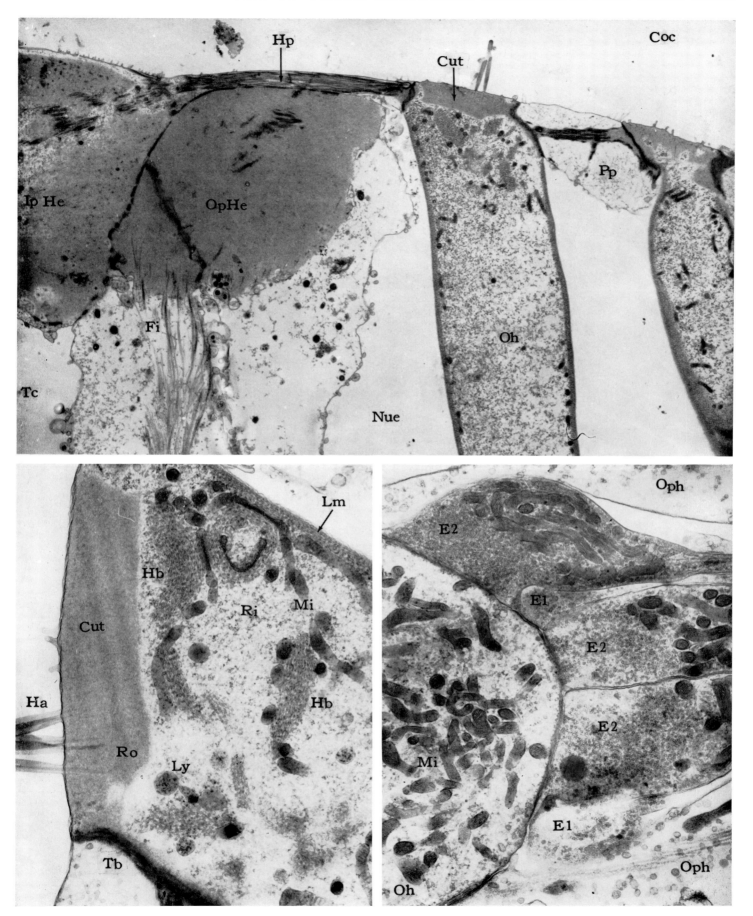

*Top Left:*

VESTIBULAR MEMBRANE.   The vestibular membrane or the membrane of Reissner separates the scala vestibuli (*Vest*) and the cochlear duct (*Coc*). The inner surface of the membrane is covered with a simple squamous, slightly cuboidal epithelium (*Ep*). The cell surface has numerous small microvilli, and the cytoplasm is pervaded by numerous vesicles. On the whole, the cells are reminiscent of the endothelial cells of blood vessels throughout the body. The surface of the vestibular membrane bordering on the perilymphatic space of the scala vestibuli, is lined with thin, extremely flat, mesenchymal epithelial cells (*Mep*) with a striking similarity to the endothelial cells of lymph capillaries elsewhere. The substantia propria of the Reissner's membrane is occupied by thin filaments (*Fi*), most of which have a reticular appearance. A thin, continuous basement membrane adheres at the surface of the epithelium, all of which faces the substantia propria.

Guinea pig cochlea. Magnification 12,500×. Ep. LH.

*Top Right:*

BASILAR MEMBRANE: ZONA PECTINATA.   This zone extends between the outer pillar cells and the crest of the spiral ligament, and therefore also forms a support for the cells of Hensen (*Hen*) with their extremely watery cytoplasm. The basilar fibers (*Fi*), here cut nearly crosswise, are smooth and straight with rare interconnections within the zona pectinata. The basement membrane material (*Bm*) is predominant with a few vague striations and some slender processes of fibroblasts (*Fib*). The tympanic covering layer (*Tcl*) toward the scala tympani (*Tymp*) has the same structural appearance as described in connection with the zona arcuata (cf. page 157).

Guinea pig cochlea. Magnification 5000×. Ep. LH.

*Bottom Left:*

VESTIBULAR LIP.   The vestibular lip serves as a point of origin for the tectorial membrane (*Tm*), which protrudes over the sensory hairs within the cochlear duct (*Coc*). Beneath and at the base of the membrane is located the internal spiral tunnel (*Isc*). The vestibular lip and the surface of the limbus spiralis are covered by rows of epithelial cells, which form cuticular plates (*Cu*) intermingled with a dense arrangement of connective tissue elements (*Co*) of the subjacent periosteum. Cells with a light cytoplasm toward the phalangeal cells are border cells (*Bo*).

Guinea pig cochlea. Magnification 2000×. Ep. LH.

*Bottom Right:*

TECTORIAL MEMBRANE.   The tectorial membrane (*Tm*) consists of numerous, densely packed and radially arranged filaments with an average thickness of 90A. The filaments seem to represent structures of the same nature as those found in soft keratin, i.e., tonofilaments (cf. page 132). The filaments are embedded in a homogeneous ground substance similar to the basement membrane of the basilar membrane (top right) or the zona pellucida of the ovum (cf. page 121). The tectorial membrane is not enveloped by a distinct thin membrane (for instance, a unit membrane), although a certain condensation or increased density is obvious at the surface of contact with the sensory hairs (arrows).

Guinea pig cochlea. Magnification 12,500×. Ep. LH.

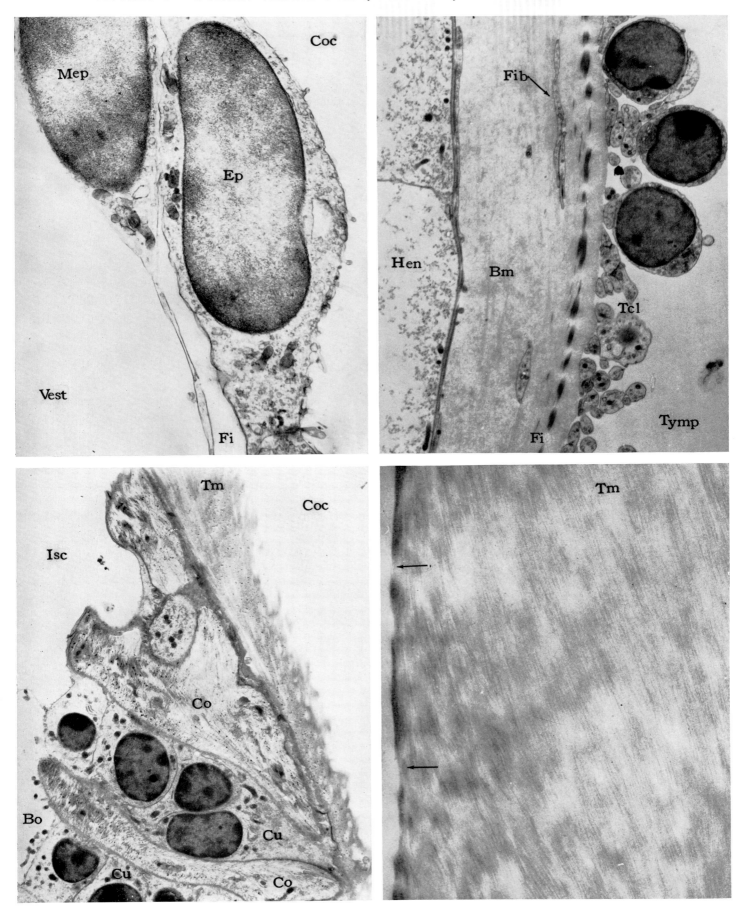

*Top:*  Longitudinally sectioned taste bud from the solitary circumvallate papilla of the mouse tongue. The taste bud is composed of two types of cells, both of which extend from a thin basement membrane and converge on the taste pore (*Po*), which opens into the circular furrow (*Fu*) of the vallate papilla. The majority of the cells have a light, vesicular cytoplasm with oval nuclei; these are the supporting (*Sup*) or sustentacular cells. The second type of cell has a narrow, dense cytoplasm with an elongated, irregularly shaped nucleus. This is the neuroepithelial taste cell (*Ep*). Both cell types have apical extensions, the so-called taste hairs (*Ha*), which project freely into the lumen of a pit formed by the protecting surface cells (*Su*) of the papilla. The taste bud is surrounded by connective tissue elements of the lamina propria (*Lp*) of the tongue.

Taste bud of circumvallate papilla. Magnification 2800×. Ep. LA.

*Bottom Left:*  The taste hairs (*Ha*) or microvilli of both cell types (*Sup* and *Ep*) contain numerous fine filaments (*Fi*), which extend down into the apical cytoplasm and are surrounded by small dense granules (*G*) and vesicles (*Ve*). The structure is not a cilium. The surface cells (*Su*) are of a nonkeratinized, squamous epithelial type. It is assumed that the filaments, granules, and vesicles facilitate the absorption and intracellular transportation of the substances tasted.

Taste pore. Magnification 10,000×. Ep. LA.

*Bottom Right:*  Toward the basement membrane (*Bm*), the bases of the supporting cells (*Sup*) are often wider and contain a less dense cytoplasm than do the neuroepithelial taste cells proper (*Ep*). On the other hand, the former contain a rich assortment of granular material (*G*). Both cell types show intragemmal, unmyelinated nerve fibers (*Ne*) in close apposition to the cell membrane. Part of a supporting cell nucleus (*Nu*) is seen. In view of the fine structural findings, it seems safe to assume that both types of cells are taste receptors.

Taste bud. Basal part. Magnification 15,000×. Ep. LA.

*References:*  246, 323, 324, 905, 1439.

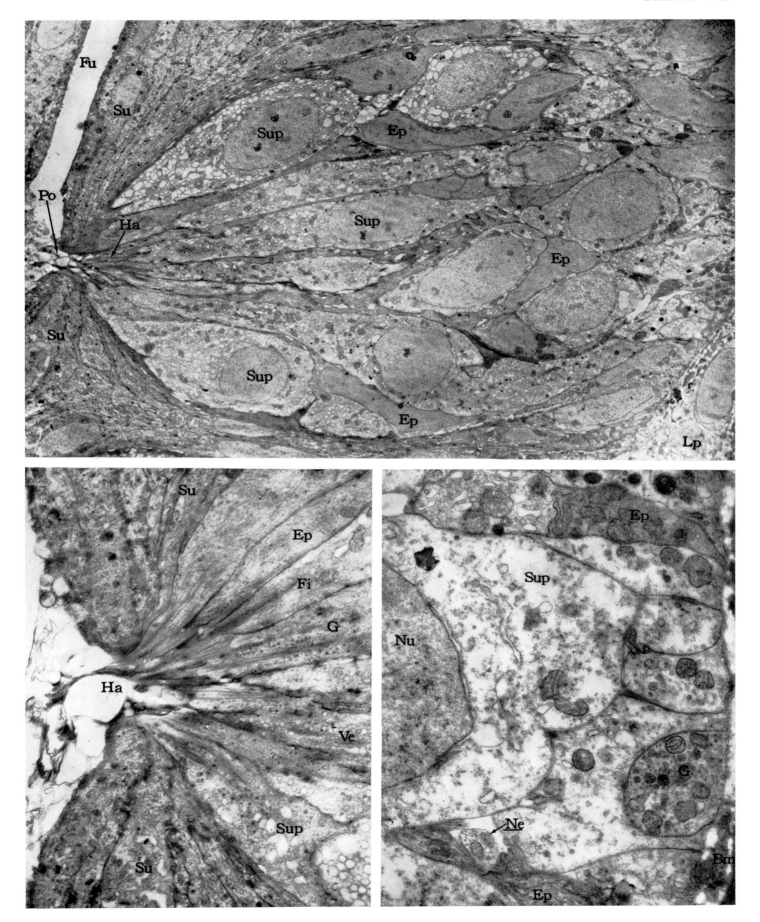

*Top:*      The olfactory mucosa is of the pseudostratified type with three cell types: supporting (*Sup*) or sustentacular cells, olfactory cells (*Of*), and basal cells (not shown in this illustration). The supporting cells have a cylindrical shape with oval nuclei arranged neatly at the same level. The basal ends taper off and their cytoplasm becomes dense. The apical surface is extensively fimbriated with long microvilli bordering on the nasal cavity (*Lu*). The olfactory cells (*Of*) have a narrow cell body, and the spherical nuclei are located at various levels beneath those of the supporting cells. Furthermore, the olfactory cell nucleus has a denser nuclear content. Apically, the olfactory cell terminates to form the so-called olfactory vesicle (*Ov*). Basally, the cytoplasm is pulled out into a nerve fiber, since this cell type actually is a bipolar nerve cell. The nerve fibers penetrate the basement membrane.

Magnification 3000×. Ep. UA.

*Bottom Left:*      Detail of two olfactory vesicles (*Ov*) and the apical portion of a supporting cell (*Sup*). The cells are joined by terminal bars (*Tb*). The microvilli (*Vi*) of the supporting cell are long, branching processes, which form a complex network around the tips of the olfactory cells. The olfactory vesicle (*Ov*) is not actually a vesicle but rather a headlike enlargement of the cell apex. The cytoplasm is rich in small vesicles (*Ve*) and mitochondria (*Mi*). Short cilia (*C*) emerge from basal corpuscles (*Bc*).

Surface structures. Magnification 29,000×. Ep. LH.

*Bottom Right:*      The basal portion of the olfactory mucosa is rather complex. The bases of the supporting cells (*Sup*) contain numerous large, dense granules, reminiscent of lysosomes. They probably correspond to the pigments referred to in light microscopy. The basal cells (*Ba*) look like undifferentiated cells in pseudostratified epithelia elsewhere in the body. The thin, narrow ends of the olfactory cells (*Of*) are identified as nerve fibers (*Ne*), surrounded more or less completely by the basal and supporting cells. Bundles of thin nerve fibers (*NeB*) begin to leave the mucosa by piercing through the basement membrane (*Bm*). The cytoplasm of both the olfactory and the supporting cells is rich in glycogen particles (*Gl*).

Basal part of mucosa. Magnification 29,000×. Ep. LH.

*References:*   90, 92, 93, 114, 245, 322, 451, 452, 1569.

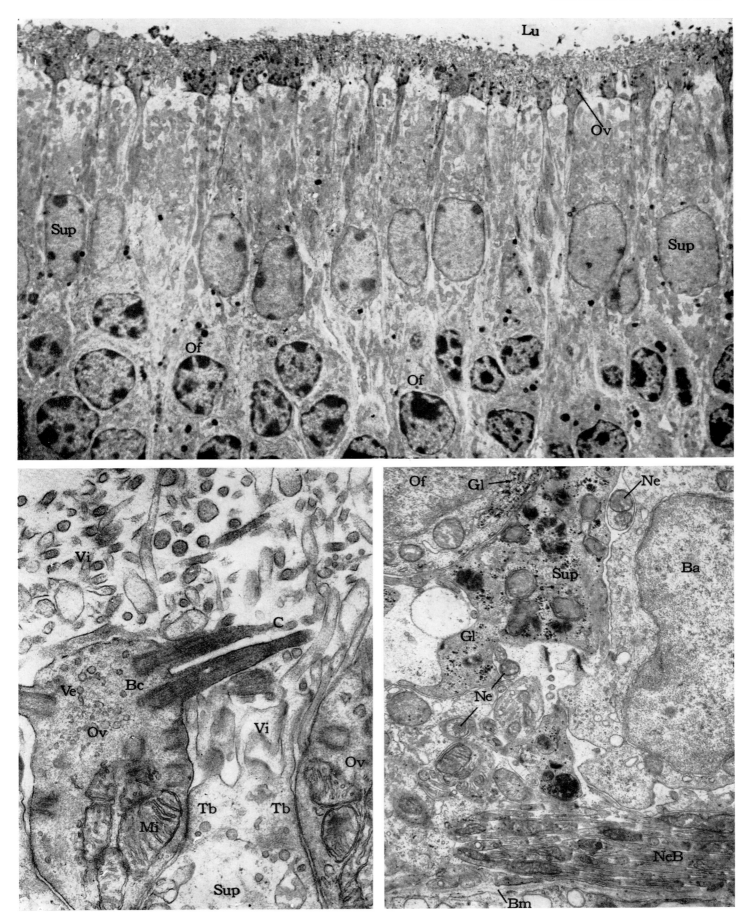

The Pacinian corpuscle (here shown in cross section) is the largest of all nerve end organs. It has the appearance of an onion and is composed of many concentric layers, which enclose the centrally located nerve ending (*Ne*). The lamellae (*L*) are formed by long and thin, highly flattened fibroblasts with a local swelling at the site of the nucleus (*Fib*). As a rule, a single fibroblast makes one complete turn unrelated to adjacent fibroblasts, but occasionally junctions (*Jct*) occur between two lamellae. The interlamellar space (*S*) varies in width and usually becomes increasingly wider toward the most peripheral region of the corpuscle (not shown). The spaces are traversed by fine collagenous fibrils, which are widely scattered and preferably oriented in parallel with the long axis of the corpuscle. The fibrils are embedded in a lymph-like fluid, which escapes when the individual lamellae are punctured by a needle, resulting in collapse of the corpuscle. It is believed that osmotic forces elevate the lamellae and maintain turgor pressure. The fibroblasts that form the lamellae are surrounded by a thin basement membrane. The entire structural complex of the outer capsules of the Pacinian corpuscle is reminiscent of the perineurium of the peripheral nerves (page 43).

The innermost layers are different from the outer layers in many respects and form the so-called inner core (*Ico*). In the adult tissue, few nuclei are seen, and the cytoplasmic lamellae are wider and lighter than the outer ones. Furthermore, the lamellae are arranged bilaterally with two intervening clefts (arrows) establishing an open connection with the innermost interlamellar space of the complete outer lamellae. The plasma membranes of neighboring inner core lamellae come in close contact with each other as in the young myelin sheaths. Basement membranes do not coat the surfaces of these lamellae, and only rarely does one find occasional reticular filaments in the intercellular spaces. The organization of the inner core suggests that the cells that form the bilaterally arranged lamellae are more likely of the Schwann cell type than that of a fibroblast.

The nerve ending itself (*Ne*) contains numerous small mitochondria and neurofilaments but few vesicular structures of the synaptic type. The cytoplasmic lamellae closest to the nerve axis cylinder are small and filamentous and are characterized by a high degree of electron density.

The encapsulated nerve ending of the Pacinian corpuscle represents a deep pressure or tension receptor, which mediates deep sensibility and joint sensibility. Since it is a certain deformation of the corpuscle that stimulates the embedded nerve fiber, it seems likely that only the slightest pressure or tension on the concentric layers of cells and intercellular fluid will be highly intensified by the layered arrangement.

Cat pancreas. Magnification 1800×. Ep. LH.

*References:* 787a, 1049a.

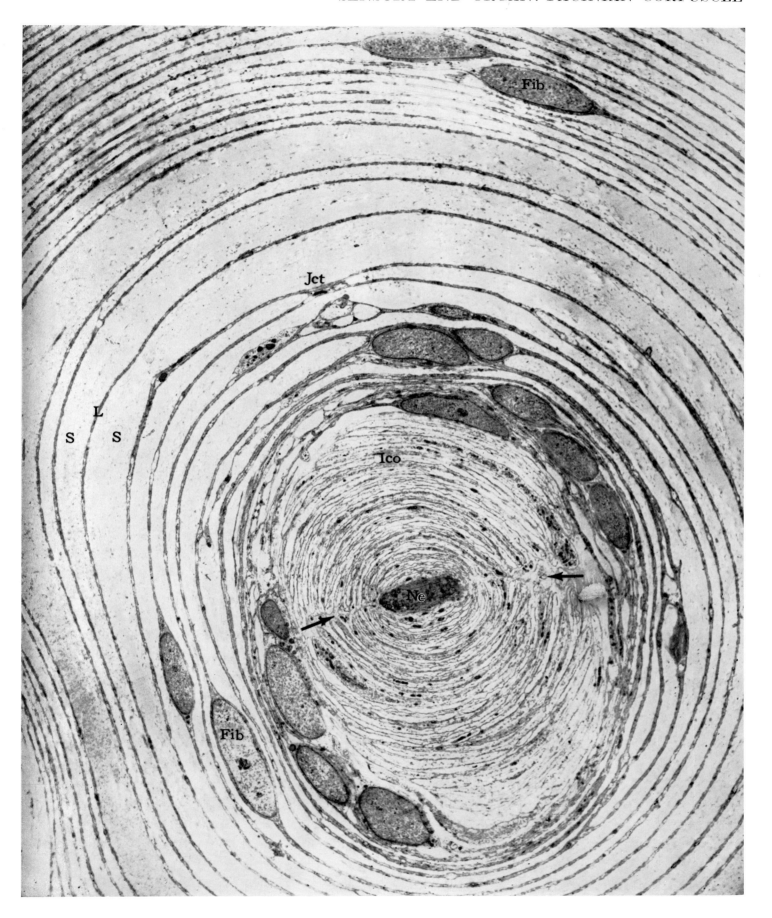

# REFERENCES

1. ACKERMAN, G. A.: Histochemistry of the centrioles and centrosomes of the leukemic cells from human myeloblastic leukemia. J. Biophys. Biochem. Cytol., 11:717–719, 1961.

2. AFZELIUS, B. A.: The ultrastructure of the nuclear membrane of the sea urchin oocyte as studied with the electron microscope. Exp. Cell Res., 8:147–158, 1955.

3. AFZELIUS, B. A.: Electron microscopy of the sperm tail. Results obtained with a new fixative. J. Biophys. Biochem. Cytol., 5:269–278, 1959.

4. ALBERT, H. M.: Electron microscopy of cardiac muscle during and after cold cardioplegia. Circulation, 24:875–876, 1961.

5. VON ALBERTINI, A.: Demonstration elektronenmikroskopischer Kapillarbefunde. Pathol. et Microbiol., 23:207–211, 1960.

6. ALBRIGHT, J. T.: Electron microscope studies of keratinization as observed in gingiva and cheek mucosa. Ann. N. Y. Acad. Sci., 85:351–361, 1960.

7. AMANO, S.: The structure of the centrioles and spindle body as observed under the electron and phase contrast microscope. A new extension-fiber theory concerning mitotic mechanism in animal cells. Cytologia, 22:193–212, 1957.

8. ÅNBERG, Å.: The ultrastructure of the human spermatozoon. Acta Obstet. Gynecol. Scand., 36:Suppl. 2, 1957. 133 p.

9. ANDERSON, C. E.: Formation, structure and function of cartilage. Calif. Med., 91:321–326, 1959.

10. ANDERSON, E.: The tubular system in the striated muscle cell. In: Stockholm Conf. Electron Micros. 1956. Proceed. pp. 208–210. Academic Press, New York, 1957.

11. ANDERSON, E.: The ultramicroscopic structure of a reptilian kidney. J. Morph., 106:205–241, 1960.

12. ANDERSON, E. and BEAMS, H. W.: Evidence from electron micrographs for the passage of material through pores of the nuclear membrane. J. Biophys. Biochem. Cytol., 2:439–444, 1956. Suppl.

13. ANDERSON, E. and BEAMS, H. W.: Observations on the ultramicroscopic anatomy of a mammalian ovum. Anat. Rec., 134:525–526, 1959.

14. ANDERSON, E. and BEAMS, H. W.: Cytological observations on the fine structure of the guinea pig ovary with special reference to the oogonium, primary oocyte and associated follicle cells. J. Ultrastructure Res., 3:432–446, 1960.

15. ANDERSON, M. S. and RECANT, L.: Fine structural alterations in the rat kidney following intraperitoneal bovine albumin. Am. J. Path., 40:555–569, 1962.

16. ANDERSSON-CEDERGREN, E.: Ultrastructure of motor end plate and sarcoplasmic components of mouse skeletal muscle fiber as revealed by three-dimensional reconstructions from serial sections. J. Ultrastructure Res., Suppl. 1:1–191, 1959.

17. ANDERSSON-CEDERGREN, E. and SJÖSTRAND, F. S.: The ultrastructural organization of the contractile elements in skeletal muscle. Acta Physiol. Scand., 42:Suppl. 145:15–16, 1957.

18. ANDRÉ, J.: Contribution à la connaissance du chondriome. Étude de ses modifications ultrastructurales pendant la spermatogénèse. J. Ultrastructure Res., Suppl. 3: 1–185, 1962.

19. ANDRES, K. H.: Untersuchungen über den Feinbau von Spinalganglien. Z. Zellforsch., 55:1–48, 1961.

20. ANDRES, K. H.: Untersuchungen über morphologische Veränderungen in Spinalganglien während der retrograden Degeneration. Z. Zellforsch., 55:49–79, 1961.

21. ANDREW, W.: An electron microscope study of age changes in the liver of the mouse. Am. J. Anat., 110:1–18, 1962.

22. ANDREWS, M. W. and SIKORSKI, J.: A contribution to the structure of keratin. In: Stockholm Conf. Electron Micros. 1956. Proceed. pp. 300–303. Academic Press, New York, 1957.

23. ARAKAWA, K.: An electron microscopic observation on hepatic cells of albino rats after DL-ethionine administration: I. Changes of the rough surfaced elements of endoplasmic reticulum. J. Electronmicroscopy, 8:54–64, 1960.

24. ARWILL, T.: Studies on the ultrastructure of dental tissues. I. Some microstructural details of the dentine. Acta Morphol. Neerlando-Scandinavica, 3:147–156, 1960.

25. ASHFORD, T. P. and PORTER, K. R.: Cytoplasmic components in hepatic cell lysosomes. J. Cell Biol., 12:198–202, 1962.

26. ASHWORTH, C. T., ERDMANN, R. R., and ARNOLD, N. J.: Age changes in the renal basement membrane in rats. Am. J. Path., 36:165–179, 1960.

27. ASHWORTH, C. T., RACE, G. J., and MOLLENHAUER, H. H.: Study of functional activity of adrenocortical cells with electron microscopy. Am. J. Path., 35:425–437, 1959.

28. ASHWORTH, C. T. and SANDERS, E.: Anatomic pathway of bile formation. Am. J. Path., 37:343–355, 1960.

29. BAHR, G. F. and JENNINGS, R. B.: Ultrastructure of normal and asphyxic myocardium of the dog. Lab. Invest., 10:548–571, 1961.

30. BAIRATI, A. and GRIGNOLO, A.: Submicroscopic structure of the ox lens capsule. Naturwissenschaften, 41:263–264, 1954.

31. BAIRATI, A., PERNIS, B., FRIGERIO, G., and BAIRATI, A., JR.: Submicroscopic structure of gliofibrils. Z. mikroskop.-anat. Forsch., 63:423–426, 1958.

32. BAKER, J. R.: What is the "Golgi" controversy? J. Roy. Microscop. Soc., 74:217–221, 1955.

33. BAKER, J. R.: The Golgi controversy. Symp. Soc. Exp. Biol., 10:1–10, 1957.

34. BAKER, J. R.: Towards a solution of the Golgi problem: recent developments in cytochemistry and electron microscopy. J. Roy. Microscop. Soc., 77:116–129, 1959.

35. BANG, B. G. and BANG, F. B.: Graphic reconstruction of the third dimension from serial electron microphotographs. J. Ultrastructure Res., 1:138–146, 1957.

36. BARER, R., JOSEPH, S., and MEEK, G. A.: The origin of the nuclear membrane. Exp. Cell Res., 18:179–182, 1959.

37. BARGEN, G.: Elektronenmikroskopische Untersuchung der Kaninchenhaut (Epidermis). Z. Zellforsch., 50:459–471, 1959.

38. BARGMANN, W.: The study of the cell by electron microscopy. Problems and prospects. Deut. med. Wochschr., 81:1109–1126, 1956.

39. BARGMANN, W.: Über die Struktur der Blutkapillaren. Deut. med. Wochschr., 83:1704–1710, 1958.

40. BARGMANN, W.: Über die Bildung von Milchfett und Milcheiweiss. Milchwissenschaft, 14:99–103, 1959.

41. BARGMANN, W.: Über die Morphologie der Milchsekretion. Z. Zellforsch., 49:344–388, 1959.

42. BARGMANN, W., FLEISCHHAUER, K., and KNOOP, A.: Über die Morphologie der Milchsekretion. Z. Zellforsch., 53:545–568, 1961.

43. BARGMANN, W. and KNOOP, A.: Vergleichende elektronenmikroskopische Untersuchungen der Lungenkapillaren. Z. Zellforsch., 44: 263–281, 1956.

44. BARGMANN, W. and KNOOP, A.: Über die morphologie der Milchsekretion. Licht- und elektronenmikroskopische Studien an der Milchdrüse der Ratte. Z. Zellforsch., 49:344–388, 1959.

45. BARGMANN, W. and KNOOP, A.: Elektronenmikroskopische Untersuchungen an Plazentarzotten des Menschen (Bemerkungen zum Synzytiumproblem). Z. Zellforsch., 50:472–493, 1959.

46. BARGMANN, W. and KNOOP, A.: Vakuolenbildung und Mitochondrien. Z. Zellforsch., 51:456–466, 1960.

47. BARGMANN, W. and KNOOP, A.: Elektronenmikroskopische Untersuchungen an der Reptilien- und Vogellunge. Z. Zellforsch., 54:541–548, 1961.

48. BARGMANN, W., KNOOP, A., and SCHIEBLER, TH. H.: Histologische, cytochemische und elektronenmikroskopische Untersuchungen am Nephron (mit Berücksichtigung der Mitochondrien). Z. Zellforsch., 42:386–422, 1955.

49. BARNES, B. G. and DAVIS, J. M.: The structure of nuclear pores in mammalian tissue. J. Ultrastructure Res., 3:131–146, 1959.

50. BARNICOT, N. A. and BIRBECK, M. S. C.: The electron microscopy of human melanocytes and melanin granules. In: The Biology of Hair Growth, pp. 239–253. Eds.: W. Montagna and R. A. Ellis. Academic Press, New York, 1958.

51. BARNICOT, N. A., BIRBECK, M. S. C., and CUCKOW, F. W.: The electron microscopy of human hair pigments. Ann. Human Genet., 19:231–249, 1955.

52. BARRNETT, R. J.: The fine structural localization of acetylcholinesterase at the myoneural junction. J. Cell Biol., 12:247–262, 1962.

53. BARRNETT, R. J. and PALADE, G. E.: Enzymatic activity in the M band. J. Biophys. Biochem. Cytol., 6:163–170, 1959.

54. BARTON, A. A.: The ultrastructure of the nuclear envelope as seen in replicas from normal and neoplastic nuclei. Cancer Research, 21:198–200, 1961.

55. BARTON, A. A. and CAUSEY, G.: Electron microscopic study of the superior cervical ganglion. J. Anat., 92:399–407, 1958.

56. BATTIG, C. G. and LOW, F. N.: The ultrastructure of human cardiac muscle and its associated tissue span. Am. J. Anat., 108: 199–229, 1961.

57. BAUD, C. A.: Recherches sur la structure de la membrane nucléaire. Acta Anat., 17:113–174, 1953.

Page 170

58. BAUD, C. A.: The ultrastructure of nerve cells. J. Anat. Soc. India., 6:59–62, 1957.

59. BAUTZMANN, H. and SCHMIDT, W.: Vergleichende elektronenmikroskopische Untersuchungen am Amnion von Sauropsiden und Mammaliern (Huhn, Katze, Mensch). Z. Zellforsch., 51:571–588, 1960.

60. BEAMS, H. W., VAN BREEMEN, V. L., NEWFANG, D. M., and EVANS, T. C.: A correlated study on spinal ganglion cells and associated nerve fibers with the light and electron microscopes. J. Comp. Neurol., 96:249–281, 1952.

61. BEAMS, H. W., TAHMISIAN, T. N., ANDERSON, E., and DEVINE, R.: Studies on the fine structure of ultracentrifuged spinal ganglion cells. J. Biophys. Biochem. Cytol., 8:793–811, 1960.

62. BEAR, R. S.: The structure of collagen fibrils. Advances in Protein Chem., 7:69–160, 1952.

63. BELT, W. D.: The origin of adrenal cortical mitochondria and liposomes: a preliminary report. J. Biophys. Biochem. Cytol., 4:337–340, 1958.

64. BELT, W. D. and PEASE, D. C.: Mitochondrial structure in sites of steroid secretion. J. Biophys. Biochem. Cytol., 2:369–374, 1956. Suppl.

65. BENCOSME, S.: Studies on the terminal autonomic nervous system with special reference to the pancreatic islets. Lab. Invest., 8:629–646, 1959.

66. BENCOSME, S. A. and PEASE, D. C.: Electron microscopy of the pancreatic islets. Endocrinology, 63:1–13, 1958.

67. BENEDETTI, E. L.: Sulla struttura del mesangio di Zimmermann indigata mediante il microscopio elettronico. Acc. Lincei-Rend. d. Cl. di Sc. fis. mat. e nat., 24:597–600,1958.

68. BENEDETTI, E. L. and MARINOZZI, V.: Sulla fine struttura del tessuto intercapillare nel glomerulo di Malpighi. Rassegna di Fisiopatologia Clinica e Terapeutica, 30:1123–1144, 1958.

69. BENNETT, H. S.: The concepts of membrane flow and membrane vesiculation as mechanisms for active transports and ion pumping. J. Biophys. Biochem. Cytol., 2:99–103, 1956, Suppl.

70. BENNETT, H. S.: The sarcoplasmic reticulum of striped muscle. J. Biophys. Biochem. Cytol., 2:171–174, 1956, Suppl.

71. BENNETT, H. S.: A suggestion as to the nature of the lysosome granules. J. Biophys. Biochem. Cytol., 2:185–186, 1956, Suppl.

72. BENNETT, H. S.: Fine structure of cell nucleus, chromosomes, nucleoli, and membrane. Revs. Modern Phys., 31:297–300, 1959.

73. BENNETT, H. S.: The structure of striated muscle. In: The Structure and Function of Muscle. I. Structure, pp. 137–181. Ed.: G. H. Bourne. Academic Press, New York, 1960.

74. BENNETT, H. S., LUFT, J. H., and HAMPTON, J. C.: Morphological classification of vertebrate blood capillaries. Am. J. Physiol., 196:381–390, 1959.

75. BERGENER, M.: Die Feinstruktur des Dünndarmepithels während der physiologischen Milchresorption beim jungen Goldhamster. Z. Zellforsch., 57:428–474, 1962.

76. BERGMAN, R. A.: Intercellular bridges in ureteral smooth muscle. Bull. Johns Hopkins Hosp., 102:195–202, 1958.

77. BERGSTRAND, A.: Electron microscopic investigations of the renal glomeruli. Lab. Invest., 6:191–204, 1957.

78. BERGSTRAND, A. and BUCHT, H.: Anatomy of the glomerulus as observed in biopsy material from young and healthy human subjects. Z. Zellforsch., 48:51–73, 1958.

79. BERNHARD, W., BAUER, A., GROPP, A., HAGUENAU, F., and OBERLING, CH.: L'ultrastructure de nucléole de cellules normales et cancéreuses. Étude au microscope électronique. Exp. Cell Res., 9:88–100, 1955.

80. BERNHARD, W. and ROUILLER, C.: Close topographical relationship between mitochondria and ergastoplasm of liver cells in a definite phase of cellular activity. J. Biophys. Biochem. Cytol., 2:73–78, 1956, Suppl.

81. BERNSTEIN, M. H. and PEASE, D. C.: Electron microscopy of the tapetum lucidum of the cat. J. Biophys. Biochem. Cytol., 5:35–40, 1959.

82. BIRBECK, M. S. C. and MERCER, E. H.: The electron microscopy of the human hair follicle. Part 1. Introduction and the hair cortex. J. Biophys. Biochem. Cytol., 3:203–214, 1957.

83. BIRBECK, M. S. C. and MERCER, E. H.: The electron microscopy of the human hair follicle. Part 2. The hair cuticle. J. Biophys. Biochem. Cytol., 3:215–222, 1957.

84. BIRBECK, M. S. C. and MERCER, E. H.: The electron microscopy of the human hair follicle. Part 3. The inner root sheath and trichohyalin. J. Biophys. Biochem. Cytol., 3:223–230, 1957.

85. BIRBECK, M. S. C., MERCER, E. H., and BARNICOT, N. A.: The structure and formation of pigment granules in human hair. Exp. Cell Res., 10:505–514, 1956.

86. BJÖRKMAN, N. and FREDRICSSON, B.: The ultrastructural organization and the alkaline phosphatase activity of the epithelial surface of the bovine fallopian tube. Z. Zellforsch., 51:589–596, 1960.

87. BJÖRKMAN, N. and FREDRICSSON, B.: The bovine oviduct epithelium and its secretory process as studied with the electron microscope and histochemical tests. Z. Zellforsch., 55:500–513, 1961.

88. BLANCHETTE, E. J.: A study of the fine structure of the rabbit primary oocyte. J. Ultrastructure Res., 5:349–363, 1961.

89. BLOM, E. and BIRCH-ANDERSEN, A.: The ultrastructure of the bull sperm. I. The middle piece. Nord. Veterinärmed., 12:261–279, 1960.

90. BLOOM, G.: Studies on the olfactory epithelium of the frog and the toad with the aid of light and electron microscopy. Z. Zellforsch., 41:89–100, 1954.

91. BLOOM, G. D.: The fine structure of cyclostome cardiac muscle cells. Z. Zellforsch., 57:213–239, 1962.

Page 171

92. BLOOM, G. and ENGSTRÖM, H.: The structure of the epithelial surface in the olfactory region. Exp. Cell Res., 3:699–701, 1952.

93. BLOOM, G. and ENGSTRÖM, H.: Interciliary structures in the epithelium of the upper part of the respiratory tract. Ann. Otol., 62:15–17, 1953.

94. BLOOM, G. and NICANDER, L.: On the ultrastructure and development of the protoplasmic droplet of spermatozoa. Z. Zellforsch., 55:833–844, 1961.

95. BODINGBAUER, J. and KLIMA, J.: Licht- und elektronenmikroskopische Untersuchungen über den Feinbau des Hundehaares (Dobermannrasse) unter besonderer Berücksichtigung von geschlechts- bzw umweltbedingten Einflüssen. Mikroskopie, 15:20–29, 1960.

96. BOHLE, A.: Elektronenmikroskopische Untersuchungen über die Struktur des Gefässpols der Niere. Verhandl. deut. Ges. Pathol., 43:219–225, 1959.

97. BORELL, U., GUSTAVSON, K.-H., NILSSON, O., and WESTMAN, A.: The structure of the epithelium lining the fallopian tube of the rat in oestrus. An electron-microscopical study. Acta Obstet. Gynecol. Scand., 38:203–208, 1959.

98. BORELL, U., NILSSON, O., WERSÄLL, J., and WESTMAN, A.: Electron-microscope studies of the epithelium of the rabbit fallopian tube under different hormonal influences. Acta Obstet. Gynecol. Scand., 35:35–41, 1956.

99. BORELL, U., NILSSON, O., and WESTMAN, A.: The cyclical changes occurring in the epithelium lining the endometrial glands. An electron-microscopical study in the human being. Acta Obstet. Gynecol. Scand., 38:364–377, 1959.

100. BORYSKO, E. and BANG, F. B.: Structure of the nucleolus as revealed by the electron microscope. Bull. Johns Hopkins Hosp., 89:468–473, 1951.

101. BOURNE, G. L. and LACY, D.: Ultra-structure of human amnion and its possible relation to the circulation of amniotic fluid. Nature, 186:952–954, 1960.

102. BOYD, J. D. and HUGHES, A. F. W.: Observations on human chorionic villi using the electron microscope. J. Anat., 88:356–362, 1954.

103. BRACHET, J.: The living cell. Sci. American, 205:50–62, 1961.

104. BRADFIELD, J. R. G.: The structure of mammalian spermatozoa. In: Third Internat. Conf. Electron Micros. 1954. Proceed. pp. 599–602. Roy. Microscop. Soc., London, 1956.

105. BRANDT, P. W. and PAPPAS, G. D.: An electron microscopic study of pinocytosis in ameba. I. The surface attachment phase. J. Biophys. Biochem. Cytol., 8:675–687, 1960.

106. BRAUNSTEINER, H., FELLINGER, K., and PAKESCH, F.: Elektronenmikroskopische Untersuchungen der Prostata und der Samenblase. Wien. Klin. Wochschr., 67: 761–763, 1955.

107. VAN BREEMEN, V. L.: Intercalated discs in heart muscle studied with the electron microscope. Anat. Rec., 117:49–63, 1953.

108. VAN BREEMEN, V. L.: Ultrastructure of human muscle. I. Observation on normal striated muscle fibers. Am. J. Path., 37:215–229, 1960.

109. VAN BREEMEN, V. L.: Ultrastructure of human muscle. II. Observations on dystrophic striated muscle fibers. Am. J. Path., 37: 333–341, 1960.

110. VAN BREEMEN, V. L. and CLEMENTE, C. D.: Silver deposition in the central nervous system and the hematoencephalic barrier studied with the electron microscope. J. Biophys. Biochem. Cytol., 1:161–166, 1955.

111. VAN BREEMEN, V. L. and McCHESNEY, D. E.: Ultrastructure of the parietal cell of the human gastric gland. Anat. Rec., 139:324, 1961. (Abstract.)

112. VAN BREEMEN, V. L. and MONTGOMERY, J. D.: Ultrastructure of cytoplasmic "metasomes" found in renal proximal tubule cells. Norelco Reptr., 7:7–12, 1960.

113. VAN BREEMEN, V. L., REGER, J. R., and COOPER, W. G.: Observations on the basement membranes in rat kidney. J. Biophys. Biochem. Cytol., 2:283–285, 1956, Suppl.

114. BRETTSCHNEIDER, H.: Elektronenmikroskopische Untersuchungen an der Nasenschleimhaut. Anat. Anz., 105:194–204, 1958.

115. BRIGHTMAN, M. W.: An electron microscopic study of ferritin uptake from the cerebral ventricles of rats. Anat. Rec., 142:219, 1962. (Abstract.)

116. BRODY, I.: The keratinization of epidermal cells of normal guinea pig skin as revealed by electron microscopy. J. Ultrastructure Res., 2:482–511, 1959.

117. BRODY, I.: An ultrastructural study on the role of the keratohyalin granules in the keratinization process. J. Ultrastructure Res., 3:84–104, 1959.

118. BRODY, I.: The ultrastructure of the tonofibrils in the keratinization process of normal human epidermis. J. Ultrastructure Res., 4:264–297, 1960.

119. BRODY, I.: The ultrastructure of the epidermis in psoriasis vulgaris as revealed by electron microscopy. 1. The dermo epidermal junction and the stratum basale in parakeratosis without keratohyalin. J. Ultrastructure Res., 6:304–323, 1962.

120. BRODY, I.: The ultrastructure of the epidermis in psoriasis vulgaris as revealed by electron microscopy. 2. The stratum spinosum in parakeratosis without keratohyalin. J. Ultrastructure Res., 6:324–340, 1962.

121. BRODY, I.: The ultrastructure of the epidermis in psoriasis vulgaris as revealed by electron microscopy. 3. Stratum intermedium in parakeratosis without keratohyalin. J. Ultrastructure Res., 6:341–353, 1962.

122. BRODY, I.: The ultrastructure of the epidermis in psoriasis vulgaris as revealed by electron microscopy. 4. Stratum corneum in parakeratosis without keretohyalin. J. Ultrastructure Res., 6:354–367, 1962.

123. BROWN, A. L.: Microvilli of the human jejunal

epithelial cell. J. Cell Biol., 12:623–627, 1962.

124. BROWN, C. A. and RIS, H.: Amphibian oocyte nucleoli. J. Morph., 104:377–414, 1959.

125. BROWN, D. B., DELOR, C. J., GREIDER, M., and FRAJOLA, W. J.: The electron microscopy of human liver. Gastroenterology, 32:103–118, 1957.

126. BUCHER, O. and REALE, E.: Zur elektronenmikroskopischen Untersuchung der juxtaglomerulären Spezialeinrichtungen der Niere. I. Problemstellung und erste Beobachtungen. Z. Zellforsch., 54:167–181, 1961.

127. BUCHER, O. and REALE, E.: Zur elektronenmikroskopischen Untersuchung der juxtaglomerulären Spezialeinrichtungen der Niere. III. Die epitheloiden Zellen der Arteriola afferens. Z. Zellforsch., 56:344–358, 1962.

128. BUCK, R. C.: The fine structure of endothelium of large arteries. J. Biophys. Biochem. Cytol., 4:187–190, 1958.

129. BUNGE, M. B., BUNGE, R. P., and PAPPAS, G. D.: Electron microscopic demonstration of connections between glia and myelin sheaths in the developing mammalian central nervous system. J. Cell Biol., 12:448–453, 1962.

130. BUNGE, R. P., BUNGE, M. B., and RIS, H.: Electron microscopic study of demyelination in an experimentally induced lesion in adult cat spinal cord. J. Biophys. Biochem. Cytol., 7:685–696, 1960.

131. BUNGE, M. B., BUNGE, R. P., and RIS, H.: Ultrastructural study of remyelination in an experimental lesion in adult cat spinal cord. J. Biophys. Biochem. Cytol., 10:67–94, 1961.

132. BURGOS, M. H. and FAWCETT, D. W.: Studies on the fine structure of the mammalian testis. I. Differentiation of the spermatids in cat (Felis domestica). J. Biophys. Biochem. Cytol., 1:287–300, 1955.

133. BURGOS, M. H. and FAWCETT, D. W.: An electron microscope study of spermatid differentiation in the toad, *Bufo arenarum* Hensel. J. Biophys. Biochem. Cytol., 2:223–240, 1956.

134. BURGOS, M. H. and WISLOCKI, G. B.: The cyclic changes in the mucosa of the guinea pig's uterus, cervix and vagina and in the sexual skin, investigated by the electron microscope. Endocrinology, 63:106–121, 1958.

135. BURNSTOCK, G. and PROSSER, C. L.: Conduction in smooth muscles: comparative electrical properties. Am. J. Physiol., 199:553–559, 1960.

136. CACHERA, R. and DARNIS, F.: Examen du foie humain au microscope électronique. Semaine hôp., 31:2187–3000, 1955.

137. CAESAR, R.: Die Feinstruktur von Milz und Leber bei experimenteller Amyloidose. Z. Zellforsch., 52:653–673, 1960.

138. CAESAR, R.: Elektronenmikroskopischer Nachweis von Fettpartikeln im Disseschen Raum. Z. Zellforsch., 54:793–802, 1961.

139. CAESAR, R., EDWARDS, G. A., and RUSKA, H.: Architecture and nerve supply of mammalian smooth muscle tissue. J. Biophys. Biochem. Cytol., 3:867–878, 1957.

140. CAESAR, R., EDWARDS, G. A., and RUSKA, H.: Electron microscopy of the impulse conducting system of the sheep heart. Z. Zellforsch., 48:698–719, 1958.

141. CAMERON, D. A.: The fine structure of osteoblasts in the metaphysis of the tibia of the young rat. J. Biophys. Biochem. Cytol., 9:583–595, 1961.

142. CAMERON, D. A. and ROBINSON, R. A.: Electron microscopy of epiphyseal and articular cartilage matrix in the femur of the newborn infant. J. Bone and Joint Surg., 40:163–170, 1958.

143. CAMPICHE, M.: Les inclusions lamellaires des cellules alvéolaires dans le poumon du Raton. Relations entre l'ultrastructure et la fixation. J. Ultrastructure Res., 3:302–312, 1960.

144. CAMPICHE, M., PROD'HOM, S., and GAUTIER, A.: Étude au microscope électronique du poumon de prématurés morts en détresse respiratoire. Ann. Paediat., 196:81–95, 1961.

145. CARASSO, N.: Rôle de l'ergastoplasme dans l'élaboration du glycogène au cours de la formation du "paraboloïde" des cellules visuelles. Compt. rend. acad. sci., 250:600–602, 1960.

146. CARLSEN, F., KNAPPEIS, G. G., and BUCHTHAL, F.: Ultrastructure of the resting and contracted striated muscle fiber at different degrees of stretch. J. Biophys. Biochem. Cytol., 11:95–117, 1961.

147. CARLSON, H. E.: Electron microscopy of the kidney in health and disease. Southern Med. J., 54:985–992, 1961.

148. CARO, L. G.: Electron microscopic radioautography of thin sections: the Golgi zone as a site of protein concentration in pancreatic acinar cells. J. Biophys. Biochem. Cytol., 10:37–45, 1961.

149. CARR, I. A.: Microvilli of the cells of the human adrenal cortex. Nature, 182:607–608, 1958.

150. CARSTEN, P.-M.: Das elektronenmikroskopische Bild des Disseschen Raumes. Berl. med., 12:545–549, 1961.

151. CARSTEN, P.-M.: Elektronenmikroskopische Untersuchungen an der Sinuswand menschlicher fetaler Lebern. Z. Zellforsch., 54:252–261, 1961.

152. CAULFIELD, J. B. and TRUMP, B. F.: Correlation of ultrastructure with function in the rat kidney. Am. J. Path., 40:199–218, 1962.

153. CAUSEY, G.: Electron microscopic observations on the mucous membrane of the stomach and of exfoliated cells. Proc. Roy. Soc. Med., 53:171–174, 1960.

154. CAUSEY, G. and HOFFMAN, H.: The relation between the Schwann cell and the axon in peripheral nerves. J. Anat., 90:1–4, 1956.

155. CAUSEY, G. and HOFFMAN, H.: The ultrastructure of the synaptic area in the superior cervical ganglion. J. Anat., 90:502–507, 1956.

156. CEDERGREN, B., GYLLENSTEN, L., and WERSÄLL,

Page 173

J.: Pulmonary damage caused by oxygen poisoning. An electron microscopic study in mice. Acta Paediatrica, 48:477–494, 1959.

157. CHALLICE, C. E., BULLIVANT, S., and SCOTT, D. B.: The fine structure of some cytoplasmic inclusions of oxyntic cells. Exp. Cell Res., 13:488–492, 1957.

158. CHALLICE, C. E. and EDWARDS, G. A.: The intercalated disc of the goldfish heart. Experientia, 16:70–72, 1960.

159. CHALLICE, C. E. and EDWARDS, G. A.: Some observations on the intercalated disc. In: European Regional Conf. Electron Micros., Delft 1960. Proceed. Vol. II, pp. 774–777. De Nederlandse Vereniging voor Electronenmicroscopie, Delft 1961.

160. CHALLICE, C. E. and LACY, D.: Fine structure of exocrine cells of the pancreas. Nature, 174:1150, 1954.

161. CHANDRA, S.: The reversal of mitochondrial membrane. J. Cell Biol., 12:503–513, 1962.

162. CHAPMAN, G. B. and DAWSON, A. B.: Fine structure of the larval anuran epidermis with special reference to the figures of Eberth. J. Biophys. Biochem. Cytol., 10: 425–435, 1961.

163. CHAPMAN, J. A.: Morphological and chemical studies of collagen formation. I. The fine structure of guinea pig granulomata. J. Biophys. Biochem. Cytol., 9:639–651, 1961.

164. CHAPMAN, J. A.: Fibroblasts and collagen. Brit. Med. Bull., 18:233–237, 1962.

165. CHAPMAN, N. D., GOLDSWORTHY, P. D., VOLWILER, W., NYHUS, L. M., and MARTINIS, A. J.: The isolated perfused bovine liver. J. Exp. Med., 113:981–996, 1961.

166. CHARLES, A.: Electron microscope observations on hardening in the hair follicle. Exp. Cell Res., 18:138–149, 1959.

167. CHARLES, A.: An electron microscope study of cornification in the human skin. J. Invest. Dermatol., 33:65–74, 1959.

168. CHARLES, A.: Human elastic fibers. Electron microscopic appearances of the elastic fibres of human skin in thin section. Brit. J. Dermatol., 73:57–60, 1961.

169. CHARLES, A. and INGRAM, J. T.: Electron microscope observations of the melanocyte of the human epidermis. J. Biophys. Biochem. Cytol., 6:41–44, 1959.

170. CHARLES, A. and SMIDDY, F. G.: The tonofibrils of the human epidermis. J. Invest. Dermatol., 29:327–338, 1957.

171. CHASE, W. H.: The surface membrane of pulmonary alveolar walls. Exp. Cell Res., 18:15–28, 1959.

172. CHAUVEAU, J., MOULE, Y., ROUILLER, C., and SCHNEEBELI, J.: Isolation of smooth vesicles and free ribosomes from rat liver microsomes. J. Cell Biol., 12:17–29, 1962.

173. CHIQUOINE, A. D.: The development of the zona pellucida of the mammalian ovum. Am. J. Anat., 106:149–169, 1960.

174. CHIQUOINE, A. D.: An electron microscope study of vitally stained ovaries and ovaries from argyric mice. Anat. Rec., 139:29–35, 1961.

175. CHOI, J. K.: Light and electron microscopy of toad urinary bladder. Anat. Rec., 139: 214–215, 1961. (Abstract).

176. CHRISTENSEN, A. K. and CHAPMAN, G. B.: Cup-shaped mitochondria in interstitial cells of the albino rat testis. Exp. Cell Res., 18: 576–579, 1959.

177. CHRISTENSEN, A. K. and FAWCETT, D. W.: The normal fine structure of opossum testicular interstitial cells. J. Biophys. Biochem. Cytol., 9:653–670, 1961.

178. CHRISTIE, A. C.: A study of the Kultschitzky (argentaffin) cell with the electron microscope, after fixation by osmium tetroxide. Quart. J. Microscop. Sci., 96:295–299, 1955.

179. CLARK, S. L., JR.: Cellular differentiation in the kidneys of newborn mice studied with the electron microscope. J. Biophys. Biochem. Cytol., 3:349–362, 1957.

180. CLARK, S. L., JR.: The ingestion of proteins and colloidal materials by columnar absorptive cells of the small intestine in suckling rats and mice. J. Biophys. Biochem. Cytol., 5:41–50, 1959.

181. CLARK, S. L., JR.: The localization of alkaline phosphatase in tissues of mice using the electron microscope. Am. J. Anat., 109: 57–83, 1961.

182. CLARK, S. L., JR.: The reticulum of lymph nodes in mice studied with the electron microscope. Am. J. Anat., 110:217–257, 1962.

183. CLARK, W. H.: Electron microscope studies of nuclear extrusions in pancreatic acinar cells of the rat. J. Biophys. Biochem. Cytol., 7:345–352, 1960.

184. CLARK, W. H. and HIBBS, R. G.: Electron microscope studies of the human epidermis. The clear cell of Masson (dendritic cell or melanocyte). J. Biophys. Biochem. Cytol., 4:679–684, 1958.

185. CLARK, W. H., WATSON, M. C., and WATSON, B. E. M.: Two kinds of "clear" cells in the human epidermis. With a report of a modified dopa reaction for electron microscopy. Am. J. Path., 39:333–344, 1961.

186. CLAUDE, A.: "Microbodies" et lysosomes: une étude au microscope électronique. Arch. intern. Physiol. et Biochem., 68:672–673, 1960.

187. CLEMENS, H. J.: Elektronenoptische Untersuchungen über den Bau der Alveolenwand in der Rattenlunge. Z. Zellforsch., 40:1–7, 1954.

188. CLEMENS, H. J.: Elektronenmikroskopische Beachtungen an der Lungenalveole. Gegenbaurs Jahrbuch, 94:471–492, 1954.

189. CLERMONT, Y.: The submicroscopic structure responsible for the cytoplasmic basophilia of the rat spermatid. Exp. Cell Res., 11: 214–217, 1956.

190. CLERMONT, Y.: The Golgi zone of the rat spermatid and its role in the formation of cytoplasmic vesicles. J. Biophys. Biochem. Cytol., 2:119–122, 1956. Suppl.

191. CLERMONT, Y. and HAGUENAU, F.: Examen au microscope électronique de la zone de Golgi des spermatides de rat. Compt. rend. acad. sci., 241:708–710, 1955.

192. COHEN, A. I.: Electron microscopic observations on the lens of the neonatal albino mouse. Am. J. Anat., 103:219–246, 1958.

193. COHEN, A. I.: The ultrastructure of the rods of the mouse retina. Am. J. Anat., 107:23–48, 1960.

194. COHEN, A. I.: Electron microscopic observations of the internal limiting membrane and optic fiber layer of the retina of the rhesus monkey (M. mulatta). Am. J. Anat., 108:179–197, 1961.

195. COHEN, A. I.: The fine structure of the extra-foveal receptors of the rhesus monkey. Exp. Eye Res., 1:128–136, 1961.

196. COHEN, A. S., WEISS, L., and CALKINS, E.: A study of the fine structure of the spleen in experimental amyloidosis of the rabbit. Clin. Res., 6:237, 1958. (Abstract.)

197. COHEN, A. S., WEISS, L., and CALKINS, E.: Electron microscopic observations of the spleen during the induction of experimental amyloidosis in the rabbit. Am. J. Path., 37:413–431, 1960.

198. COHN, Z. A. and HIRSCH, J. G.: The isolation and properties of the specific cytoplasmic granules of rabbit polymorphonuclear leucocytes. J. Exp. Med., 112:983–1004, 1960.

199. COLWIN, A. L. and COLWIN, L. H.: Egg membrane lytic activity of sperm extract and its significance in relation to sperm entry in *Hydroides hexagonus* (Annelida). J. Biophys. Biochem. Cytol., 7:321–328, 1960.

200. COLWIN, A. L. and COLWIN, L. H.: Fine structure of the spermatozoon of *Hydroides hexagonus* (Annelida) with special reference to the acrosomal region. J. Biophys. Biochem. Cytol., 10:211–230, 1961.

201. COLWIN, A. L. and COLWIN, L. H.: Changes in the spermatozoon during fertilization in *Hydroides hexagonus* (Annelida). J. Biophys. Biochem. Cytol., 10:255–274, 1961.

202. COLWIN, L. H. and COLWIN, A. L.: Formation of sperm entry holes in the vitelline membrane of *Hydroides hexagonus* (Annelida) and evidence of their lytic origin. J. Biophys. Biochem. Cytol., 7:315–320, 1960.

203. COLWIN, L. H. and COLWIN, A. L.: Changes in the spermatozoon during fertilization in *Hydroides hexagonus* (Annelida) I. Passage of the acrosomal region through the vitelline membrane. J. Biophys. Biochem. Cytol., 10:231–254, 1961.

204. CONDIE, R. M., HOWELL A. E., JR., and GOOD, R. A.: Studies on the problem of preservation of myelin sheath ultrastructure: Evaluation of fixation, dehydration, and embedding techniques. J. Biophys. Biochem. Cytol., 9:429–443, 1961.

205. COOPER, J. H.: The basement membrane-elastica system of the dermo-epidermal junction. Nature, 178:643–644, 1956.

206. COSSEL, L.: Elektronmikroskopische Befunde an Leber- sinusoiden und -epithelien bei verschiedenen Funktionszuständen der Leber. Verhandl. deut. Ges. Pathol., 43: 204–208, 1959.

207. COSSEL, L.: Elektronenmikroskopische Untersuchungen zur Frage des Dissesschen Raumes in der Leber. Klin. Wochschr., 37:743–753, 1959.

208. COSSEL, L.: Beitrag zur submikroskopischen Morphologie des Stoffaustausches und intracellulären Stofftransportes in der Leber. Acta Hepatosplen., 8:264–278, 1961.

209. COTTE, G.: Quelques problèmes posés par l'ultrastructure des lipides de la cortico-surrénale. J. Ultrastructure Res., 3:186–209, 1959.

210. COTTE, G. and COTTE, N.: Étude ultrastructurale d'images de fonte holocrine dans la cortico-surrénale. Z. Zellforsch., 54:182–198, 1961.

211. COTTE, G. and PICARD, D.: Recherches sur les lipides de la cortico-surrénale: aspects ultrastructuraux. Compt. rend. soc. biol., 153:1221–1223, 1959.

212. COUTEAUX, R.: Observations sur l'ultrastructure de la jonction musculo-tendineuse. Compt. rend. acad. sci., 249:964–966, 1959.

213. COUTEAUX, R.: Motor end-plate structure. In: The Structure and Function of Muscle. I. Structure, pp. 337–380. Ed.: G. H. Bourne. Academic Press, New York, 1960.

214. CRAIG, E. L., FRAJOLA, W. J., and GREIDER, M. H.: An embedding technique for electron microscopy using Epon 812. J. Cell Biol., 12:190–194, 1962.

215. DAEMS, W. TH.: The micro-anatomy of the smallest biliary pathways in mouse liver tissue. Acta Anat., 46:1–24, 1961.

216. DAEMS, W. TH. and VAN RIJSSEL, TH. G.: The fine structure of the peribiliary dense bodies in mouse liver tissue. J. Ultrastructure Res., 5:263–290, 1961.

217. DALHAMN, T.: Mucous flow and ciliary activity in the trachea of healthy rats and rats exposed to respiratory irritant gases. Acta Physiol. Scand., 36:Suppl. 123:1–161, 1956.

218. DALTON, A. J.: Structural details of some of the epithelial cell types in the kidney of the mouse as revealed by the electron microscope. J. Natl. Cancer Inst., 11:1163–1185, 1951.

219. DALTON, A. J.: Electron micrography of epithelial cells of the gastrointestinal tract and pancreas. Am. J. Anat., 89:109–133, 1951.

220. DALTON, A. J.: A study of the Golgi material of hepatic and intestinal epithelial cells with the electron microscope. Z. Zellforsch., 36: 522–540, 1952.

221. DALTON, A. J.: Electron microscopy of the epithelial cell types of the stomach and intestine. J. Natl. Cancer Inst., 13:983, 1953.

222. DALTON, A. J.: Electron microscopy of tissue sections. Int. Rev. Cytol., 2:403–417, 1953.

223. DALTON, A. J.: Golgi apparatus and secretion granules. In: The Cell. Vol. II, pp. 603–619. Eds.: J. Brachet and A. E. Mirsky. Academic Press, New York, 1961.

224. DALTON, A. J. and Felix, M. D.: Studies on the Golgi substance of the epithelial cells of the epididymis and duodenum of the mouse. Am. J. Anat., 92:277–305, 1953.

225. DALTON, A. J. and FELIX, M. D.: Cytological and cytochemical characteristics of the Golgi substance of epithelial cells of the epididymis, in situ, in homogenates and after isolation. Am. J. Anat., 94:171–207, 1954.

226. DALTON, A. J. and FELIX, M. D.: A study of the Golgi substance and ergastoplasm in a series of mammalian cell types. In: Symposium on the Fine Structure of Cells. 8th Congress of Cell Biology, Leiden, Holland, 1954, pp. 274–293. Noordhoff, Groningen, 1955.

227. DALTON, A. J. and FELIX, M. D.: A comparative study of the Golgi complex. J. Biophys. Biochem. Cytol., 2:79–84, 1956. Suppl.

228. DALTON, A. J. and FELIX, M. D.: Electron microscopy of mitochondria and the Golgi complex. Symp. Soc. Exp. Biol., 10:148–159, 1957.

229. DALTON, A. J., KAHLER, H., and LLOYD, B. J.: The structure of the free surface of a series of epithelial cell types in the mouse as revealed by electron microscope. Anat. Rec., 111:67–72, 1951.

230. DALTON, A. J., KAHLER, H., STRIEBICH, M. J., and LLOYD, B.: Finer structure of hepatic, intestinal and renal cells of mouse as revealed by the electron microscope. J. Natl. Cancer Inst., 11:439–461, 1950.

231. DALTON, A. J., KAHLER, H., STRIEBICH, M. J., and LLOYD, B.: Structural details of some of the epithelial cell types in the mouse as revealed by the electron microscope. J. Natl. Cancer Inst., 11:1163–1185, 1951.

232. DALTON, A. J. and ZEIGEL, R. F.: A simplified method of staining thin sections of biological material with lead hydroxide for electron microscopy. J. Biophys. Biochem. Cytol., 7:409–410, 1960.

233. DANIELLI, J. F.: Surface chemistry and cell membranes. In: Surface Phenomena in Chemistry and Biology, pp. 246–265. Pergamon Press, New York, 1958.

234. DAVID, H.: Über einen Nucleolus mit Membran. Z. Zellforsch., 53:50–54, 1960.

235. DAVID, H.: Zur submikroskopischen Morphologie intrazellulärer Gallenkapillaren. Acta Anat., 47:216–224, 1961.

236. DAVID, H.: Zur morphologie der Leberzellmembran. Z. Zellforsch., 55:220–234, 1961.

237. DAVID-FERREIRA, J. F. and DAVID-FERREIRA, K.: L'ultrastructure des plaquettes sanguines. Mise en évidence du glycogène. Z. Zellforsch., 56:789–802, 1962.

238. DAVIS, J. M.: Structure of the walls of the bile "canaliculi" in mammalian liver cells. Nature, 188:1123–1124, 1960.

239. DAVIS, R. and ENDERS, A. C.: Light and electron microscope studies on the parathyroid gland. In: The Parathyroids, pp. 76–92. Eds.: R. O. Greep and R. V. Talmage. Charles C Thomas, Springfield, Ill., 1961.

240. DAWSON, I. M., HOSSACK, J., and WYBURN, G. M.: Observations on the Nissl's substance, cytoplasmic filaments and the nuclear membrane of spinal ganglion cells. Proc. Roy. Soc., 144:132–142, 1955.

241. DAY, T. D. and EAVES, G.: Electron microscope observations of the ground substance of interstitial connective tissue. Biochim. Biophys. Acta, 10:203–209, 1953.

242. DEANE, H. W. and PORTER, K. R.: A comparative study of cytoplasmic basophilia and the population density of ribosomes in the secretory cells of mouse seminal vesicle. Z. Zellforsch., 52:697–711, 1960.

243. DE DUVE, C.: The enzymic heterogeneity of cell fractions isolated by differential centrifuging. Symp. soc. exp. biol., 10:50–61, 1957.

244. DE DUVE, C.: Lysosomes, a new group of cytoplasmic particles. In: Subcellular Particles, pp. 128–159. Ed.: T. Hayashi. Ronald Press, New York, 1958.

245. DE LORENZO, A. J.: Electron microscopic observations on the olfactory mucosa and olfactory nerve. J. Biophys. Biochem. Cytol., 3:839–850, 1957.

246. DE LORENZO, A. J.: Electron microscopic observations on the taste buds of the rabbit. J. Biophys. Biochem. Cytol., 4:143–148, 1958.

247. DE LORENZO, A. J.: The fine structure of synapses in the ciliary ganglion of the chick. J. Biophys. Biochem. Cytol., 7:31–36, 1960.

248. DE LORENZO, A. J.: Electron microscopy of the cerebral cortex. I. The ultrastructure and histochemistry of synaptic junctions. Bull. Johns Hopkins Hosp., 108:258–279, 1961.

249. DEMAN, J. C. H., DAEMS, W. TH., WILLIGHAGEN, R. G. J., and VAN RIJSSEL, TH. G.: Electron dense bodies in liver tissue of the mouse in relation to the activity of acid phosphatase. J. Ultrastructure Res., 4:43–57, 1960.

250. DEMPSEY, E. W.: Variations in the structure of mitochondria. J. Biophys. Biochem. Cytol., 2:305–312, 1956. Suppl.

251. DEMPSEY, E. W.: Histophysical considerations. In: The Placenta and Fetal Membranes, pp. 29–35. Ed.: C. A. Villee. Williams and Wilkins, New York, 1960.

252. DEMPSEY, E. W. and PETERSON, R. R.: Electron microscopic observations on the thyroid glands of normal, hypophysectomized, cold-exposed and thiouracil-treated rats. Endocrinology, 56:46–58, 1955.

253. DEMPSEY, E. W. and WISLOCKI, G. B.: An electron microscopic study of the blood-brain barrier in the rat, employing silver nitrate as a vital stain. J. Biophys. Biochem. Cytol., 1:245–256, 1955.

254. DEMPSEY, E. W., WISLOCKI, G. B., and AMOROSO, E. C.: Electron microscopy of the pig's placenta, with especial reference to the cell-membranes of the endometrium and chorion. Am. J. Anat., 96:65–102, 1955.

255. DE ROBERTIS, E.: The nucleo-cytoplasmic relationship and the basophilic substance

(ergastoplasm) of nerve cells (electron microscope observations). J. Histochem. Cytochem., 2:341–345, 1954.

256. DE ROBERTIS, E.: Electron microscope observations on the submicroscopic organization of the retinal rods. J. Biophys. Biochem. Cytol., 2:319–330, 1956.

257. DE ROBERTIS, E.: Submicroscopic changes of the synapse after nerve section in the acoustic ganglion of the guinea pig. J. Biophys. Biochem. Cytol., 2:503–512, 1956.

259. DE ROBERTIS, E.: Morphogenesis of the retinal rods; an electron microscope study. J. Biophys. Biochem. Cytol., 2:209–218, 1956, Suppl.

260. DE ROBERTIS, E.: Submicroscopic morphology and function of the synapse. Exp. Cell Res., Suppl. 5:347–369, 1958.

261. DE ROBERTIS, E. and BENNETT, H. S.: Submicroscopic vesicular component in the synapse. Federation Proc., 13:35, 1954. (Abstract).

262. DE ROBERTIS, E. and BENNETT, H. S.: A submicroscopic vesicular component of Schwann cells and nerve satellite cells. Exp. Cell Res., 6:543–545, 1954.

263. DE ROBERTIS, E. and BENNETT, H. S.: Some features of the submicroscopic morphology of synapses in frog and earthworm. J. Biophys. Biochem. Cytol., 1:47–58, 1955.

264. DE ROBERTIS, E. and FERREIRA, A. V.: Submicroscopic changes of the nerve endings in the adrenal medulla after stimulation of the splanchnic nerve. J. Biophys. Biochem. Cytol., 3:611–614, 1957.

265. DE ROBERTIS, E. and FRANCHI, C. M.: Electron microscope observations on synaptic vesicles in synapsis of the retinal rods and cones. J. Biophys. Biochem. Cytol., 2:307–318, 1956.

266. DE ROBERTIS, E. and GERSCHENFELD, H. M.: Submicroscopic morphology and function of glial cells. In: International Review of Neurobiology, 3:1–65. Eds.: C. C. Pfeiffer and J. R. Smythies. Academic Press, New York, 1961.

267. DE ROBERTIS, E., GERSCHENFELD, H. M., and WALD, F.: Cellular mechanism of myelination in the central nervous system. J. Biophys. Biochem. Cytol., 4:651–658, 1958.

268. DE ROBERTIS, E., GERSCHENFELD, H. M., and WALD, F.: Ultrastructure and function of glial cells. In: Structure and Function of the Cerebral Cortex. pp. 69–80. Eds.: D. B. Tower and J. B. Schade. Elsevier, Amsterdam, 1960.

269. DE ROBERTIS, E., GERSCHENFELD, H. M., and WALD, F.: Some aspects of glial function as revealed by electron microscopy. In: Fourth Internat. Conf. Electron Micros., Berlin 1958, Proceed. Vol. II, pp. 443–447. Springer Verlag, Berlin, 1960.

270. DE ROBERTIS, E., DE IARALDI, A. P., RODRIGUEZ, G., and GOMEZ, C. J.: On the isolation of nerve endings and synaptic vesicles. J. Biophys. Biochem. Cytol., 9:229–235, 1961.

271. DE ROBERTIS, E. and LASANSKY, A.: Submicroscopic organization of retinal cones of the rabbit. J. Biophys. Biochem. Cytol., 4:743–746, 1958.

272. DE ROBERTIS, E. and LASANSKY, A.: Ultrastructure and chemical organization of photoreceptors. In: The Structure of the Eye, pp. 29–52. Ed.: G. K. Smelser. Academic Press, New York, 1961.

273. DE ROBERTIS, E. and SABATINI, D. D.: Mitochondrial changes in the adrenocortex of normal hamsters. J. Biophys. Biochem. Cytol., 4:667–670, 1958.

274. DE ROBERTIS, E. and SOTELO, J. R.: Electron microscope study of cultured nervous tissue. Exp. Cell Res., 3:433–452, 1952.

275. DONAHUE, S. and PAPPAS, G. D.: The fine structure of capillaries in the cerebral cortex of the rat at various stages of development. Am. J. Anat., 108:331–347, 1961.

276. DONN, A.: The movement of ions and water across the cornea. Invest. Ophthal., 1:170–177, 1962.

277. DOWLING, J. E. and GIBBONS, I. R.: The effect of vitamin A deficiency on the fine structure of the retina. In: The Structure of the Eye, pp. 85–99. Ed.: G. K. Smelser. Academic Press, New York, 1961.

278. DRIESSENS, J., DUPONT, A., and DEMAILLE, A.: L'ultrastructure du poumon de rat, examiné au microscope électronique. Compt. rend. soc. biol., 153:611–612, 1959.

279. DRIESSEN, J., DUPONT, A., and DEMAILLE, A.: L'ultrastructure du rein du rat examiné au microscope électronique. Compt. rend. soc. biol., 153:626–628, 1959.

280. DROCHMANS, P.: Electron microscope studies of epidermal melanocytes, and the fine structure of melanin granules. J. Biophys. Biochem. Cytol., 8:165–180, 1960.

281. DROCHMANS, P.: Mise en évidence du glycogène dans la cellule hepatique par microscopie électronique. J. Biophys. Biochem. Cytol., 8:553–558, 1960.

282. DROCHMANS, P.: Morphologie du glycogène. Étude au microscope électronique de colorations négatives du glycogène particulaire. J. Ultrastructure Res., 6:141–163, 1962.

283. DUDLEY, R. H. and SPIRO, D.: The fine structure of bone cells. J. Biophys. Biochem. Cytol., 11:627–649, 1961.

284. DUNCAN, D. and HILD, W.: Mitochondrial alterations in cultures of the central nervous system as observed with the electron microscope. Z. Zellforsch., 51:123–137, 1960.

285. EAKIN, R. M. and WESTFALL, J. A.: Fine structure of photoreceptors in amphioxus. J. Ultrastructure Res., 6:531–539, 1962.

286. EASTON, J. M., GOLDBERG, B., and GREEN, H.: Demonstration of surface antigens and pinocytosis in mammalian cells with ferritin-antibody conjugates. J. Cell Biol., 12:437–443, 1962.

287. EASTON, J. M., GOLDBERG, B., and GREEN, H.: Immune cytolysis: Electron microscopic localization of cellular antigens with ferritin-antibody conjugates. J. Exp. Med., 115:275–288, 1962.

Page 177

288. EDLUND, Y. and EKHOLM, R.: Microstructure and ultrastructure of the human pancreas. Acta Chir. Scand., 113:469–471, 1957.

289. EDWARDS, G. A.: The fine structure of a multi-terminal innervation of an insect muscle. J. Biophys. Biochem. Cytol., 5:241–243, 1959.

290. EDWARDS, G. A. and CHALLICE, C. E.: The fine structure of cardiac muscle cells of new-born and suckling mice. Exp. Cell Res., 15:247–250, 1958.

291. EDWARDS, G. A., RUSKA, H., and DE HARVEN, E.: Electron microscopy of peripheral nerves and neuromuscular junctions in the wasp leg. J. Biophys. Biochem. Cytol., 4:107–114, 1958.

292. EDWARDS, G. A., RUSKA, H., DE SOUZA, S. P., and VALLEJO-FREIRE, A.: Comparative cytophysiology of striated muscle with special reference to the role of the endoplasmic reticulum. J. Biophys. Biochem. Cytol., 2:143–156, 1956. Suppl.

293. EICHNER, D.: Zur Frage der Neurofibrillen. Z. Zellforsch., 43:501–512, 1956.

294. EICHNER, D. und THEMANN, H.: Zur Frage des Netzhautglykogens beim Meerschweinchen. Z. Zellforsch., 56:231–246, 1962.

295. EKHOLM, R.: The ultrastructure of the blood capillaries in the mouse thyroid gland. Z. Zellforsch., 46:139–146, 1957.

296. EKHOLM, R.: The ultrastructure of the stimulated mouse thyroid gland. In: Fourth Internat. Conf. Electron Micros., Berlin 1958, Vol. II, pp. 378–381. Springer Verlag, Berlin, 1960.

297. EKHOLM, R.: Iodide binding in thyroid mitochondrial and microsomal fractions. J. Ultrastructure Res., 5:575–583, 1961.

298. EKHOLM, R. and EDLUND, Y.: Ultrastructure of the human exocrine pancreas. J. Ultrastructure Res., 2:453–481, 1959.

299. EKHOLM, R. and EDLUND, Y.: The mitochondria in human normal and cholestatic liver. In: Fourth Internat. Conf. Electron Micros., Berlin 1958, Vol. II, pp. 273–275. Springer Verlag, Berlin, 1960.

300. EKHOLM, R., EDLUND, Y., and ZELANDER, T.: The ultrastructure of the rat exocrine pancreas after brief ethionine exposure. J. Ultrastructure Res., 7:102–120, 1962.

301. EKHOLM, R. and SJÖSTRAND, F. S.: The ultrastructure of the thyroid gland of the mouse. In: Stockholm Conf. Electron Micros. 1956. Proceed. pp. 171–173. Academic Press, New York, 1957.

302. EKHOLM, R. and SJÖSTRAND, F. S.: The ultrastructural organization of the mouse thyroid gland. J. Ultrastructure Res., 1:178–199, 1957.

303. EKHOLM, R. and ZELANDER, T.: Nerve tissue in the mouse thyroid gland. In: European Regional Conf. Electron Micros., Delft 1960, Proceed. Vol. II, pp. 827–830. De Nederlandse Vereniging voor Electronenmicroscopie, Delft, 1961.

304. EKHOLM, R., ZELANDER, T., and EDLUND, Y.: The ultrastructural organization of the rat exocrine pancreas. I. Acinar cells. J. Ultrastructure Res., 7:61–72, 1962.

305. EKHOLM, R., ZELANDER, T., and EDLUND, Y.: The ultrastructural organization of the rat exocrine pancreas. II. Centroacinar cells, intercalary and intralobular ducts. J. Ultrastructure Res., 7:73–83, 1962.

306. ELFVIN, L. G.: The ultrastructure of unmyelinated fibers in the splenic nerve of the cat. J. Ultrastructure Res., 1:428–454, 1958.

307. ELFVIN, L. G.: Electron microscopic investigation of filament structures in unmyelinated fibers of cat splenic nerve. J. Ultrastructure Res., 5:51–64, 1961.

308. ELFVIN, L. G.: The ultrastructure of the nodes of Ranvier in cat sympathetic nerve fibers. J. Ultrastructure Res., 5:374–387, 1961.

309. ELFVIN, L. G.: Electron microscopic investigation of the plasma membrane and myelin sheath of autonomic nerve fibers in the cat. J. Ultrastructure Res., 5:388–407, 1961.

310. ELFVIN, L. G.: Electron microscopic studies on the effect of anisotonic solutions on the structure of unmyelinated splenic nerve fibers of the cat. J. Ultrastructure Res., 7:1–38, 1962.

311. ELLIOTT, G. F.: The structure of certain smooth muscles which contain "paramyosin" elements. In: Fourth Internat. Conf. Electron Micros., Berlin 1958. Proceed. Vol. II, pp. 328–330. Springer Verlag, Berlin, 1960.

312. EMMELOT, P. and BENEDETTI, E. L.: Changes in the fine structure of rat liver cells brought about by dimethylnitrosamine. J. Biophys. Biochem. Cytol., 7:393–396, 1960.

313. EMMELOT, P., MIZRAHI, I. J., NACCARATO, R., and BENEDETTI, E. L.: Changes in function and structure of the endoplasmic reticulum of rat liver cells after administration of cysteine. J. Cell Biol., 12:177–180, 1962.

314. ENDERS, A. C.: Cytological studies on corpora lutea of delayed implantation. Anat. Rec., 139:225, 1961. (Abstract).

315. ENDERS, A. C.: Observations on the fine structure of lutein cells. J. Cell Biol., 12:101–113, 1962.

316. ENGFELDT, B., GARDELL, S., HELLSTRÖM, J., IVEMARK, B., RHODIN, J., and STRANDH, J.: Effect of experimentally induced hyperparathyroidism on renal function and structure. Acta Endocrinologica, 29:15–26, 1958.

317. ENGSTRÖM, H.: The structure of tracheal cilia. Acta Oto-Laryngol., 39:360–366, 1951.

318. ENGSTRÖM, H.: The structure of the basilar membrane. Acta oto-rhino-laryng. belg., 9:531–542, 1955.

319. ENGSTRÖM, H.: On the double innervation of the sensory epithelia of the inner ear. Acta Oto-Laryngol., 49:109–118, 1958.

320. ENGSTRÖM, H.: The cortilymph, the third lymph of the inner ear. Acta Morphol. Neerl.-Scand., 3:195–204, 1960.

321. ENGSTRÖM, H.: Electron micrographic studies of the receptor cells of the organ of Corti. In: Neural Mechanisms of the Auditory and Vestibular Systems, pp. 48–64. Eds.: G. L. Rasmussen and W. Windle. Charles C Thomas, Springfield, Ill., 1961.

322. ENGSTRÖM, H. and BLOOM, G.: The structure of

the olfactory region in man. Acta Oto-Laryngol., 43:11–21, 1953.

323. ENGSTRÖM, H. and RYTZNER, C.: The fine structure of taste buds and taste fibers. Ann. Otol. Rhinol. Laryngol., 65:361–375, 1956.

324. ENGSTRÖM, H. and RYTZNER, C.: The structure of taste buds. Acta Oto-Laryngol., 46:361–367, 1956.

325. ENGSTRÖM, H. and SJÖSTRAND, F. S.: The structure and innervation of the cochlear hair cells. Acta Oto-Laryngol. 44:490–501, 1954.

326. ENGSTRÖM, H., SJÖSTRAND, F. S., and SPOENDLIN, H.: Feinstruktur der Stria vascularis beim Meerschweinchen. Pract. oto-rhino-laryng., 17:69–79, 1955.

327. ENGSTRÖM, H., SJÖSTRAND, F. S. and WERSÄLL, J.: The fine structure of the tone receptors of the guinea pig as revealed by the electron microscope. Proc. Fifth Intern. Congr. of Oto-rhino-laryngology, Amsterdam, 1953. pp. 563–568.

328. ENGSTRÖM, H. and WERSÄLL, J.: Some principles in the structure of vibratile cilia. Ann. Otol. Rhinol. Laryngol., 61:1027–1038, 1952.

329. ENGSTRÖM, H. and WERSÄLL, J.: Is there a special nutritive cellular system around the hair cells in the organ of Corti? Ann. Otol. Rhinol. Laryngol., 62:507, 1953.

330. ENGSTRÖM, H. and WERSÄLL, J.: Structure of the organ of Corti. 1. Outer hair cells. Acta Oto-Laryngol., 43:1–10, 1953.

331. ENGSTRÖM, H. and WERSÄLL, J.: Structure of the organ of Corti. 2. Supporting structures and their relations to sensory cells and nerve endings. Acta Oto-Laryngol., 43:323–334, 1953.

332. ENGSTRÖM, H. and WERSÄLL, J.: Myelin sheath structure in nerve fibre demyelinization and branching regions. Exp. Cell Res., 14:414–425, 1958.

333. ENGSTRÖM, H. and WERSÄLL, J.: The ultrastructural organization of the organ of Corti and of vestibular sensory epithelia. Exp. Cell Res., Suppl. 5:460–492, 1958.

334. ENGSTRÖM, H. and WERSÄLL, J.: Structure and innervation of the inner ear sensory epithelia. Int. Rev. Cytol., 7:535–585, 1958.

335. ERÄNKÖ, O. and HÄNNINEN, L.: Electron microscopic observations on the adrenal medulla of the rat. Acta Pathol. Microbiol. Scand., 50:126–132, 1960.

336. ESSNER, E.: An electron microscopic study of erythrophagocytosis. J. Biophys. Biochem. Cytol., 7:329–334, 1960.

337. ESSNER, E. and NOVIKOFF, A. B.: Acid phosphatase activity in hepatic lysosomes: electron microscopic demonstration of its reaction product. J. Histochem. Cytochem., 8:318, 1960. (Abstract).

338. ESSNER, E. and NOVIKOFF, A. B.: Human hepatocellular pigments and liposomes. J. Ultrastructure Res., 3:374–391, 1960.

340. ESSNER, E. and NOVIKOFF, A. B.: Localization of acid phosphatase activity in hepatic lysosomes by means of electron microscopy. J. Biophys. Biochem. Cytol., 9:773–784, 1961.

341. ESSNER, E., NOVIKOFF, A. B., and MASEK, B.: Adenosine triphosphatase and 5-nucleotidase activities in the plasma membrane of liver cells as revealed by electron microscopy. J. Biophys. Biochem. Cytol., 4:711–716, 1958.

342. ESTABLE, C., ACOSTA-FERREIRA, W., and SOTELO, J. R.: An electron microscope study of the regenerating nerve fibers. Z. Zellforsch., 46:387–399, 1957.

343. ESTABLE, C., REISSIG, M. and DE ROBERTIS, E.: Microscopic and submicroscopic structure of the synapsis in the ventral ganglion of the acoustic nerve. Exp. Cell Res., 6:255–262, 1954.

344. FARQUHAR, M. G.: Neurological structure and relationships as seen with the electron microscope. Anat. Rec., 121:291–292, 1955.

345. FARQUHAR, M. G.: Preparation of ultrathin tissue sections for electron microscopy. Review and compilation of procedures. Lab. Invest., 5:317–337, 1956.

346. FARQUHAR, M. G.: Review of normal and pathologic glomerular ultrastructure. Proc. of the Annual Conf. on the Nephrotic Syndrome, 10th Conference, pp. 2–25, 1959.

347. FARQUHAR, M. G.: Electron microscopy of renal biopsies. Bull. N. Y. Acad. Med., 36:419–423, 1960.

348. FARQUHAR, M. G. and HARTMANN, J. E.: Neurological structure and relationships as revealed by electron microscopy. J. Neuropathol. Exp. Neurol., 16:18–39, 1957.

349. FARQUHAR, M. G. and PALADE, G. E.: Behavior of colloidal particles in the glomerulus. Anat. Rec., 133:378, 1959. (Abstract.)

350. FARQUHAR, M. G. and PALADE, G. E.: Segregation of ferritin in glomerular protein absorption droplets. J. Biophys. Biochem. Cytol., 7:297–304, 1960.

351. FARQUHAR, M. G. and PALADE, G. E.: Glomerular permeability. II. Ferritin transfer across the glomerular capillary wall in nephrotic rats. J. Exp. Med., 114:699–716, 1961.

352. FARQUHAR, M. G. and PALADE, G. E.: Functional evidence for the existence of a third cell type in the renal glomerulus. Phagocytosis of filtration residues by a distinctive "third" cell. J. Cell Biol., 13:55–87, 1962.

353. FARQUHAR, M. G. and WELLINGS, S. R.: Electron microscopic evidence suggesting secretory granule formation within the Golgi apparatus. J. Biophys. Biochem. Cytol., 3:319–322, 1957.

354. FARQUHAR, M. G., WISSIG, S. L., and PALADE, G. E.: Glomerular permeability. I. Ferritin transfer across the normal glomerular capillary wall. J. Exp. Med., 113:47–66, 1961.

355. FASSKE, E. and THEMANN, H.: Über das Deckepithel der menschlichen Mundschleimhaut. Licht- und elektronenmikroskopische Untersuchungen. Z. Zellforsch., 49:447–463, 1959.

Page 179

356. FAWCETT, D. W.: The study of epithelial cilia and sperm flagella with the electron microscope. Laryngoscope, 64:557–567, 1954.

357. FAWCETT, D. W.: Observations on the cytology and electron microscopy of the hepatic cells. J. Natl. Cancer Inst., 15:1475–1502, 1955, Suppl.

358. FAWCETT, D. W.: Observations on the submicroscopic structure of small arteries, arterioles and capillaries. Anat. Rec., 124:401, 1956. (Abstract.)

359. FAWCETT, D. W.: Structural specialization of the cell surface. In: Frontiers in Cytology, pp. 19–41. Ed.: S. L. Palay. Yale University Press, New Haven, 1958.

360. FAWCETT, D. W.: The structure of the mammalian spermatozoon. Int. Rev. Cytol., 7:195–234, 1958.

361. FAWCETT, D. W.: The fine structure of capillaries, arterioles and small arteries. In: The Microcirculation, pp. 1–27. Eds: S. R. M. Reynolds and B. W. Zweifach. University of Illinois Press, Urbana, 1959.

362. FAWCETT, D. W.: The membranes of the cytoplasm. Lab. Invest., 10:1162–1188, 1961.

363. FAWCETT, D. W.: Intercellular bridges. Exp. Cell Res. Suppl. 8:174–187, 1961.

364. FAWCETT, D. W.: Cilia and flagella. In: The Cell, Vol. II, pp. 217–297. Eds.: J. Brachet and A. E. Mirsky. Academic Press, New York, 1961.

365. FAWCETT, D. W. and BURGOS, M. H.: Studies on the fine structure of the mammalian testis. II. The human interstitial tissue. Am. J. Anat., 107:245–269, 1960.

366. FAWCETT, D. W. and ITO, S.: Observations on the cytoplasmic membranes of testicular cells, examined by phase contrast and electron microscopy. J. Biophys. Biochem. Cytol., 4:135–142, 1958.

367. FAWCETT, D. W., ITO, S., and SLAUTTERBACH, D.: The occurrence of intracellular bridges in groups of cells exhibiting synchronous differentiation. J. Biophys. Biochem. Cytol., 5:453–460, 1959.

368. FAWCETT, D. W. and PORTER, K. R.: A study of the fine structure of ciliated epithelia. J. Morph., 94:221–282, 1954.

370. FAWCETT, D. W. and REVEL, J. P.: The sarcoplasmic reticulum of a fast-acting fish muscle. J. Biophys. Biochem. Cytol., 10:89–109, 1961 Suppl.

371. FAWCETT, D. W. and SELBY, C. C.: Observations on the fine structure of the turtle atrium. J. Biophys. Biochem. Cytol., 4:63–72, 1958.

372. FEARNHEAD, R. W.: Secretory products of ameloblasts. In: Electron Microscopy in Anatomy, pp. 241–260. Eds.: J. D. Boyd, F. R. Johnson, and J. D. Lever. Williams and Wilkins, Baltimore, 1961.

373. FEENEY, L. and HOGAN, M. J.: Electron microscopy of the human choroid. I. Cells and supporting structures. Am. J. Ophthal., 51:1057–1071, 1961.

374. FEENEY, L. and HOGAN, M. J.: Electron microscopy of the human choroid. II. The choroidal nerves. Am. J. Ophthal., 51:1072–1083, 1961.

375. FEENEY, L. and HOGAN, M. J.: Electron microscopy of the human choroid. III. The blood vessels. Am. J. Ophthal., 51:1084–1097, 1961.

376. FEENEY, M. L. and GARRON, L. K.: Descemet's membrane in the human peripheral cornea. A study by light and electron microscopy. Anat. Rec., 136:192, 1960. (Abstract).

377. FELDHERR, C. M.: The nuclear annuli as pathways for nucleocytoplasmic exchanges. J. Cell Biol., 14:65–72, 1962.

378. FELDMAN, J. D., VAZQUEZ, J. J., and KURTZ, S. M.: Maturation of the rat fetal thyroid. J. Biophys. Biochem. Cytol., 11:365–383, 1961.

379. FELLINGER, K., BRAUNSTEINER, H., and PAKESCH, F.: Elektronenmikroskopische Beobachtungen zur Frage des Disseschen Raumes. Wien. klin. Wochschr., 65:738–740, 1953.

380. FELIX, M. D.: Observations on the surface cells of the mouse omentum as studied with the phase-contrast and electron microscopes. J. Natl. Cancer Inst., 27:713–745, 1961.

381. FELIX, M. D. and DALTON, A. J.: A comparison of mesothelial cells and macrophages in mice after the intraperitoneal inoculation of melanin granules. J. Biophys. Biochem. Cytol., 2:109–114, 1956, Suppl.

382. FERNÁNDEZ-MORÁN, H.: Electron microscope observations on the structure of the myelinated nerve fiber sheath. Exp. Cell Res., 1:143–149, 1950.

383. FERNÁNDEZ-MORÁN, H.: Sheath and axon structures in the internode portion of vertebrate myelinated nerve fibers. Exp. Cell Res., 1:309–340, 1950.

384. FERNÁNDEZ-MORÁN, H.: The submicroscopic organization of vertebrate nerve fibers. An electron microscope study of myelinated and unmyelinated nerve fibers. Exp. Cell Res., 3:282–359, 1952.

385. FERNÁNDEZ-MORÁN, H.: The fine structure of vertebrate and invertebrate photoreceptors as revealed by low-temperature electron microscopy. In: The Structure of the Eye, pp. 521–556. Ed.: G. K. Smelser. Academic Press, New York, 1961.

386. FERNÁNDEZ-MORÁN, H. and BROWN, R. (editors): Symposium on submicroscopic organization and function of nerve cells. Exp. Cell Res., 1958, Suppl. 5.

387. FERNER, H.: Bau und Struktur der Speicheldrüsen unter Berücksichtigung eigener elektronenmikroskopischer Beobachtungen am Menschen. Deut. zahnärztl. Z., 16:128–142, 1961.

388. FERNER, H. and GANSLER, H.: Elektronenmikroskopische Untersuchungen an der Glandula submandibularis und Parotis des Menschen. Z. Zellforsch., 55:148–178, 1961.

389. FERREIRA, D.: L'ultrastructure des cellules du pancréas endocrine chez l'embryon et la rat nouveau-né. J. Ultrastructure Res., 1:14–25, 1957.

390. FERREIRA, J. F. D.: Sur la structure et le pouvoir phagocytaire des plaquettes sanguines. Z. Zellforsch., 55:89–103, 1961.

Page 180

391. Fick, K., Fricke, R., Gattow, G., Hartmann, F., and Schwarz, W.: Untersuchungen über die Struktur und Funktion des Bindegewebes. 5. Die Differenzierung des Sehnenbindegewebes während des Wachstums und ihre Beeinflussung durch desmotrope Pharmaka. Z. Rheumaforsch., 19:293–310, 1960.

392. Filshie, B. K. and Rogers, G. E.: The fine structure of α-keratin. J. Mol. Biol., 3:784–786, 1961.

393. Filshie, B. K. and Rogers, G. E.: An electron microscope study of the fine structure of feather keratin. J. Cell Biol., 13:1–12, 1962.

394. Finck, H.: Epoxy resins in electron microscopy. J. Biophys. Biochem. Cytol., 7:27–30, 1960.

395. Fine, B. S. and Tousimis, A. J.: The structure of the vitreous body and the suspensory ligaments of the lens. Arch. Ophthal., 65:95–110, 1961.

396. Fine, B. S. and Zimmerman, L. E.: Müller's cells and the "middle limiting membrane" of the human retina. Invest. Ophthal., 1:304–326, 1962.

397. Finean, J. B.: Further observations on the structure of myelin. Exp. Cell Res., 5:202–215, 1953.

398. Finean, J. B.: The effects of osmium tetroxide on the structure of the myelin in sciatic nerve. Exp. Cell Res., 6:283–292, 1954.

399. Finean, J. B.: The molecular organization of nerve myelin. Acta Neurol. Psychiat. Belg., 57:462–471, 1957.

400. Finean, J. B.: Electron microscope and x-ray diffraction studies of the effects of dehydration on the structure of nerve myelin. I. Peripheral nerve. J. Biophys. Biochem. Cytol., 8:13–29, 1960.

401. Finean, J. B.: Electron microscope and x-ray diffraction studies of the effects of dehydration on the structure of nerve myelin. II. Optic nerve. J. Biophys. Biochem. Cytol., 8:31–37, 1960.

402. Finean, J. B.: Chemical Ultrastructure in Living Tissues. Charles C Thomas, Springfield, Illinois, 1961.

403. Finean, J. B. and Robertson, J. D.: Lipids and the fine structure of myelin. Brit. Med. Bull., 14:267–273, 1958.

404. Finean, J. B., Sjöstrand, F. S., and Steinmann, E.: Submicroscopic organization of some layered lipoprotein structures (nerve myelin, retinal rods, and chloroplasts). Exp. Cell Res., 5:557–559, 1953.

405. Fitton-Jackson, S.: The formation of connective and skeletal tissues. Proc. Roy. Soc. London, 142B:536–548, 1954.

406. Fitton-Jackson, S.: The morphogenesis of avian tendon. Proc. Roy. Soc. London, 144B:556–572, 1956.

407. Fitton-Jackson, S.: The fine structure of the developing bone in the embryonic fowl. Proc. Roy. Soc. London, 146B:270–280, 1957.

408. Fitton-Jackson, S. and Randall, J. T.: The fine structure of bone. Nature, 178:798, 1956.

409. Fitton-Jackson, S. and Smith, R. H.: Fibro-genesis of connective and skeletal tissues in the embryonic fowl. Symp. Soc. Exp. Biol., 9:89–96, 1955.

410. Fitton-Jackson, S. and Smith, R. H.: Studies on the biosynthesis of collagen. I. The growth of fowl osteoblasts and the formation of collagen in tissue culture. J. Biophys. Biochem. Cytol., 3:897–912, 1957.

411. Florey, H. W.: Electron microscopic observations on goblet cells of the rat's colon. Quart. J. Exp. Physiol., 45:329–336, 1960.

412. Florey, H. W.: A series of electron micrographs of the intima of blood vessels. Proc. Roy. Soc. Med., 53:13–14, 1960.

413. Florey, H. W.: The structure of normal and inflamed small blood vessels of the mouse and rat colon. Quart. J. Exp. Physiol., 46:119–122, 1961.

414. Florey, H. W., Poole, J. C. F., and Meek, G. A.: Endothelial cells and "cement" lines. J. Pathol. Bacteriol., 77:625–636, 1959.

415. Fraley, E. E. and Weiss, L.: An electron microscopic study of the lymphatic vessels in the penile skin of the rat. Am. J. Anat., 109:85–101, 1961.

416. Franchi, L. L.: Electron microscopy of oocyte-follicle cell relationships in the rat ovary. J. Biophys. Biochem. Cytol., 7:397–398, 1960.

417. Frank, R., Frank, P., Klein, M., and Fontaine, R.: L'os compacte humaine normal au microscope électronique. Arch. d'Anat. microsc. et de Morphol. experim., 44:191–206, 1955.

418. Fredricsson, B.: Studies on the morphology and histochemistry of the fallopian tube epithelium. Acta Anat., 37:3–23, 1959. Suppl.

419. Freeman, J. A.: The ultrastructure of the double membrane systems of mitochondria. J. Biophys Biochem. Cytol., 2:353–354, 1956, Suppl.

420. Freeman, J. A. and Spurlock, B. O.: A new epoxy embedment for electron microscopy. J. Cell Biol., 13:437–443, 1962.

421. Frei, J. V. and Sheldon, H.: A small granular component of the cytoplasm of keratinizing epithelia. J. Biophys. Biochem. Cytol., 11:719–724, 1961.

422. Frei, J. V. and Sheldon, H.: Corpus intra cristam: A dense body within mitochondria of cells in hyperplastic mouse epidermis. J. Biophys. Biochem. Cytol., 11:724–729, 1961.

423. French, J. E., Florey, H. W., and Morris, B.: The absorption of particles by the lymphatics of the diaphragm. Quart. J. Exp. Physiol., 45:88–103, 1960.

424. Frenkel, G.: Elektronenmikroskopische Untersuchungen der mukösen Endstücke der Glandulae labiales et buccales des Menschen. Deut. zahnärztl. Z., 14:1459–1474, 1959.

425. Fresen, O. and Wellensiek, H. J.: Zur elektronenmikroskopischen Struktur des Lymphknotens. Verhandl. deut. Ges. Pathol., 42:353–365, 1959.

426. Friedmann, I.: The ultrastructural organization of sensory epithelium in the develop-

ing fowl embryo otocyst. J. Laryng., 73:779–794, 1959.

427. FRIEDMANN, I.: Electron microscope observations on "in vitro" cultures of the isolated fowl embryo otocyst. J. Biophys. Biochem. Cytol., 5:263–268, 1959.

428. FRIEDMANN, I.: Attachment zones of cells in organ cultures of the isolated fowl embryo otocyst. J. Ultrastructure Res., 5:44–50, 1961.

429. FRIEDMANN, I.: Cytology of the ear. Brit. Med. Bull., 18:209–213, 1962.

430. FUJITA, H.: An electron microscopic study of the adrenal cortical tissue of the domestic fowl. Z. Zellforsch., 55:80–88, 1961.

431. FUJITA, H. and MACHINO, M.: On the follicle formation of the thyroid gland in the chick embryo. Exp. Cell Res., 25:204–207, 1961.

432. FUJITA, M.: The fine structure of the epithelial cell of the mouse seminal vesicle studied with the electron microscope. Kurume. Med. J., 22:536–558, 1959.

433. GAEDE, K., RUNGE, W., and CARBONELL, L.: Elektronenmikroskopische Differenzierung der Inselzellgranula des Pankreas bei der Ratte. Z. Zellforsch., 49:690–693, 1959.

434. GALAMBOS, R.: A glia-neural theory of brain function. Proc. Natl. Acad. Sci., U. S., 47:129–136, 1961.

435. GALINDO, B. and IMAEDA, T.: Electron microscope study of the white pulp of the mouse spleen. Anat. Rec., 143:399–415, 1962.

436. GALL, J. G.: Observations on the nuclear membrane with the electron microscope. Exp. Cell Res., 7:197–200, 1954.

437. GALL, J. G.: On the submicroscopic structure of chromosomes. Mutation. Brookhaven Symp. Biol., 8:17–32, 1956.

438. GALL, J. G.: Small granules in the amphibian oocyte nucleus and their relationship to RNA. J. Biophys. Biochem Cytol., 2:393–396, 1956. Suppl.

439. GALL, J. G.: Centriole replication. A study of spermatogenesis in the snail *Viviparus*. J. Biophys. Biochem. Cytol., 10:163–193, 1961.

440. GANSLER, H.: Elektronenmikroskopische Untersuchungen am Uterusmuskel der Ratte unter Follikelhormonwirkung. Arch. pathol. Anat. Physiol., Virchows., 329:235–244, 1956.

441. GANSLER, H.: Beitrag zur Ultrastruktur der marklosen Nervenfasern. Verhandl. deut. Ges. Pathol., 41:345–351, 1957.

442. GANSLER, H.: Elektronenmikroskopische Untersuchungen am Uterusmuskel der Ratte. In: Stockholm Conf. Electron Micros. 1956. Proceed. pp. 210–212. Academic Press, New York, 1957.

443. GANSLER, H.: Beitrag zur elektronenmikroskopischen Histologie der Haut. Acta Neuroveget. Vienna., 18:320–334, 1958.

444. GANSLER, H.: Phasenkontrast- und elektronenmikroskopische Untersuchungen zur Morphologie und Funktion der glatten Muskulatur. Z. Zellforsch., 52:60–92, 1960.

445. GANSLER, H.: Phasenkontrast- und elektronenmikroskopische Untersuchungen zur Innervation der glatten Muskulatur. Acta Neuroveget. Vienna., 22:192–211, 1961.

446. GANSLER, H.: Struktur und Funktion der glatten Muskulatur II. Licht-und elektronenmikroskopische Befunde an Hohlorganen von Ratte, Meerschweinchen und Mensch. Z. Zellforsch., 55:724–762, 1961.

447. GANSLER, H. and ROUILLER, C.: Modifications physiologiques et pathologiques du chondriome. Schweiz. Z. Path. Bakt., 19:217–243, 1956.

449. GARRON, L. K. and FEENEY, M. L.: Electron microscopic studies of the human eye. II. Study of the trabeculae by light and electron microscopy. Arch. Ophthal., 62:966–973, 1959.

450. GARRON, L. K., FEENEY, M. L., HOGAN, M., and McEWEN, W.: Electron microscopic studies of the human eye: I. Preliminary investigations of the trabeculas. Am. J. Ophthal., 40:27–35, 1958.

451. GASSER, H. S.: Olfactory nerve fibers. J. Gen. Physiol., 39:473–496, 1956.

452. GASSER, H. S.: Comparison of the structure as revealed with the electron microscope and the physiology of the unmyelinated fibers in the skin nerves and in the olfactory nerves. Exp. Cell Res., Suppl., 5:3–17, 1958.

453. GATENBY, J. B.: Light and electron microscopy of the Golgi apparatus. Dalton-Felix granules and cortical substances. La Cellule, 57:243–268, 1955.

454. GATENBY, J. B.: The Golgi apparatus. J. Roy. Microscop. Soc., 74:134–161, 1955.

455. GAUTIER, A. and BERNHARD, W.: Étude au microscope électronique du rein de rat normal. Les tubes contournés et la bordure en brosse. Compt. rend. soc. biol., 144:1479–1482, 1950.

456. GAUTIER, A. and DIOMEDE-FRESA, V.: Étude au microscope électronique de l'ergastoplasme des glandes salivaires du rat. Mikroskopie, 8:23–31, 1953.

457. GAY, H.: Nucleo-cytoplasmic relations in salivary gland cells of Drosophila. Proc. Natl. Acad. Sci., U.S., 41:370–375, 1955.

458. GAY, H.: Chromosome-nuclear membrane-cytoplasmic interrelations in Drosophila. J. Biophys. Biochem. Cytol., 2:407–414, 1956, Suppl.

459. GELBER, D., MOORE, D. H., and RUSKA, H.: Observations of the myo-tendon junction in mammalian skeletal muscle. Z. Zellforsch., 52:396–400, 1960.

460. GEREN, B. B.: The formation from the Schwann cell surface of myelin in the peripheral nerves of chick embryos. Exp. Cell Res., 7:558–562, 1954.

461. GEREN, B. B.: Structural studies of the formation of the myelin sheath in peripheral nerve fibers. In: Symposium on Cellular Mechanisms in Differentiation and Growth, pp. 213–220. Ed.: D. Rudnick. Princeton University Press, Princeton, 1956.

462. GEREN, B. B. and SCHMITT, F. O.: Electron microscope studies of the Schwann cell and its constituents with particular reference to their relation to the axon. In:

Symposium on the Fine Structure of Cells. 8th Congress of Cell Biology, Leiden, Holland, 1954, pp. 251–260. Noordhoff, Groningen, 1955.

463. GEREN, B. B. and SCHMITT, F. O.: The structure of the Schwann cell and its relation to the axon in certain invertebrate nerve fibers. Proc. Natl. Acad. Sci., U.S., 40: 863–870, 1954.

464. GHOSH, A., BERN, H. A., GHOSH, I., and NISHIOKA, R. S.: Nature of the inclusions in the lumbosacral neurons of birds. Anat. Rec., 143:195–217, 1962.

465. GIBBONS, I. R. and BRADFIELD, J. R. G.: The fixation of cell nuclei by osmium tetroxide. Biochim. Biophys. Acta, 22:506–513, 1956.

466. GIESEKING, R.: Elektronenmikroskopische Beobachtungen an Mitochondrien aus Leberzellen. Mikroskopie, 9:186–191, 1954.

467. GIESEKING, R.: Elektronenoptische Beobachtungen im Alveolarbereich der Lunge. Beitr. pathol. Anat. allgem. Pathol., 116:177–199, 1956.

468. GIESEKING, R.: Aufnahme und Ablagerung von Fremdstoffen in der Lunge nach elektronenoptischen Untersuchungen. Ergeb. Pathol., 38:92–126, 1958.

469. GIESEKING, R.: Elektronenoptische Beobachtung der Stoffaufnahme in die Alveolarwand. Verhandl. deut. Ges. Pathol., 41:336–340, 1958.

470. GILEV, V. P.: A study of myofibril sarcomere structure during contraction. J. Cell Biol., 12:135–147, 1962.

471. GLIMSTEDT, G. and WOHLFART, G.: Electron microscopic studies on peripheral nerve regeneration. Lunds Univ. Årsskr. N.F. Avd. 2, 56:1–22, 1960.

472. GLOOR, F.: Über die Ultrastruktur der Pankreaskapillaren (Elektronenmikroskopische Untersuchungen am exokrinen Pankreas der weissen Maus). Acta Anat., 35:63–84, 1958.

473. GODMAN, G. C. and PORTER, K. R.: Chondrogenesis, studied with the electron microscope. J. Biophys. Biochem. Cytol., 8:719–760, 1960.

474. GOLDEN, S. L.: Mucous membrane of the small intestine as examined with aid of an electron microscope (in Russian). Doklady Akad. Nauk. U.S.S.R., 106:721–724, 1956.

475. GOLDFISCHER, S., ARIAS, I. M., ESSNER, E., and NOVIKOFF, A. B.: Cytochemical and electron microscopic studies of rat liver with reduced capacity to transport conjugated bilirubin. J. Exp. Med., 115:467–474, 1962.

476. GOLDSTEIN, D. J.: Some histochemical observations of human striated muscle. Anat. Rec., 134:217–237, 1959.

477. GONZALES, F. and KARNOVSKY, M. J.: Electron microscopy of osteoclasts in healing fractures of rat bone: J. Biophys. Biochem. Cytol., 9:299–316, 1961.

478. GOOD, C. H.: Ultrastructure of the cerebellar cortex, with special reference to the synapse. Anat. Rec., 139:231–232, 1961. (Abstract).

479. GRANBOULAN, N.: Étude au microscope électronique des cellules de la lignée lymphocytaire normale. Rev. Hématol., 15:52–71, 1960.

480. GRANGER, B. and BAKER, R. F.: Electron microscopic investigation of the striated border of intestinal epithelium. Anat. Rec., 107:423–441, 1950.

481. GRASSÉ, P.-P.: Ultrastructure, polarité et reproduction de l'appareil de Golgi. Compt. rend. acad. sci., 245:1278–1281, 1957.

482. GRASSÉ, P., CARASSO, N., and FAVARD, P.: Les dictoyosomes (appareil de Golgi) et leur ultra-structure. Compt. rend. acad. sci., 241:1243–1245, 1955.

483. GRAY, E. G.: Electron microscopy of neuroglial fibrils of the cerebral cortex. J. Biophys. Biochem. Cytol., 6:121–122, 1959.

484. GRAY, E. G.: Axo-somatic and axo-dendritic synapses of the cerebral cortex: an electron microscope study. J. Anat., 93:420–433, 1959.

485. GRAY, E. G.: Electron microscopy of synaptic contacts on dendrite spines of the cerebral cortex. Nature, 183:1592–1593, 1959.

486. GRAY, E. G.: Regular organization of material in certain mitochondria of neuroglia of lizard brain. J. Biophys. Biochem. Cytol., 8:282–285, 1960.

487. GRAY, E. G.: Ultrastructure of synapses of the cerebral cortex and of certain specialisations of neuroglial membranes. In: Electron Microscopy in Anatomy, pp. 54–73. Eds.: J. D. Boyd, F. R. Johnson, and J. D. Lever. Williams and Wilkins, Baltimore, 1961.

488. GRAY, M., BLANK, H., and RAKE, G.: Electron microscopy of normal human skin. J. Invest. Dermatol., 19:449–457, 1952.

489. GREEN, D. E.: Mitochondrial structure and function. In: Subcellular Particles, pp. 84–103. Ed.: T. Hayashi. New York, Ronald Press, 1959.

490. GRIMLEY, P.: Cardiac desmosomes of the toad. J. Appl. Phys., 31:1833, 1960. (Abstract).

491. GRIMLEY, P. M. and EDWARDS, G. A.: The ultrastructure of cardiac desmosomes in the toad and their relationship to the intercalated disc. J. Biophys. Biochem. Cytol., 8:305–318, 1960.

492. GRONIOWSKI, J. und DJACZENKO, W.: Die Feinstruktur des Lungengewebes nach dem Beginn der Atmung. Z. Zellforsch., 53:639–644, 1961.

493. DE GROODT, M., LAGASSE, A., and SEBRUYNS, M.: Subendothelial space between the ovarian interstitial cell and the endothelial lining of the blood sinusoids. Nature, 180:1431–1432, 1957.

494. DE GROODT, M., LAGASSE, A., and SEBRUYNS, M.: Fine structure of the alveolar wall of the lung. Nature, 181:1066–1067, 1958.

495. GROSS, J.: Collagen. Sci. American, 204:120–130, 1961.

496. GROSS, J. and SCHMITT, F. O.: The structure of human skin collagen as studied with the electron microscope. J. Exp. Med., 88:555–568, 1947.

497. GRUNBAUM, B. W. and WELLINGS, S. R.: Electron microscopy of cytoplasmic structures

in frozen-dried mouse pancreas. J. Ultrastructure Res., 4:73–80, 1960.

498. GRUNER, J.-E.: La structure fine du fuseau neuromusculaire humain. Rev. Neurol., 104:490–507, 1961.

499. GUSEK, W.: Zur ultramikroskopischen Cytologie der Belegzellen in der Magenschleimhaut des Menschen. Z. Zellforsch., 55:790–809, 1961.

500. GUSEK, W.: Elektronenoptische Untersuchungen über die Ultrastruktur von Mastzellen. Arch. klin. exp. Dermatol., 213:573–581, 1961.

501. HACKENSELLNER, H. A. and DAVID, H.: Vergleichende elektronenmikroskopische Untersuchungen am Endothel grosser Gefässe. Frankfurt. Z. Pathol., 71:194–202, 1961.

502. HAGER, H.: Elektronenmikroskopische Untersuchungen über die Feinstruktur der Blutgefässe und perivasculären Räume im Säugetiergehirn. Acta Neuropathol. Berlin., 1:9–33, 1961.

503. HAGER, H., HIRSCHBERGER, W., and SCHOLZ, W.: Electron microscopic changes in brain tissue of Syrian hamsters following acute hypoxia. Aerospace Med., 31:379–387, 1960.

504. HAGUENAU, F.: L'appareil de Golgi vu au microscope électronique. Bull. microscop. appl., 5:18–20, 1955.

505. HAGUENAU, F.: The ergastoplasm; its history, ultrastructure and biochemistry. Int. Rev. Cytol., 7:425–483, 1958.

506. HAGUENAU, F.: Les myofilaments de la cellule myoepthéliale. Étude au microscope électronique. Compt. rend. acad. sci., 249:182–184, 1959.

507. HAGUENAU, F. and BERNHARD, W.: Aspect de la substance de Nissl au microscope électronique. Exp. Cell Res., 4:496–498, 1953.

508. HAGUENAU, F. and BERNHARD, W.: L'appareil de Golgi dans les cellules normales et cancéreuses de vertébrés. Rappel historique et étude au microscope électronique. Arch. anat. micr., 44:27–55, 1955.

509. HAGUENAU, F. and BERNHARD, W.: Particularités structurales de la membrane nucleaire. Étude au microscope électronique de cellules normales et cancéreuses. Bull. assoc. franç. étude cancer, 42:537–544, 1955.

510. HALL, B. V.: Studies of the normal glomerular structure by electron microscopy. Proc. Ann. Conf. Nephrotic Syndrome, 5th Conf., pp. 1–39, 1953.

511. HALL, B. V: Further studies of the normal structure of the renal glomerulus. Proc. Ann. Conf. Nephrotic Syndrome, 6th Conf., 1–39, 1954.

512. HALL, B. V.: The protoplasmic basis of glomerular ultrafiltration. Am. Heart J., 54:1–9, 1957.

513. HALL, B. V. and ROTH, L. E.: Preliminary studies on the development and differentiation of cells and structures of the renal corpuscle. In: Stockholm Conf. Electron

Micros. 1956. Proceed. pp. 176–179. Academic Press, New York, 1957.

514. HALL, C. E.: Introduction to Electron Microscopy. McGraw-Hill, New York, 1953.

515. HALL, D. A., REED, R., and TURNBRIDGE, R. E.: Electron microscope studies of elastic tissue. Exp. Cell Res., 8:35–48, 1955.

516. HALLY, A. D.: The fine structure of the Paneth cell. J. Anat., 92:268–277, 1958.

517. HALLY, A. D.: The fine structure of the gastric parietal cell in the mouse. J. Anat., 93:217–225, 1959.

518. HALLY, A. D.: Functional changes in the vacuole-containing bodies of the gastric parietal cell. Nature, 183:408, 1959.

519. HALLY, A. D.: Electron microscopy of the unusual Golgi apparatus within the gastric parietal cell. J. Anat., 94:425–431, 1960.

520. HALLY, A. D.: The secretory changes produced by pilocarpine in the gastric parietal cell of the mouse. In: Electron Microscopy in Anatomy, pp. 225–234. Eds.: J. D. Boyd, F. R. Johnson, and J. D. Lever. Williams and Wilkins, Baltimore, 1961.

521. HAMA, K.: The fine structure of the desmosomes in frog mesothelium. J. Biophys. Biochem. Cytol., 7:575–576, 1960.

522. HAMA, K.: The fine structure of some blood vessels of the earthworm, Eisenia foetida. J. Biophys. Biochem. Cytol., 7:717–724, 1960.

523. HAMA, K.: On the existence of filamentous structures in endothelial cell of the amphibian capillary. Anat. Rec., 139:437–441, 1961.

524. HAMPTON, J.: An electron microscope study of the hepatic uptake and excretion of submicroscopic particles injected into the blood stream and into the bile duct. Acta Anat., 32:262–291, 1958.

525. HAMPTON, J. C.: An electron microscope study of the source and distribution of ferritin in hepatic parenchymal cells of the newborn rabbit. Blood, 15:480–490, 1960.

526. HAMPTON, J. C.: Electron microscopic study of extrahepatic biliary obstruction in the mouse. Lab. Invest., 10:502–513, 1961.

527. HAMPTON, J. C.: An electron microscopic study of the reaction of intestinal epithelial cells to corn oil, sucrose and casein administered by gavage. Anat. Rec., 139:306, 1961. (Abstract.)

528. HAMPTON, J. C. and QUASTLER, H.: Combined autoradiography and electron microscopy of thin sections of intestinal epithelial cells of the mouse labeled with H³-thymidine. J. Biophys. Biochem. Cytol., 10:140–144, 1961.

529. HAN, S. S.: The ultrastructure of lymph nodes. Anat. Rec., 136:206, 1960. (Abstract.)

530. HAN, S. S.: The ultrastructure of reticular connective tissue cells and plasma cells in the rat lymph node. Anat. Rec., 139:235, 1961. (Abstract.)

531. HAN, S. S.: The ultrastructure of the mesenteric lymph node of the rat. Am. J. Anat., 109:183–225, 1961.

532. HANCOX, N. M. and BOOTHROYD, B.: Motion

picture and electron microscope studies on the embryonic avian osteoclast. J. Biophys. Biochem. Cytol., 11:651–661, 1961.

533. HANSON, J. and HUXLEY, H. E.: The structural basis of contraction in skeletal muscle. Symp. Soc. Exp. Biol., 9:228–264, 1955.

534. HANSON, J. and LOWY, J.: Structure of smooth muscles. Nature, 180:906–909, 1957.

535. HANSON, J. and LOWY, J.: The structure of the muscle fibres in the translucent part of the adductor of the oyster *Crassostrea angulata*. Proc. Roy. Soc. London, 154 B: 173–196, 1961.

536. HARMAN, J. N., O'HEGARTY, M. T., and BYRNES, C. K.: The ultrastructure of human smooth muscle. Exp. Molecular Pathol., 1:204–228, 1962.

537. HARTMAN, R. E., SMITH, R. B. W., HARTMAN, R. S., BUTTERWORTH, C. E., JR., and MOLESWORTH, J. M.: The electron microscopy of human intestinal epithelium obtained with the Crosby intestinal biopsy capsule. J. Biophys. Biochem. Cytol., 5:171–172, 1959.

538. HARTMAN, R. S., BUTTERWORTH, C. E., JR., HARTMAN, R. E., CROSBY, W. H., and SHIRAI, A.: An electron microscopic investigation of the jejunal epithelium in sprue. Gastroenterology, 38:506–516, 1960.

539. HARTMAN, R. S., HARTMAN, R. E., and CONRAD, M. E., JR.: Ferritin in the human intestinal epithelium. J. Appl. Phys., 31: 1841, 1960. (Abstract.)

540. HARTMANN, J. F.: An electron optical study of sections of central nervous system. J. Comp. Neurol., 99:201–247, 1953.

541. HARTMANN, J. F.: Electron microscopy of motor cells following section of axons. Anat. Rec., 118:19–34, 1954.

542. HARTMANN, J. F.: Electron microscopy of mitochondria in the central nervous system. J. Biophys. Biochem. Cytol., 2:375–378, 1956, Suppl.

543. HARTROFT, P. M. and NEWMARK, L. N.: Electron microscopy of renal juxtaglomerular cells. Anat. Rec., 139:185–199, 1961.

544. DE HARVEN, E.: Un constituant du cytoplasme révélé par la microscopie électronique: le réticulum endoplasmique. Ann. soc. roy. sci. méd. et nat. Bruxelles, 12:5–14, 1959.

545. DE HARVEN, E. and BERNHARD, W.: Étude au microscope électronique de l'ultrastructure du centriole chez les vertébrés. Z. Zellforsch., 45:375–398, 1956.

546. DE HARVEN, E. and COËRS, C.: Electron microscope study of the human neuromuscular junction. J. Biophys. Biochem. Cytol., 6:7–10, 1959.

547. DE HARVEN, E. and COËRS, C.: Electron microscopic observations on human neuromuscular junctions. In: Electron Microscopy in Anatomy, pp. 261–266. Eds.: J. D. Boyd, F. R. Johnson, and J. D. Lever. Williams and Wilkins, Baltimore, 1961.

548. HASHIMOTO, M., KOMORI, A., KOSAKA, M., MORI, Y., SHIMOYAMA, T., and AKASHI, K.: Electron microscopic studies on the smooth muscle of the human uterus. J. Japan. Obstet. Gynecol., 7:115–121, 1960.

549. HASHIMOTO, M., KOSAKA, M., MORI, Y., KOMORI, A., and AKASHI, K.: Electron microscopic studies on the epithelium of the chorionic villi of the human placenta (Report I). J. Japan. Obstet. Gynecol., 7:44–52, 1960.

550. HASHIMOTO, M., KOSAKA, M., SHIMOYAMA, T., HIRASAWA, T., KOMORI, A., KAWASAKI, T., and AKASHI, K.: Electron microscopic studies of the epithelium of the chorionic villi of the human placenta (Report II). J. Japan. Obstet. Gynecol., 7:122–129, 1960.

551. HASHIMOTO, M., SHIMOYAMA, T., MORI, Y., KOMORI, A., KOSAKA, M., and AKASHI, K.: Electron microscopic observations on the secretory process in the fallopian tube of the rabbit (Report II). J. Japan. Obstet. Gynecol., 6:384–391, 1959.

552. HASHIMOTO, M., SHIMOYAMA, T., MORI, Y., KOMORI, A., TOMITA, H., and AKASHI, K.: Electron microscopic observations on the secretory process in the fallopian tube of the rabbit (Report I). J. Japan. Obstet. Gynecol., 6:235–243, 1959.

553. HATT, P.-Y.: Activité sécrétoire de la paroi des artérioles rénales. Démonstration cytologique au cours de l'ischémie rénale expérimentale. Compt. rend. acad. sci., 252: 1851–1853, 1961.

554. HATT, P.-Y. and ROUILLER, C.: Les ultrastructures pulmonaires et le régime de la petit circulation. I. Au cours du rétrécissement mitral serré. Semaine hôp. Paris, Pathol. et Biol., 6:1371–1397, 1958.

555. HAUBRICH, W. S., WATSON, J. H. L., O'DRISCOLL, W., and VALENTINE, V.: Electron microscopy of the free border of the human intestinal epithelial cell. Henry Ford Hospital Med. Bull., 7:113–122, 1959.

556. HAY, E. D.: Fine structure of an unusual intracellular supporting network in the Leydig cells of amblystoma epidermis. J. Biophys. Biochem. Cytol., 10:457–463, 1961.

557. HAYASHI, T. (ed.): Subcellular Particles. A symposium held during the meeting of the Society of General Physiologists at the Marine Biological Laboratory, Woods Hole, Massachusetts, 1958. Ronald Press, New York, 1959.

558. HAYEK, H., BRAUNSTEINER, H., and PAKESCH, F.: Über die Veränderlichkeit der Microvilli der Alveolar-epithelien bei Temperaturveränderungen. Wien. Z. inn. Med. Grenzg., 38:165–169, 1957.

559. HAYWARD, A. F.: Electron microscopic observations on absorption in the epithelium of the guinea pig gall bladder. Z. Zellforsch. 56:197–202, 1962.

560. HELANDER, H. F.: A preliminary note of the ultrastructure of the argyrophile cells of the mouse gastric mucosa. J. Ultrastructure Res., 5:257–262, 1961.

561. HELANDER, H. F.: Ultrastructure of fundus glands in the mouse gastric mucosa. J. Ultrastructure Res., Suppl., 4:1–123, 1962.

562. HELANDER, H. and EKHOLM, R.: Ultrastructure of epithelial cells in the fundus glands of the mouse gastric mucosa. J. Ultrastructure Res., 3:74–83, 1959.

563. HELANDER, H.: The ultrastructural organization of the fundus glands in the mouse gastric mucosa. In: European Regional Conf. Electron Micros., Delft 1960, Proceed. Vol. II, pp. 849–852. De Nederlandse Vereniging voor Electronenmicroscopie, Delft, 1961.

564. HELLSTRÖM, B.: "Harmonic precision"—a new concept in ultramicrotomy. Sci. Tools, 5:33–43, 1958.

565. HELLSTRÖM, K. E. and NILSSON, O.: In vitro investigation of the ciliated and secretory cells in the rabbit fallopian tube. Exp. Cell Res., 12:180–181, 1957.

566. HERMAN, L.: An electron microscope study of the salamander thyroid during hormonal stimulation. J. Biophys. Biochem. Cytol., 7:143–150, 1960.

567. HERMAN, L. and FITZGERALD, P. J.: The degenerative changes in pancreatic acinar cells caused by DL-ethionine. J. Cell Biol., 12:277–296, 1962.

568. HERMAN, L. and FITZGERALD, P. J.: Restitution of pancreatic acinar cells following ethionine. J. Cell Biol., 12:297–312, 1962.

569. HERMAN, L., FITZGERALD, P. J., WEISS, M., and POLEVOY, I. S.: Electron microscope observations of degenerating and regenerating pancreas following ethionine administration. In: Fourth Internat. Conf. Electron Micros., Berlin 1958, Vol. II, pp. 372–378. Springer Verlag, Berlin, 1960.

570. HERMAN, L., STUCKEY, J. W., and HOFFMAN, B. F.: Electron microscopy of Purkinje fibers and ventricular muscle of dog heart. Circulation, 24:954, 1961. (Abstract.)

571. HERMODSSON, L. H.: Electron microscopy of the exocrine pancreas cells from the cat. In: European Regional Conf. Electron Microsc., Delft 1960. Proceed. Vol. II, pp. 853–856. De Nederlandse Vereniging voor Electronenmicroscopie, Delft, 1961.

572. VON HERRATH, E.: Bau und Funktion der normalen Milz. Walter De Gruyter, Berlin, 1958.

573. HESS, A.: The fine structure of young and old spinal ganglia. Anat. Rec., 123:399–423, 1955.

574. HESS, A.: The fine structure and morphological organization of non-myelinated nerve fibers. Proc. Roy. Soc., 144:496–506, 1956.

575. HESS, A.: Further histochemical studies on the presence and nature of the ground substance of the central nervous system. J. Anat., 92:298–303, 1958.

575a. HESS, A.: The fine structure of nerve cells and fibers, neuroglia, and sheaths of the ganglion chain in the cockroach (Periplaneta americana). J. Biophys. Biochem. Cytol., 4:731–742, 1958.

576. HESS, A. and LANSING, A. I.: The fine structure of peripheral nerve fibers. Anat. Rec., 117:175–200, 1953.

577. HIBBS, R. G.: Electron microscopy of developing cardiac muscle in chick embryos. Am. J. Anat., 99:17–52, 1956.

578. HIBBS, R. G., BURCH, G. E., and PHILLIPS, J. H.: The fine structure of the small blood vessels of normal human dermis and subcutis. Am. Heart J., 56:662–670, 1958.

579. HIBBS, R. G., BURCH, G. E., and PHILLIPS, J. H.: Electron-microscopic observations on the human mast cell. Am. Heart J., 60:121–127, 1960.

580. HIBBS, R. G. and CLARK, W. H.: Electron microscope studies of the human epidermis: the cell boundaries and topography of the stratum malpighii. J. Biophys. Biochem. Cytol., 6:71–76, 1959.

581. HIFT, H., YOUNG, W. P., GOTT, V. L., and CRUMPTON, C. W.: Electron microscope studies of human and dog heart biopsies. Circulation, 24:955, 1961. (Abstract.)

582. HILD, W.: Das Neuron. In: Handbuch der mikroskopischen Anatomie des Menschen, Vol. 4/1, pp. 1–184. Eds.: W. Möllendorf and W. Bargmann. Springer Verlag, Berlin, 1959.

583. HILL, J. M., SMITH, A., and FIORELLO, O.: Electron microscopy of "foam cells" in the spleen. J. Appl. Phys., 32:1643, 1961. (Abstract.)

584. HIMES, M. and POLLISTER, A. W.: An electron microscopic study of intranuclear glycogen inclusions in tadpole livers. Anat. Rec., 132:453–454, 1958.

585. HIRSCH, G. C.: Der Arbeitszyklus im Pankreas und die Entstehung der Eiweisse. Versuch eines synthetischen Bildes nach der Elektronen-Mikroskopie und Biochemie. Naturwissenschaften, 45:349–358, 1958.

586. HO, S.: The endoplasmic reticulum of gastric parietal cells. J. Biophys. Biochem. Cytol., 11:333–347, 1961.

587. HODGE, A. J.: Studies on the structure of muscle. III. Phase contrast and electron microscopy of dipteran flight muscle. J. Biophys. Biochem. Cytol., 1:361–380, 1955.

588. HODGE, A. J.: The fine structure of striated muscle. A comparison of insect flight muscle with vertebrate and invertebrate skeletal muscle. J. Biophys. Biochem. Cytol., 2:131–142, 1956, Suppl.

589. HODGE, A. J., HUXLEY, H. E., and SPIRO, D.: Electron microscope studies on ultrathin sections of muscle. J. Exp. Med., 99:201–206, 1954.

590. HOFFMAN, H. J. and GRIGG, G. W.: An electron microscopic study of mitochondria formation. Exp. Cell Res., 15:118–131, 1958.

591. HOLLMANN, K. H.: L'ultrastructure de la glande mammaire normale de la sourie en lactation. J. Ultrastructure Res., 2:423–443, 1959.

592. HOLLMANN, K. H.: La cytologie de la glande mammaire au microscope électronique. Bull. Soc. Roy. Belge Gynec. Obstet. 30:353–358, 1960.

593. HOLMBERG, Å.: Studies of the ultrastructure of the non-pigmented epithelium in the ciliary body. Acta Ophthal., 33:377–381, 1955.

594. HOLMBERG, Å.: Ultrastructural changes in the ciliary epithelium following inhibition of secretion of aqueous humour in the rabbit eye. Thesis. Karolinska Institutet, Stockholm, 1957, pp. 1–77.

595. HOLMBERG, Å.: Ultrastructure of the ciliary epithelium. Arch. Ophthal., 62:935–948, 1959.

596. HOLMBERG, Å.: The ultrastructure of the capillaries in the ciliary body. Arch. Ophthal., 62:949–951, 1959.

597. HOLMBERG, Å.: Differences in ultrastructure of normal human and rabbit ciliary epithelium. Arch. Ophthal., 62:952–955, 1959.

598. HOLMBERG, Å.: Some characteristic components of the ciliary epithelium. Am. J. Ophthal., 48:426–428, 1959.

599. HOLMBERG, Å.: The fine structure of the inner wall of Schlemm's canal. Arch. Ophthal., 62:956–958, 1959.

600. HOLMBERG, Å. and BECKER, B.: The effect of hypothermia on aqueous humor dynamics. II. Ultrastructural changes in the rabbit ciliary epithelium. Am. J. Ophthal., 49:1134–1140, 1960.

601. HOLT, S. J. and HICKS M.: Studies on formalin fixation for electron microscopy and cytochemical staining purposes. J. Biophys. Biochem. Cytol., 11:37–45, 1961.

602. HOLT, S. J. and HICKS, R. M.: The localization of acid phosphatase in rat liver as revealed by combined cytochemical staining and electron microscopy. J. Biophys. Biochem. Cytol., 11:47–66, 1961.

603. HOLTER, H.: How things get into cells. Sci. American, 205:167–180, 1961.

604. HONJIN, R.: Ultrastructure of the Golgi apparatus of the nerve cells. Fol. Anat. Japon., 29:117–131, 1956.

605. HORSTMANN, E.: Zur Frage der Struktur markhaltiger zentraler Nervenfasern. Z. Zellforsch., 45:18–30, 1956.

606. HORSTMANN, E.: Zur Elektronenmikroskopie der Epidermis. In: Handbuch der mikroskopischen Anatomie des Menschen. Vol. 3, pp. 486–488. Eds.: W. Möllendorf and W. Bargmann. Springer Verlag, Berlin, 1957.

607. HORSTMANN, E.: Zur Elektronenmikroskopie des Nucleolus und Karyoplasmas. Verhandl. deut. Ges. Pathol., 41:361–364, 1958.

608. HORSTMANN, E.: Die elektronenmikroskopische Struktur der Haut. Arch. klin. exp. Dermatol., 211:18–35, 1960.

609. HORSTMANN, E.: Elektronenmikroskopische Untersuchungen zur Spermiohistogenese beim Menschen. Z. Zellforsch., 54:68–89, 1961.

610. HORSTMANN, E.: Elektronenmikroskopie des menschlichen Nebenhodenepithels. Z. Zellforsch., 57:692–718, 1962.

611. HORSTMANN, E. and KNOOP, A.: Zur Struktur des Nukleolus und des Kernes. Z. Zellforsch., 46:100–107, 1957.

612. HORSTMANN, E. and KNOOP, A.: Elektronmikroskopische Studien an der Epidermis. I. Rattenpfote. Z. Zellforsch., 47:348–362, 1958.

613. HOWATSON, A. F.: The structure of pigeon breast muscle mitochondria. J. Biophys. Biochem. Cytol., 2:363–368, 1956. Suppl.

614. HUDSON, G. and HARTMANN, J. F.: The relationship between dense bodies and mitochondria in motor neurons. Z. Zellforsch., 54:147–157, 1961.

615. HUECK, H. and KLEIFELD, O.: Ein elektronmikroskopischer Beitrag zur Feinstruktur der Linsenfaser. Arch. Ophthalmol. Graefe's., 160:20–25, 1958.

616. HUHN, D., STEINER, J. W., und MOVAT, H. Z.: Die Feinstruktur des Mesangiums im Nierenglomerulum von Hund und Maus. Z. Zellforsch., 56:213–230, 1962.

617. HUTTER, R. V. P.: Electron microscopic observations on platelets from human blood. Am. J. Clin. Pathol., 28:447–460, 1957.

618. HUXLEY, H. E.: Electron microscope studies of the organization of the filaments in striated muscle. Biochim. Biophys. Acta, 12:387–394, 1953.

619. HUXLEY, H. E.: Muscular contraction. Endeavour, 15:177–188, 1956.

620. HUXLEY, H. E.: The double array of filaments in cross-striated muscle. J. Biophys. Biochem. Cytol., 3:631–648, 1957.

621. HUXLEY, H. E.: The structure of striated muscle. In: Molecular Biology, pp. 1–16. Ed.: D. Nachmansohn. Academic Press, New York, 1960.

622. HUXLEY, H. and HANSON, J.: Changes in the cross-striations of muscle during contraction and stretch in their structural interpretation. Nature, 173:971–986, 1954.

623. IRIE, M.: Electron microscopic observation on the various mammalian thyroid glands (in Japanese). Arch. Histol. Japon., 19:39–74, 1960.

624. ITAGI, K.: Electron microscopic observations of pulmonary alveolar structures. Acta Tuberc. Japon., 122:35–52, 1955.

625. ITAGI, K.: Electron microscopic observation of pulmonary alveolar structures of laboratory mammals. Acta Tuberc. Japon., 6:75–90, 1956.

626. ITAGI, K.: On the epithelial covering tissue of the alveolar walls of human lung. Acta Tuberc. Japon., 6:91–98, 1956.

627. ITO, S.: The endoplasmic reticulum of gastric parietal cells. J. Biophys. Biochem. Cytol., 11:333–347, 1961.

628. IURATO, S.: Structure submicroscopique des cellules ciliées de l'organe de Corti. J. franç. otorhinolaryng., 9:67–75, 1960.

629. IURATO, S.: Submicroscopic structure of the membranous labyrinth. I. The tectorial membrane. Z. Zellforsch., 52:105–128, 1960.

630. IURATO, S.: Submicroscopic structure of the membranous labyrinth. 2. The epithelium of Corti's organ. Z. Zellforsch., 53:259–298, 1961.

631. IURATO, S.: Submicroscopic structure of the membranous labyrinth. III. The supporting structure of Corti's organ (basilar membrane, limbus spiralis and spiral ligament). Z. Zellforsch., 56:40–96, 1962.

632. IURATO, S. and DE PETRIS, S.: Submicroscopic structure and nature of the limbus spiralis, the basilar membrane and the spiral ligament. In: European Regional Conf. Electron Micros., Delft 1960, Proceed. Vol. II, pp. 814–817. De Nederlandse Vereniging voor Electronenmicroscopie, Delft, 1961.

633. IZQUIERDO, L. and VIAL, J. D.: Electron microscope observations on the early develop-

ment of the rat. Z. Zellforsch., 56:157–179, 1962.

634. JAKUS, M. A.: The fine structure of the cornea. Acta Conc. Ophthal., 17:461–464, 1954.

635. JAKUS, M. A.: Studies on the cornea. I. The fine structure of the rat cornea. Am. J. Ophthal., 38:40–53, 1954.

636. JAKUS, M. A.: Studies on the cornea. II. The fine structure of Descemet's membrane. J. Biophys. Biochem. Cytol., 2:243–252, 1956, Suppl.

637. JAKUS, M. A.: Comparative fine structure of the corneal stroma. J. Appl. Phys., 28:1371, 1957. (Abstract.)

638. JAKUS, M. A.: The fine structure of certain ocular tissues. In: Fourth Internat. Conf. Electron Micros., Berlin 1958. Proceed. Vol. II, pp. 344–347. Springer Verlag, Berlin, 1960.

639. JAKUS, M. A.: The fine structure of the human cornea. In: The Structure of the Eye, pp. 343–380. Ed.: G. K. Smelser. Academic Press, New York, 1961.

640. JAKUS, M. A.: Further observations on the fine structure of the cornea. Invest. Ophthal., 1:202–225, 1962.

641. JAMES, J. A. and ASHWORTH, C. T.: Some features of glomerular filtration and permeability revealed by electron microscopy after intraperitoneal injection of dextran in rats. Am. J. Path., 38:515–525, 1961.

642. JOHANSEN, E. and PARKS, H. F.: Electron microscopic observations on the three-dimensional morphology of apatite crystallites of human dentine and bone. J. Biophys. Biochem. Cytol., 7:743–746, 1960.

643. JOHNSTON, H. S.: An investigation of small intestine cells using the electron microscope. J. Med. Lab. Technol., 13:445–456, 1956.

644. JONES, O. P.: Origin of megakaryocyte granules from Golgi vesicles. Anat. Rec., 138:105–114, 1960.

645. JUNG, F.: Zür Feinstruktur der roten Blutzelle. Folia Haematol., 73:401–404, 1956.

646. JUNG, F., RIND, H., and STOBBE, H.: Über Retikulocyten. Folia Haematol., 75:295–316, 1958.

647. JUNQUEIRA, L. C. and HIRSCH, G. C.: Cell secretion: a study of pancreas and salivary glands. Int. Rev. Cytol., 5:323–364, 1956.

648. KAJIKAWA, K.: Structure of collagen fibrils as revealed by electron microscopy. J. Electronmicroscopy Chiba, 10:1–6, 1961.

649. KAJIKAWA, K.: The fine structure of fibroblasts of mouse embryo skin. J. Electronmicroscopy Chiba, 10:131–144, 1961.

650. KANWAR, K. C.: What constitutes "apparato reticolare interno" of Golgi in the goblet cells of vertebrate intestine? Experientia, 17:228–229, 1961.

651. KARNOVSKY, M. J.: Simple methods for "staining with lead" at high pH in electron microscopy. J. Biophys. Biochem. Cytol., 11:729–732, 1961.

652. KARRER, H. E.: The ultrastructure of mouse lung. General architecture of capillary and alveolar walls. J. Biophys. Biochem. Cytol., 2:241–252, 1956.

653. KARRER, H. E.: The ultrastructure of mouse lung. Fine structure of the capillary endothelium. Exp. Cell Res., 11:542–547, 1956.

654. KARRER, H. E.: An electron microscopic study of the fine structure of pulmonary capillaries and alveoli of the mouse. Bull. Johns Hopkins Hosp., 98:65–83, 1956.

655. KARRER, H. E.: The ultrastructure of mouse lung. A note on the fine structure of mitochondria and endoplasmic reticulum of the bronchiolar epithelium. J. Biophys. Biochem. Cytol., 2:115–118, 1956. Suppl.

656. KARRER, H. E.: The ultrastructure of mouse lung. Some remarks regarding the fine structure of the alveolar basement membrane. J. Biophys. Biochem. Cytol., 2:287–292, 1956. Suppl.

657. KARRER, H. E.: Electron microscopic study of bronchiolar epithelium of normal mouse lung. Preliminary report. Exp. Cell Res., 10:237–241, 1956.

658. KARRER, H. E.: Fine structure of the tunica propria in bronchioles of young adult mice. J. Appl. Phys., 28:1372, 1957. (Abstract.)

659. KARRER, H. E.: The alveolar macrophage. J. Appl. Phys., 29:1621, 1958. (Abstract.)

660. KARRER, H. E.: The fine structure of connective tissue in the tunica propria of bronchioles. J. Ultrastructure Res., 2:96–121, 1958.

661. KARRER, H. E.: The ultrastructure of mouse lung. The alveolar macrophage. J. Biophys. Biochem. Cytol., 4:693–700, 1958.

662. KARRER, H. E.: The striated musculature of blood vessels. I. General cell morphology. J. Biophys. Biochem. Cytol., 6:383–392, 1959.

663. KARRER, H. E.: Cell interconnections in normal human cervical epithelium. J. Biophys. Biochem. Cytol., 7:181–184, 1960.

664. KARRER, H. E.: Electron microscopic study of the phagocytosis process in lung. J. Biophys. Biochem. Cytol., 7:357–366, 1960.

665. KARRER, H. E.: The striated musculature of blood vessels. II. Cell interconnections and cell surface. J. Biophys. Biochem. Cytol., 8:135–150, 1960.

666. KARRER, H. E.: Electron microscopic observations on developing chick embryo liver. The Golgi complex and its possible role in the formation of glycogen. J. Ultrastructure Res., 4:149–165, 1960.

667. KARRER, H. E.: Electron microscopic study of glycogen in chick embryo liver. J. Ultrastructure Res., 4:191–212, 1960.

668. KARRER, H. E.: Electron microscope study of developing chick embryo aorta. J. Ultrastructure Res., 4:420–454, 1960.

669. KARRER, H. E.: The alveolar macrophage. In: Fourth Internat. Conf. Electron Micros., Berlin 1958. Proceed. Vol. II. pp. 415–417. Springer Verlag, Berlin, 1960.

670. KARRER, H. E.: An electron microscope study of the aorta in young and in aging mice. J. Ultrastructure Res., 5:1–27, 1961.

671. KARRER, H. E.: Electron microscope observa-

tions on chick embryo liver. Glycogen, bile, canaliculi, inclusion bodies and hematopoiesis. J. Ultrastructure Res., 5:116–141, 1961.

672. KATZ B.: Mechanisms of synaptic transmission. Rev. Modern Phys., 31:524–531, 1959.

673. KAUTZ, J. and DE MARSH, Q. B.: Fine structure of the nuclear membrane in cells from the chick embryo: On the nature of the so-called "pores" in the nuclear membrane. Exp. Cell Res., 8:394–396, 1955.

674. KAWAGUTI, S. and IKEMOTO, N.: Electron microscopy on the smooth muscle of a cat's urinary bladder. Biol. J. Okayama Univ., 3:159–168, 1957.

675. KAWAGUTI, S. and KOBAYASHI, T.: Electron microscopic study of the cardiac myogenesis in a mammalian embryo. Biol. J. Okayama Univ., 6:53–60, 1960.

676. KAYE, G. I.: Studies on the cornea. III. The fine structure of the frog cornea and the uptake and transport of colloidal particles by the cornea in vivo. J. Cell Biol., 15:241–258, 1962.

677. KAYE, G. I. and PAPPAS, G. D.: Studies on the cornea. I. The fine structure of the rabbit cornea and the uptake and transport of colloidal particles by the cornea in vivo. J. Cell Biol., 12:457–479. 1962.

678. KAYE, G. I., PAPPAS, G. D., and DONN, A.: An electron microscope study of the rabbit corneal endothelium in relation to its uptake and transport of colloidal particles. Anat. Rec., 139:244–245, 1961. (Abstract.)

679. KAYE, G. I., PAPPAS, G. D., DONN, A., and MALLETT, N.: Studies on the cornea. II. The uptake and transport of colloidal particles by the living rabbit cornea in vitro. J. Cell Biol., 12:481–501, 1962.

680. KAYE, J. S.: Changes in the fine structure of mitochondria during spermatogenesis. J. Morph., 102:347–400, 1958.

681. KAYE, J. S.: Changes in the fine structure of nuclei during spermatogenesis. J. Morph., 103:311–330, 1958.

682. KEECH, M. K.: The effect of collagenase and trypsin on collagen. Anat. Rec., 119:139–159, 1954.

683. KEECH, M. K.: Electron microscope study of the normal rat aorta. J. Biophys. Biochem. Cytol., 7:533–538, 1960.

684. KEECH, M. K.: Electron microscope study of the lathyritic rat aorta. J. Biophys. Biochem. Cytol., 7:539–546, 1960.

685. KEMP, N. E.: Electron microscopy of growing oocytes of Rana pipiens. J. Biophys. Biochem. Cytol., 2:281–292, 1956.

686. KEMP, N. E.: Differentiation of the cortical cytoplasm and inclusions in oocytes of the frog. J. Biophys. Biochem. Cytol., 2:187–190, 1956. Suppl.

687. KERR, D. N. S. and MUIR, A. R.: A demonstration of the structure and disposition of ferritin in the human liver cell. J. Ultrastructure Res., 3:313–319, 1960.

688. KIKUTH, W., SCHLIPKÖTER, H. W., and SCHROETELER, P.: Vergleichende Unter-suchungen der Mitochondrien in Rattenlungen nach intratrachealer Injektion von Kieselsäure. In: Stockholm Conf. Electron Micros., 1956. Proceed. pp. 246–248. Academic Press, New York, 1957.

689. KIMURA, R. and WERSÄLL, J.: Termination of the olivo-cochlear bundle in relation to the outer hair cells of the organ of Corti in guinea pig. Acta Oto-Laryngol., 55:11–32, 1962.

690. KINGSLEY SMITH, B. V. and LACY, D.: Residual bodies of seminiferous tubules of the rat. Nature, 184:249–251, 1959.

691. KISCH, B.: Electron microscopic investigation of the lungs (capillaries and specific cells). Exp. Med. Surg., 13:101–117, 1955.

692. KISCH, B.: Studies in comparative electron microscopy of the heart. II. Guinea pig and rat. Exp. Med. Surg., 13:404–428, 1955.

693. KISCH, B.: The mechanism of axon reflexes. An electron microscopic consideration. Exp. Med. Surg., 15:221–227, 1958.

694. KISCH, B.: Electron microscopy of cardiac nerves. Am. J. Cardiol., 2:475–478, 1958.

695. KISSEN, A. T. and CRAIG, E. L.: Electron microscopy of human iris. J. Appl. Phys., 30:2040, 1959. (Abstract.)

696. KLUG, H.: Elektronenmikroskopische Untersuchungen Über die Wirkung von Röntgenstrahlen auf die Zellkernstrukturen der Milz. Radiobiol. Radiother., 2:301–314, 1961.

697. KNAPPEIS, G. G. and CARLSEN, F.: Electron microscopical study of skeletal muscle during isotonic (afterload) and isometric contraction. J. Biophys. Biochem. Cytol., 2:201–211, 1956.

698. KNAPPEIS, G. G. and CARLSEN, F.: The ultrastructure of the Z-disc in skeletal muscle. J. Cell Biol., 13:323–335, 1962.

699. KNESE, K. -H. and KNOOP, A. -M.: Elektronenoptische Untersuchungen über die periostale Osteogenese. Z. Zellforsch., 48:455–478, 1958.

700. KNESE, K. -H. and KNOOP, A. -M.: Über den Ort der Bildung des Mukopolysaccharid-proteinkomplexes in Knorpelgewebe. Elektronenmikroskopische und histochemische Untersuchungen. Z. Zellforsch., 53:201–258, 1961.

701. KNESE, K. -H. and KNOOP, A. -M.: Elektronenmikroskopische Beobachtungen über die Zellen in der Eröffnungszone des Epiphysenknorpels. Z. Zellforsch., 54:1–38, 1961.

702. KNESE, K. -H. and KNOOP, A. -M.: Chondrogenese und Osteogenese. Elektronenmikroskopische und lichtmikroskopische Untersuchungen. Z. Zellforsch., 55:413–468, 1961.

703. KNOOP, E., WORTMANN, A., and KNOOP, A. -M.: Der elektronenmikroskopische Nachweis der Fettkügelchenhüllen. Milchwissenschaft, 13:154–159, 1958.

704. KNOOP, E., WORTMANN, A., and KNOOP, A.-M.: Die Hüllen der Milchfettkügelchen im elektronenmikroskopischen Bild. Naturwissenschaften, 45:418, 1958.

Page 189

705. KOGA, H.: The fine structure of cytotrophoblast in mouse placenta studied with the electron microscope. J. Kurume Med. Assoc., 22:1669–1690, 1959.

706. KÖPPEL, G.: Elektronenmikroskopische Untersuchungen zur Funktionsmorphologie der Thrombocyten und zum Gerinnungsablauf im normalen menschlichen Nativblut. Z. Zellforsch., 47:401–439, 1958.

707. KRAHL, V. E.: The respiratory portions of the lung: An account of their finer structure. Bull. School Med. Univ. Maryland, 40:101–124, 1955.

708. KRAUSS, M. and VAN ANTWERP, W. R.: Connections between myofibrils as seen in electron micrographs of vertebrate striated muscle. Exp. Cell Res., 11:637–666, 1956.

709. KUBOTA, K., KUSHIDA, T., and OGATA, S.: Cytological studies on human testes. Anat. Rec., 136:226, 1960. (Abstract.)

709a. KUROSUMI, K.: Electron microscopic analysis of the secretion mechanism. Int. Rev. Cytol., 11:1–124, 1961.

710. KUROSUMI, K., SHIBASAKI, S., UCHIDA, G., and TANAKA, Y.: Electron microscopic studies on the gastric mucosa of normal rats. Arch. Histol. Japon., 15:587–624, 1958.

711. KUROSUMI, K., YAMAGISHI, M., and SEKINE, M.: Mitrochondrial deformation and apocrine secretory mechanism in the rabbit submandibular organ as revealed by electron microscopy. Z. Zellforsch., 55:297–312, 1961.

712. KURTZ, S. M.: The electron microscopy of the developing human renal glomerulus. Exp. Cell Res., 14:355–367, 1958.

713. KURTZ, S. M.: A new method for embedding tissues in Vestopal W. J. Ultrastructure Res., 5:468–469, 1961.

714. KURTZ, S. M.: The fine structure of the lamina densa. Lab. Invest., 10:1189–1208, 1961.

715. KURTZ, S. M. and FELDMAN, J. D.: Experimental studies on the formation of the glomerular basement membrane. J. Ultrastructure Res., 6:19–27, 1962.

716. KURTZ, S. M. and MCMANUS, J. F. A.: A reconsideration of the development, structure, and disease of the human renal glomerulus. Am. Heart J., 58:357–371, 1959.

717. KURTZ, S. M. and MCMANUS, J. F. A.: The fine structure of the human glomerular basement membrane. J. Ultrastructure Res., 4:81–87, 1960.

718. LACY, D. and CHALLICE, C. E.: The structure of the Golgi apparatus in vertebrate cells examined by light and electron microscopy. Symp. Soc. Exp. Biol., 10:62–91, 1957.

719. LACY, D. and TAYLOR, A. B.: Fat absorption by epithelial cells of the small intestine of the rat. Am. J. Anat., 110:155–185, 1962.

720. LACY, P. E.: Electron microscopic identification of different cell types in the islets of Langerhans of the guinea pig, rat, rabbit and dog. Anat. Rec., 128:255–268, 1957.

721. LACY, P. E.: Electron microscopy of the normal islets of Langerhans. Studies in the dog, rabbit, guinea pig and rat. Diabetes, 6:498–507, 1957.

722. LACY, P. E.: Electron microscopic and fluorescent antibody studies on islets of Langerhans. Exp. Cell Res., Suppl. 7:296–308, 1959.

723. LACY, P. E.: Electron microscopy of the beta cell of the pancreas. Am. J. Med., 31:851–859, 1961.

724. LACY, P. E. and CARDEZA, A. F.: Electron microscopy of guinea pig pancreas. Effect of cobalt on the acini and islets. Diabetes, 7:368–374, 1958.

725. LACY, P. E., CARDEZA, A. F., and WILSON, W. D.: Electron microscopy of the rat pancreas. Effects of glucagon administration. Diabetes, 8:36–44, 1959.

726. LACY, P. E. and HARTCROFT, W. S.: Electron microscopy of the islets of Langerhans. Ann. N. Y. Acad. Sci., 82:287–300, 1959.

727. LACY, P. E. and WILLIAMSON, J. R.: Electron microscopic and fluorescent antibody studies of islet cell adenomas. Anat. Rec., 136:227–228, 1960. (Abstract.)

728. LADEN, E. L., GETHNER, P., and ERICKSON, J. O.: Electron microscopic study of keratohyalin in the formation of keratin. J. Invest. Dermatol., 28:325–327, 1957.

729. LADMAN, A. J.: The fine structure of the rod-bipolar cell synapse in the retina of the albino rat. J. Biophys. Biochem. Cytol., 4:459–466, 1958.

730. LADMAN, A. J.: Electron microscopic observations on the fine structure of Müller cells in the retina of the cat. Anat. Rec., 139:247, 1961. (Abstract.)

731. LADMAN, A. J. and YOUNG, W. C.: An electron microscopic study of the ductuli efferentes and rete testis of the guinea pig. J. Biophys. Biochem. Cytol., 4:219–226, 1958.

732. LAITINEN, E. A.: An electron microscope investigation of the connective tissue in the alveolar wall of the normal and the bronchiectatic human lung. Acta Pathol. Microbiol. Scand., 49:136–150, 1960.

733. LANDES, E. and KAPPESSER, W.: Elektronenoptische Untersuchungen über die Ultrastruktur des menschlichen Spermatozoenkerns. Hautarzt, 9:463–466, 1958.

734. LANGE, R.: Zur Histologie und Zytologie der Glandula parathyreoidea des Menschen. Licht- und elektronenmikroskopische Untersuchungen an Epithelkörperadenomen. Z. Zellforsch., 53:765–828, 1961.

735. LANGER, E. and HUHN, S.: Der submikroskopische Bau der Myoepithelzelle. Z. Zellforsch., 47:507–516, 1958.

736. LARSEN, J. F.: Electron microscopy of the implantation site in the rabbit. Am. J. Anat., 109:319–334, 1961.

737. LARSEN, J. F.: Electron microscopy of the uterine epithelium in the rabbit. J. Cell Biol., 14:49–64, 1962.

738. LARSEN, J. F. and DAVIES, J.: The paraplacental chorion and accessory fetal membranes of the rabbit. Histology and electron microscopy. Anat. Rec., 143:27–45, 1962.

739. LASANSKY, A.: Morphological bases for a nursing role of glia in the toad retina. Electron microscope observations. J. Biophys. Biochem. Cytol., 11:237–243, 1961.

740. LASANSKY, A. and DE ROBERTIS, E.: Submicroscopic changes in visual cells of the rabbit induced by iodoacetate. J. Biophys. Biochem. Cytol., 5:245–249, 1959.

741. LASANSKY, A. and DE ROBERTIS, E.: Electron microscopy of retinal photoreceptors. The use of chromatin following formaldehyde fixation as a complimentary technique to osmium tetroxide. J. Biophys. Biochem. Cytol., 7:493–498, 1960.

742. LATTA, H.: Collagen in normal rat glomeruli. J. Ultrastructure Res., 5:364–373, 1961.

743. LATTA, H.: The plasma membrane of glomerular epithelium. J. Ultrastructure Res., 6:407–412, 1962.

744. LATTA, H. and MAUNSBACH, A. B.: The juxtaglomerular apparatus as studied electron microscopically. J. Ultrastructure Res., 6:547–561, 1962.

745. LATTA, H. and MAUNSBACH, A. B.: Relations of the centrolobular region of the glomerulus to the juxtaglomerular apparatus. J. Ultrastructure Res., 6:562–578, 1962.

746. LATTA, H., MAUNSBACH, A. B., and MADDEN, S. C.: The centrolobular region of the renal glomerulus studied by electron microscopy. J. Ultrastructure Res., 4:455–472, 1960.

747. LATTA, H., MAUNSBACH, A. B., and MADDEN, S. C.: Cilia in different segments of the rat nephron. J. Biophys. Biochem. Cytol., 11:248–252, 1961.

748. LATTA, H., STONE, R. S., BENCOSME, S. A., and MADDEN, S. C.: Mechanisms for movement of fluid in renal tubule cells. In: Electron Microscopy in Anatomy, pp. 235–240. Eds.: J. D. Boyd, F. R. Johnson, and J. D. Lever. Williams and Wilkins, Baltimore, 1961.

749. LAWN, A. M.: Observations on the fine structure of the gastric parietal cells of the rat. J. Biophys. Biochem. Cytol., 7:161–166, 1960.

750. LAWN, A. M.: The use of potassium permanganate as an electron-dense stain for sections of tissue embedded in epoxy resin. J. Biophys. Biochem. Cytol., 7:197–198, 1960.

751. LEBLOND, C. P. and CLERMONT, Y.: The cell web, a fibrillar structure found in a variety of cells in animal tissues. Anat. Rec., 136:230, 1960. (Abstract.)

752. LEESON, C. R. and JACOBY, F.: An electron microscopic study of the rat submaxillary gland during its post-natal development and in the adult. J. Anat., 93:287–295, 1959.

753. LEESON, C. R. and THREADGOLD, L. T.: The differentiation of the epidermis in *Rana pipiens*. Acta Anat., 44:159–173, 1961.

754. LEESON, T. S.: The fine structure of the mesonephros of the 17-day rabbit embryo. Exp. Cell Res., 12:670–672, 1957.

755. LEESON, T. S.: An electron microscopic study of the mesonephros and metanephros of the rabbit. Am. J. Anat., 105:165–196, 1959.

756. LEESON, T. S.: Electron microscopy of the developing kidney: an investigation into the fine structure of the mesonephros and metanephros of the rabbit. J. Anat., 94:100–106, 1960.

757. LEESON, T. S.: Electron microscopy of intertubular tissue in the hamster kidney. Anat. Rec., 136:231, 1960. (Abstract.)

758. LEESON, T. S.: Fine structure of the developing trachea. J. Appl. Phys., 31:1844, 1960. (Abstract.)

759. LEESON, T. S.: The development of the trachea in the rabbit, with particular reference to its fine structure. Anat. Anz., 110:214–223, 1961.

760. LEESON, T. S.: An electron microscope study of the postnatal development of the hamster kidney. With particular reference to the intertubular tissue. Lab. Invest., 10:466–480, 1961.

761. LEESON, T. S. and KALANT, H.: Effects of in vivo decalcification on ultrastructure of adult rat liver. J. Biophys. Biochem. Cytol., 10:95–104, 1961.

762. LEESON, T. S. and SPEAKMAN, J. S.: The fine structure of extracellular material in the pectinate ligament (trabecular meshwork) of the human iris. Acta Anat., 46: 363–379, 1961.

763. LEHMAN, F. E.: Der Feinbau von Kern und Zytoplasma in seiner Beziehung zu generellen Zellfunktionen. Ergeb. med. Grundlagenforsch., 1:111–137, 1956.

765. LEHNINGER, A. L.: The enzymic and morphologic organization of the mitochondria. Pediatrics, 26:466–475, 1960.

766. LEHNINGER, A. L.: How cells transform energy. Sci. American, 205:63–73, 1961.

767. LEHRER, G. M. and ORNSTEIN, L.: The ultrastructure of the mammalian neuromuscular junction (NMJ). Anat. Rec., 133:303, 1959, (Abstract.)

768. LENZ, H.: Elektronenmikroskopische Untersuchungen der Dentinentwicklung. Deut. Zahn-, Mund-, Kieferheilk, 30:367–381, 1959.

769. LEVER, J. D.: Electron microscopic observations on the normal and denervated adrenal medulla of the rat. Endocrinology, 57:621–635, 1955.

770. LEVER, J. D.: Electron microscopic observations on the adrenal cortex. Am. J. Anat., 97:409–430, 1955.

771. LEVER, J. D.: Remarks on the electron microscopy of the rat corpus luteum: and comparison with earlier observations on the adrenal cortex. Anat. Rec., 124:111–126, 1956.

772. LEVER, J. D.: The subendothelial space in certain endocrine tissues. J. Biophys. Biochem. Cytol., 2:293–296, 1956. Suppl.

773. LEVER, J. D.: Fine structural appearances in the rat parathyroid. J. Anat., 91:73–81, 1957.

774. LEVER, J. D.: Cytological appearances in the normal and activated parathyroid of the rat: a combined study by electron and light microscopy with certain quantitative assessments. J. Endocrinol., 17:210–217, 1958.

775. LEVER, J. D.: A method of staining sectioned

tissues with lead for electron microscopy. Nature, 186:810–811, 1960.

776. LEVER, J. D.: The detection of intracellular iron in rat duodenal epithelium. In: Electron Microscopy in Anatomy, pp. 278–286. Eds.: J. D. Boyd, F. R. Johnson, and J. D. Lever. Williams and Wilkins, Baltimore, 1961.

777. LEVER, J. D. and JEACOCK, M.: Islet cell appearances in the normal and experimental cat pancreas. An electron microscopic and histochemical study. Anat. Rec., 136:233, 1960. (Abstract.)

778. LILLIBRIDGE, C.: Electron microscopic criteria for identifying human oxyntic and pepsin producing cells in biopsy material. Anat. Rec., 136:234, 1960. (Abstract.)

779. LILLIBRIDGE, C. B.: Membranes of the human pepsinogen granule. J. Biophys. Biochem. Cytol., 10:145–149, 1961.

780. LINDNER, E.: Die submikroskopische Morphologie des Herzmuskels. Z. Zellforsch., 45:702–746, 1957.

781. LINDNER, E.: Submikroskopische Untersuchungen über die Herzentwicklung beim Hühnchen. Verhandl. Anat. Ges., 22:305–317, 1957.

782. LINDNER, E.: Die submikroskopische Morphologie des Herzmuskels. Z. Zellforsch., 45:702–746, 1957.

783. LINDNER, E.: Myofibrils in the early development of chick embryo hearts as observed with the electron microscope. Anat. Rec., 136:234–235, 1960. (Abstract.)

784. LINDNER, J. and GUSEK, W.: Elektronenmikroskopische Untersuchungen an Lymphknoten nach Dextranzufuhr. Frankfurt. Z. Pathol., 70:367–388, 1960.

785. LION, G., MAERTENS, C., and VANDERMEERSSCHE, G.: Submicroscopic morphology of the retinal pigment epithelium. In: Stockholm Conf. Electron Micros., 1956. Proceed. pp. 196–197. Academic Press, New York, 1957.

786. LISCHKA, G.: Die Zellstrukturen des Dünndarmepithels in ihrer Abhängigkeit von der physikalisch-chemischen Beschaffenheit des Darminhalts. III. Hydronium- und Hydroxylionen. Z. Zellforsch., 56:498–514, 1962.

787. LITTLE, K.: Electron microscope studies on human dental enamel. J. Roy. Microscop. Soc., 78:58–66, 1959.

787a. LOEWENSTEIN, W. R.: Biological transducers. Sci. American, 203:98–108, 1960.

788. LONGLEY, J. B., BANFIELD, W. G., and BRINDLEY, D. C.: Structure of the rete mirabile in the kidney of the rat as seen with the electron microscope. J. Biophys. Biochem. Cytol., 7:103–106, 1960.

789. LOOSLI, C. G. and POTTER, E. L.: Pre- and postnatal development of the respiratory portion of the human lung. With special reference to the elastic fibers. Am. Rev. Respirat. Diseases, 80:5–23, 1959.

790. LOW, F. N.: Electron microscopy of the rat lung. Anat. Rec., 113:437–449, 1952.

791. LOW, F. N.: The pulmonary alveolar epithelium of laboratory mammals and man. Anat. Rec., 117:241–264, 1953.

792. LOW, F. N.: Ultrastructure of the pulmonary alveolar wall. Anat. Rec., 118:429–430, 1954.

793. LOW, F. N.: The electron microscopy of sectioned lung tissue after varied duration of fixation in buffered osmium tetroxide. Anat. Rec., 120:827–852, 1954.

794. LOW, F. N.: Mitochondrial structure. J. Biophys. Biochem. Cytol., 2:337–340, 1956. Suppl.

795. LOW, F. N.: The extracellular portion of the human blood-air barrier and its relation to tissue space. Anat. Rec., 139:105–123, 1961.

796. LOW, F. N.: Microfibrils: Fine filamentous components of the tissue space. Anat. Rec., 142:131–137, 1962.

797. LOW, F. N. and CLEVENGER, M. R.: Polyester-methacrylate embedments for electron microscopy. J. Cell Biol., 12:615–621, 1962.

798. LOW, F. N. and DANIELS, C. W.: Electron microscopy of the rat lung. Anat. Rec., 113:437–450, 1952.

799. LOW, F. N. and FREEMAN, J. A., SR.: Electron microscopic atlas of normal and leukemic human blood. McGraw-Hill, New York, 1958.

800. LOW, F. N. and SAMPAIO, M. M.: The pulmonary alveolar epithelium as an entodermal derivative. Anat. Rec., 127:51–64, 1957.

801. LUFT, J. H.: Permanganate—a new fixative for electron microscopy. J. Biophys. Biochem. Cytol., 2:799–801, 1956.

802. LUFT, J. H.: Improvements in epoxy resin embedding methods. J. Biophys. Biochem. Cytol., 9:409–414, 1961.

803. LUFT, J. H. and HECHTER, O.: An electron microscopic correlation of structure with function in the isolated perfused cow adrenal. Preliminary observations. J. Biophys. Biochem. Cytol., 3:615–620, 1957.

804. LUSE, S. A.: Electron microscopic observations of the central nervous system. J. Biophys. Biochem. Cytol., 2:531–542, 1956.

805. LUSE, S. A.: Formation of myelin in the central nervous system of mice and rats as studied with the electron microscope. J. Biophys. Biochem. Cytol., 2:777–784, 1956.

807. LUSE, S. A.: Electron microscopy of glial cells. Anat. Rec., 124:329–330, 1956. (Abstract.)

808. LUSE, S. A.: Electron microscopic observations of the central nervous system. In: Inhibitions of the Nervous System and Gamma-Aminobutyric Acid, pp. 29–33. Ed.: E. Roberts. Pergamon Press, New York, 1960.

809. LUSE, S. A.: Fixation and embedding of mammalian brain and spinal cord for electron microscopy. J. Ultrastructure Res., 4:108–112, 1960.

810. LUSE, S. A.: Histochemical implications of electron microscopy of the central nervous system. J. Histochem. Cytochem., 8:398–411, 1960.

811. LUSE, S. A.: The ultrastructure of normal and abnormal oligodendroglia. Anat. Rec., 138:461–492, 1960.

812. LUSE, S. A. and HARRIS, B.: Electron mi-

croscopy of the brain in experimental edema. J. Neurosurg., 17:439–446, 1960.

813. LUSE, S. A. and McDOUGAL, D. B.: Electron-microscopic observations on allergic encephalomyelitis in the rabbit. J. Exp. Med., 112:735–742, 1960.

814. McALEAR, J. H., CAMOUGIS, G., and THIBODEAU, L. F.: Mapping of large areas with the electron microscope. J. Biophys. Biochem. Cytol., 10:133–135, 1961.

815. McALEAR, J. H. and EDWARDS, G. A.: Continuity of plasma membrane and nuclear membrane. Exp. Cell Res., 16:689–692, 1959.

816. McLEAN, F. C.: The ultrastructure and function of bone. Science, 127:451–456, 1958.

817. McQUADE, H. A. and EVANS, T. C.: The electron microscopy of the response of follicular epithelium cells of rat thyroid to autolysis, ligation, and irradiation by iodine-131. Radiation Res., 11:520–534, 1959.

818. McQUADE, H. A., SEAMAN, W., and PORPORIS, A. A.: Electron microscopy of irradiated cells of the follicular epithelium of the rat thyroid. Radiation Res., 4:532–540, 1956.

819. MACKAY, B., MUIR, A. R., and PETERS, A.: Observations on the terminal innervation of segmental muscle fibers in amphibia. Acta Anat., 40:1–12, 1960.

820. MAEDA, J.: Electron microscopy of retinal vessels. I. Human retina. Acta Soc. Ophthal. Japon., 62:1002–1017, 1958.

821. MAJNO, G. and PALADE, G. E.: Studies on inflammation. I. The effect of histamine and serotonin on vascular permeability. An electron microscopic study. J. Biophys. Biochem. Cytol., 11:571–605, 1961.

822. MALHOTRA, S. K.: A comparative histochemical study of the Golgi apparatus. Quart. J. Microscop. Sci., 102:83–87, 1961.

823. MALHOTRA, S. K. and MEEK, G. A.: The electron microscopy of the "Golgi apparatus" in the Purkinje cells of owls. J. Microscop. Sci., 101:389–394, 1960.

824. MANNI, E.: Submicroscopic changes of the parotid gland caused by functional rest and secretory nerve stimulation. In: Fourth Internat. Conf. Electron Micros., Berlin 1958. Proceed. Vol. II, pp. 365-368. Springer Verlag, Berlin, 1960.

825. MARINOZZI, V.: La structure de l'alvéole pulmonaire, etudiée au moyen de la technique de l'imprégnation à l'argent. In: Fourth Internat. Conf. Electron Micros., Berlin 1958. Proceed. Vol. II, pp. 412–415. Springer Verlag, Berlin, 1960.

826. MARINOZZI, V.: Silver impregnation of ultrathin sections for electron microscopy. J. Biophys. Biochem. Cytol., 9:121–133, 1961.

827. MARK, J. S. T.: An electron microscope study of uterine smooth muscle. Anat. Rec., 125:473–494, 1956.

828. MARTIN, A. V. W.: Electron microscope studies of collagenous fibres in bone. Biochim. Biophys. Acta, 10:42–48, 1953.

829. MARTIN, A. V. W.: An electron microscope study of the cartilaginous matrix in the developing tibia of the fowl. J. Embryol. Exp. Morphol., 2:38–43, 1954.

830. MATOLTSY, A. G. and BALSAMO, C. A.: A study of the components of the cornified epithelium of human skin. J. Biophys. Biochem. Cytol., 1:339–360, 1955.

831. MATOLTSY, A. G. and ODLAND, G. F.: Investigation of the structure of the cornified epithelium of the human skin. J. Biophys. Biochem. Cytol., 1:191–196, 1955.

832. MATTISSON, A. G. M. and BIRCH-ANDERSON, A.: On the fine structure of the mitochondria and its relation to oxidative capacity in muscles in various invertebrates. J. Ultrastructure Res., 6:205–228, 1962.

833. MAUNSBACH, A. B., MADDEN, S. C., and LATTA, H.: Variations in fine structure of renal tubular epithelium under different conditions of fixation. J. Ultrastructure Res., 6:511–530, 1962.

834. MAURICE, D. M.: The structure and transparency of the cornea. J. Physiol., London, 136:263–286, 1957.

835. MAURO, A.: Satellite cell of skeletal muscle fibers. J. Biophys. Biochem. Cytol., 9:493–495, 1961.

836. MAURO, A. and ADAMS, R.: The structure of the sarcolemma of the frog skeletal muscle fiber. J. Biophys. Biochem. Cytol., 10:177–185, 1961. Suppl.

837. MAYNARD, E. A., SCHULTZ, R. L., and PEASE, D. C.: Electron microscopy of the vascular bed of rat cerebral cortex. Am. J. Anat. 100:409–433, 1957.

838. MAYOR, H. D., HAMPTON, C., and ROSARIO, B.: A simple method for removing the resin from epoxy-embedded tissue. J. Biophys. Biochem. Cytol., 9:909–910, 1961.

839. MEEK, G. A. and MOSES, M. J.: Microtubulation of the inner membrane of the nuclear envelope. J. Biophys. Biochem. Cytol., 10:121–131, 1961.

840. MENEFEE, M. G.: Some fine structure changes occurring in the epidermis of embryo mice during differentiation. J. Ultrastructure Res., 1:49–61, 1957.

841. MERCER, E. H.: The fine structure of keratin. Textile Res. J., 27:860–866, 1957.

842. MERCER, E. H.: The electron microscopy of keratinized tissues. In: The Biology of Hair Growth, pp. 91–111. Eds. W. Montagna and R. A. Ellis. Academic Press, New York, 1958.

843. MERCER, E. H. and BIRBECK, M. S. C.: Electron Microscopy: A Handbook for Biologists. Blackwell Scientific Publ., Oxford, 1961.

844. MERIEL, P., MOREAU, G., SUC, J.-M., PUTOIS, J., and REGNIER, C.: Application de la microscopie électronique a l'étude du rein humain. Compt. rend. acad. sci., 246: 2600–2602, 1958.

845. MERKER, H.-J.: Elektronmikroskopische Untersuchungen am Bindegewebe normaler und pathologischer Lebern des Menschen. Berlin. Med., 10:265–271, 1959.

846. MERKER, H.-J.: Das elektronenmikroskopische Bild der Haftstellen (Desmosomen) im Vaginalepithel der Ratte. Berlin. Med., 12:555–558, 1961.

847. MERKER, H.-J.: Elektronenmikroskopische Untersuchungen über die Fibrillogenese in der Haut Menschlicher Embryonen. Z. Zellforsch., 53:411–430, 1961.

848. MERKER, H.-J.: Elektronenmikroskopische Untersuchungen über die Bildung der Zona pellucida in den Follikeln des Kaninchenovars. Z. Zellforsch., 54:677–688, 1961.

849. MERRIAM, R. W.: On the fine structure and composition of the nuclear envelope. J. Biophys. Biochem. Cytol., 11:559–570, 1961.

850. MERRIAM, R. W.: Some dynamic aspects of the nuclear envelope. J. Cell Biol., 12:79–90, 1962.

851. MERRIAM, R. W. and KOCH, W. E.: The relative concentration of solids in the nucleolus, nucleus, and cytoplasm of the developing nerve cell of the chick. J. Biophys. Biochem. Cytol., 7:151–160, 1960.

852. MERRILLERS, N. C. R.: The fine structure of muscle spindles in the lumbrical muscles of the rat. J. Biophys. Biochem. Cytol., 7:725–742, 1960.

853. METUZALS, J.: Ultrastructure of myelinated nerve fibers and nodes of Ranvier in the central nervous system of the frog. In: European Regional Conf. Electron Micros., Delft 1960. Proceed. Vol. II, pp. 799–802. De Nederlandse Vereniging voor Elektronenmikroskopie, Delft, 1961.

854. MEYER, W. E.: Das praktische Auflösungsvermögen von Elektronenmikroskopen. Optik, 18:101–114, 1961.

855. MEYER, H. and QUEIROGA, L. T.: An electron microscope study of embryonic heart muscle cells grown in tissue cultures. J. Biophys. Biochem. Cytol., 5:169–170, 1959.

856. MEYER, J. S. and HARTROFT, W. S.: Hepatic lipid produced by polyphagia in albino rats. Am. J. Path., 36:365–391, 1960.

857. MILLER, A. and PAUTARD, F. G. E.: Electron microscope observations on apatite crystallites in human dentine and enamel. In: Fourth Internat. Conf. Electron Micros., Berlin 1958. Proceed. Vol. II, pp. 357–361. Springer Verlag, Berlin, 1960.

858. MILLER, F.: Orthologie und Pathologie der Zelle im elektronenmikroskopischen Bild. Verhandl. deut. Ges. Pathol., 42:261–332, 1959.

859. MILLER, F.: Hemoglobin absorption by the cells of the proximal convoluted tubule in mouse kidney. J. Biophys. Biochem. Cytol., 8:689–718, 1960.

860. MILLER, F.: Lipoprotein granules in the cortical collecting tubules of mouse kidney. J. Biophys. Biochem. Cytol., 9:157–170, 1961.

861. MILLER, F. and SITTE, H.: Elektronenmikroskopische Untersuchungen an Mäusenieren nach intraperitonalen Eiweissgaben. Verhandl. deut. Ges. Pathol., 39:183–190, 1956.

862. MILLINGTON, P. F. and FINEAN, J. B.: Electron microscope studies of the structure of the microvilli on principal epithelial cells of rat jejunum after treatment in hypo- and hypertonic saline. J. Cell Biol., 14:125–139, 1962.

863. MILLONIG, G.: Advantages of a phosphate buffer for OsO$_4$ solutions in fixation. J. Appl. Phys., 32:1637, 1961. (Abstract.)

864. MILLONIG, G.: A modified procedure for lead staining of thin sections. J. Biophys. Biochem. Cytol., 11:736–739, 1961.

865. MILLONIG, G. and PORTER, K. R.: Structural elements of rat liver cells involved in glycogen metabolism. In: European Regional Conf. Electron Micros., Delft 1960, Proceed. Vol. II, pp. 655–659. De Nederlandse Vereniging voor Elektronenmicroscopie, Delft, 1961.

866. MISSOTTEN, L.: Étude des synapses de la rétine humaine au microscope électronique. In: European Regional Conf. Electron Micros., Delft 1960. Proceed. Vol. II, pp. 818–821. De Nederlandse Vereniging voor Elektronenmicroscopie, Delft, 1961.

867. MOE, H.: The ultrastructure of Brunner's glands of the cat. J. Ultrastructure Res., 4:58–72, 1960.

868. MOE, H. and BEHNKE, O.: Cytoplasmic bodies containing mitochondria, ribosomes and rough surfaced endoplasmic membranes in the epithelium of the small intestine of newborn rats. J. Cell Biol., 13:168–171, 1962.

869. MOE, H., BEHNKE, O., and ROSTGAARD, J.: Staining of osmium fixed vestopal embedded tissue sections for light microscopy. Acta Anat., 48:142–148, 1962.

870. MOE, R.: Electron microscopic morphology of lymphatic sinuses. Anat. Rec., 136:245–246, 1960. (Abstract.)

871. MOERICKE, V. and WOHLFARTH-BOTTERMAN, K. E.: Zur Funktionellen Morphologie der Speicheldrüsen von Homopteren. Die Hauptzellen der Hauptdrüse von Myzus Persicae (Sulz.), Aphididae. Z. Zellforsch., 51:157–184, 1960.

872. MOERICKE, V. and WOHLFARTH-BOTTERMAN, K. E.: Zur Funktionellen Morphologie der Speicheldrüsen von Homopteren. Die Ausführgänge der Speicheldrüsen von Myzus Persicae (Sulz.) Aphididae. Z. Zellforsch., 53:25–49, 1960.

873. MÖLBERT, E. and ARNESEN, K.: Elektronenmikroskopische Untersuchungen zur Ultrastruktur der Nebennierenrinde der weissen Maus. (Zugleich ein Beitrag zur Struktur und Funktion der Mitochondrien). Beitr. pathol. Anat. allgem. Pathol., 122:31–56, 1960.

874. MÖLBERT, E. DUSPIVA, F., and VON DEIMLING, O.: Die histochemische Lokalisation der Phosphatase in der Tubulusepithelzelle der Mäuseniere im elektronenmikroskopischen Bild. Histochemie, 2:5–22, 1960.

875. MÖLBERT, E. R. G., DUSPIVA, F., and VON DEIMLING, O. H.: The demonstration of alkaline phosphatase in the electron microscope. J. Biophys. Biochem. Cytol., 7:387–390, 1960.

876. MOLLENHAUER, H. H., WHALEY, W. G., and LEECH, J. H.: Cell ultrastructure responses to mechanical injury. A preliminary report. J. Ultrastructure Res., 4:473–481, 1960.

877. MOLLENHAUER, H. H. and ZEBRUN, W.: Permanganate fixation of the Golgi complex and other cytoplasmic structures of mammalian testes. J. Biophys. Biochem. Cytol., 8:761–775, 1960.

878. MOLNAR, Z.: Development of the parietal bone of young mice. I. Crystals of bone mineral in frozen dried preparations. J. Ultrastructure Res., 3:39–45, 1959.

879. MONROE, B. G.: Electron microscopy of the thyroid. Anat. Rec., 116:345–362, 1953.

880. MONTAGNA, W.: The Structure and Function of Skin. Academic Press, New York, 1956.

881. MOODY, M. F. and ROBERTSON, J. D.: The fine structure of some retinal photoreceptors. J. Biophys. Biochem. Cytol., 7:87–92, 1960.

882. MOORE, D. H.: Problems in methacrylate embedding. In: Fourth Internat. Conf. Electron Micros., Berlin 1958. Proceed. Vol. II, pp. 37–39. Springer Verlag, Berlin, 1960.

883. MOORE, D. H. and GRIMLEY, P. M.: Problems in methacrylate embedding for electron microscopy. J. Biophys. Biochem. Cytol., 3:255–260, 1957.

884. MOORE, D. H. and RUSKA, H.: Electron microscope study of mammalian cardiac muscle cells. J. Biophys. Biochem. Cytol., 3:261–268, 1957.

885. MOORE, D. H. and RUSKA, H.: The fine structure of capillaries and small arteries. J. Biophys. Biochem. Cytol., 3:457–462, 1957.

886. MOORE, R. D., MUMAW, V. R., and SCHOENBERG, M. D.: Optical microscopy of ultrathin tissue sections. J. Ultrastructure Res., 4:113–116, 1960.

887. MOORE, R. D., MUMAW, V. R., and SCHOENBERG, M. D.: The transport and distribution of colloidal iron and its relation to the ultrastructure of the cell. J. Ultrastructure Res., 5:244–256, 1961.

888. MORALES, R., DUNCAN, D., and NALL, D.: A note on the fine structure of endothelium in old mice. Texas Repts. Biol. Med., 18:247–253, 1960.

889. MORELAND, J. E.: Electron microscopic studies of mitochondria in cardiac and skeletal muscle from hibernated ground squirrels. Anat. Rec., 142:155–167, 1962.

890. MORICARD, R.: Fonction méiogène et fonction oestrogène du follicule ovarien des mammifères. (Cytologie golgienne, traceurs, microscopie électronique.) Ann. Endocrinol., 19:943–967, 1958.

891. MOSES, M. J.: Studies on nuclei using correlated cytochemical light and electron microscope techniques. J. Biophys. Biochem. Cytol., 2:397–406, 1956.

892. MOSES, M. J.: Breakdown and reformation of the nuclear envelope at cell division. In: Fourth Internat. Conf. Electron Micros., Berlin 1958. Proceed. Vol. II, pp. 230–233. Springer Verlag, Berlin, 1960.

893. MOUSSA, T. and KHATTAB, F. I.: An experimental study of the relation between the Golgi apparatus, mitochondria and secretion in the surface epithelium of the mammalian stomach. J. Morph., 101:191–207, 1957.

894. MOYER, F.: Electron microscope observations on the origin, development, and genetic control of melanin granules in the mouse eye. In: The Structure of the Eye, pp. 469–486. Ed.: G. K. Smelser. Academic Press, New York, 1961.

895. MUELLER, C. B.: The structure of the renal glomerulus. Am. Heart J., 55:304–322, 1958.

896. MUELLER, C. B., MASON, A. D., and STOUT, D. G.: Anatomy of the glomerulus. Am. J. Med., 18:267–276, 1955.

897. MOULÉ, Y., ROUILLER, C., and CHAUVEAU, J.: A biochemical and morphological study of rat liver microsomes. J. Biophys. Biochem. Cytol., 7:547–558, 1960.

898. MUIR, A. R.: An electron microscope study of the embryology of the intercalated disc in the heart of the rabbit. J. Biophys. Biochem. Cytol., 3:193–202, 1957.

899. MUIR, A. R.: Observations on the fine structure of the Purkinje fibers in the ventricles of the sheep's heart. J. Anat., 91:251–258, 1957.

900. MUIR, A. R. and PETERS, A.: Quintuple-layered membrane junctions at terminal bars between endothelial cells. J. Cell Biol., 12:443–448, 1962.

901. MUNGER, B. L.: A phase and electron microscopic study of cellular differentiation in pancreatic acinar cells of the mouse. Am. J. Anat., 103:1–34, 1958.

902. MUNGER, B. L.: A light and electron microscope study of cellular differentiation in the pancreatic islets of the mouse. Am. J. Anat., 103:275–312, 1958.

903. MUNGER, B. L.: The mode of secretion of alpha granules of pancreatic islet alpha cells. Anat. Rec., 139:258, 1961. (Abstract.)

904. MUNGER, B. L.: The morphologic sequence of secretion in the parathyroid glands as compared to other endocrine organs. Anat. Rec., 142:261, 1962. (Abstract.)

905. MURRAY, R. G. and MURRAY, A.: The fine structure of the taste buds of Rhesus and Cynomalgus monkeys. Anat. Rec., 138:211–233, 1960.

906. MUSCATELLO, U., ANDERSSON-CEDERGREN, E., AZZONE, G. F., and VON DER DECKEN, A.: The sarcotubular system of frog skeletal muscle. A morphological and biochemical study. J. Biophys. Biochem. Cytol., 10:201–218, 1961, Suppl.

907. MUTA, T.: The fine structure of the interstitial cell in the mouse ovary studied with the electron microscope. Kurume Med. J., 5:167–185, 1958.

908. NILSSON, O.: Electron microscopy of the glandular epithelium in the human uterus. I. Follicular phase. J. Ultrastructure Res., 6:413–421, 1962.

909. NILSSON, O.: Electron microscopy of the glandular epithelium in the human uterus.

II. Early and late luteal phase. J. Ultrastructure Res., 6:422–431, 1962.

910. NILSSON, O.: Correlation of structure to function of the luminal cell surface in the uterine epithelium of mouse and man. Z. Zellforsch., 56:803–808, 1962.

911. NISHIKAWA, M.: Electron microscopical study of the morphogenesis of collagen fibers. Arch. Histol. Japon., 14:463–483, 1958.

912. NORDMANN, M.: Die Lebenswandlungen und Struktur der Kapillaren. Verhandl. deut. Ges. Kreislaufforschung, 24:41–56, 1958.

913. NORDMANN, M. and BÄSSLER, R.: Elektronenoptische Untersuchungen an Kapillaren. Verhandl. deut. Ges. Pathol., 42:320–325, 1958.

914. NORDMANN, M. and WOLF, E.: Elektronenoptische Untersuchungen des Pankreas unter normalen und abnormen Stoffwechsellagen. Arch. Pathol. Anat. Physiol. Virchows, 333:54–67, 1960.

915. NORRIS, J. L.: The normal histology of the esophageal and gastric mucosae of the frog, *Rana pipiens*. J. Exp. Zool., 141:155–173, 1959.

916. NORTH, R. J. and POLLAK, J. K.: An electron microscope study on the variation of nuclear-mitochondrial proximity in developing chick liver. J. Ultrastructure Res., 5:497–503, 1961.

917. NOSEDA, I.: Elektronenmikroskopische Untersuchungen an der normalen Schilddrüse mit besonderer Berücksichtigung der Sekretionsvorgänge. Z. mikrosk.-anat. Forsch., 60:192–204, 1954.

918. NOVIKOFF, A. B.: Electron microscopy: cytology of cell fractions. Science, 124:969–972, 1956.

920. NOVIKOFF, A. B.: Biochemical heterogeneity of the cytoplasmic particles of rat liver. Symp. Soc. Exp. Biol., 10:92–109, 1957.

922. NOVIKOFF, A. B.: The proximal tubule cell in experimental hydronephrosis. J. Biophys. Biochem. Cytol., 6:136–138, 1959.

923. NOVIKOFF, A. B.: The biochemical cytology of liver. Bull. N. Y. Acad. Med., 35:67–70, 1959.

924. NOVIKOFF, A. B.: Cell heterogeneity within the hepatic lobule of the rat (staining reaction). J. Histochem. Cytochem., 7:240–244, 1959.

925. NOVIKOFF, A. B.: Mitochondria (chondriosomes). In: The Cell, Vol. II, pp. 299–421. Eds.: J. Brachet and A. E. Mirsky. Academic Press, New York, 1961.

926. NOVIKOFF, A. B.: Lysosomes and related particles. In: The Cell, Vol. II, pp. 423–488. Eds.: J. Brachet and A. E. Mirsky. Academic Press, New York, 1961.

927. NOVIKOFF, A. B., BEAUFAY, H., and DEDUVE, C.: Electron microscopy of liposome rich fractions from rat liver. J. Biophys. Biochem. Cytol., 2:179–184, 1956, Suppl.

929. NOVIKOFF, A. B. and ESSNER, E.: The liver cell: Some new approaches to its study. Am. J. Med., 29:102–131, 1960.

930. NOVIKOFF, A. B. and ESSNER, E.: Cytolysomes and mitochondrial degeneration. J. Cell Biol., 15:140–146, 1962.

931. NOVIKOFF, A. B. and PODBER, E.: The contributions of differential centrifugation to the intracellular localization of enzymes. J. Histochem. Cytochem., 5:552–564, 1957.

932. NOVIKOFF, A. B., SHIN, W.-Y., and DRUCKER, J.: Mitochondrial localization of oxidative enzymes: Staining results with two tetrazolium salts. J. Biophys. Biochem. Cytol., 9:47–61, 1961.

933. NOWELL, P. and BERWICK, L.: The surface ultrastructure of normal and leukemic rat lymphocytes. Cancer Res., 18:1067–1069, 1958.

934. NYLEN, M. U. and SCOTT, D. B.: An electron microscopic study of the early stages of dentinogenesis. U. S. Dept. of Health, Education & Welfare, Public Health Service Publ. No. 613. Washington, D. C., 1958.

935. NAGANO, T.: The structure of cytoplasmic bridges in dividing spermatocytes of the rooster. Anat. Rec., 141:73–79, 1961.

936. NAGANO, T.: Observations on the fine structure of the developing spermatid in the domestic chicken. J. Cell Biol., 14:193–205, 1962.

937. NAPOLITANO, L. and FAWCETT, D. W.: The fine structure of brown adipose tissue in the newborn mouse and rat. J. Biophys. Biochem. Cytol., 4:685–692, 1958.

938. NEBEL, B. R. and HACKETT, E. M.: Synaptinemal complexes in primary spermatocytes of the mouse: The effect of elevated temperature and some observations on the structure of these complexes in control material. Z. Zellforsch., 55:556–565, 1961.

939. NELSON, L.: Cytochemical studies with the electron microscope. III. Sulfhydryl groups of rat spermatozoa. J. Ultrastructure Res., 4:182–190, 1960.

940. NELSON, E., BLINZINGER, K., and HAGER, H.: Electron microscopic observations on subarachnoid and perivascular spaces of the Syrian hamster brain. Neurology, 11:285–295, 1961.

941. NEMETSCHEK, TH. and SCHULZ, H.: Kasuistischer Beitrag zur elektronenoptischen Untersuchung von Staub in der Lunge. Arch. Gewerbepathol. Gewerbehyg., 14:673–677, 1956.

941a. NEWMAN, S. B., BORYSKO, E., and SWERDLOW, M.: Ultra-microtomy by a new method. J. Res. Natl. Bur. Standards, 43:183–199, 1949.

942. NICANDER, L. and BANE, A.: Fine structure of boar spermatozoa. Z. Zellforsch., 57:390–405, 1962.

943. NIESSING, K. and VOGELL, W.: Das elektronenoptische Bild der sorgenannten Grundsubstanz der Hirnrinde. Z. Naturforsch., 12b: 641–646, 1957.

944. NIESSING, K. and VOGELL, W.: Elektronenmikroskopische Untersuchungen über Strukturveränderungen in der Hirnrinde beim Ödem und ihre Bedeutung für das Problem der Grundsubstanz. Z. Zellforsch., 52:216–237, 1960.

945. NILSSON, O.: Observations on a type of cilia in the rat oviduct. J. Ultrastructure Res., 1:170–177, 1957.

946. NILSSON, O.: Electron microscopy of the fallo

pian tube epithelium of rabbit in oestrus. Exp. Cell Res., 14:341–354, 1958.

947. NILSSON, O.: Influence of estradiol on the ultrastructure of mouse uterine surface epithelium. Exp. Cell Res., 14:434–435, 1958.

948. NILSSON, O.: Ultrastructure of mouse uterine surface epithelium under different estrogenic influences. I. Spayed animals and oestrous animals. J. Ultrastructure Res., 1:375–396, 1958.

949. NILSSON, O.: Ultrastructure of mouse uterine surface epithelium under different estrogenic influences. II. Early effect of estrogen administered to spayed animals. J. Ultrastructure Res., 2:73–95, 1958.

950. NILSSON, O.: Ultrastructure of mouse uterine surface epithelium under different estrogenic influences. III. Late effect of estrogen administered to spayed animals. J. Ultrastructure Res., 2:185–199, 1958.

951. NILSSON, O.: Ultrastructure of mouse uterine surface epithelium under different estrogenic influences. IV. Uterine secretion. J. Ultrastructure Res., 2:331–341, 1959.

952. NILSSON, O.: Ultrastructure of mouse uterine surface epithelium under different estrogenic influences. V. Continuous administration of estrogen. J. Ultrastructure Res., 2:342–351, 1959.

953. NILSSON, O.: Ultrastructure of mouse uterine surface epithelium under different estrogenic influences. VI. Changes of some cell components. J. Ultrastructure Res., 2:373–387, 1959.

954. OBERLING, CH., GAUTIER, A., and BERNHARD, W.: La structure des capillaires glomérulaires vue au microscope électronique. Presse méd., 59:938–940, 1951.

955. OBERLING, CH. and HATT, P.-Y.: Étude de l'appareil juxtaglomérulaire du rat au microscope électronique. Ann. anat. pathol., 5:441–474, 1960.

956. OBERLING, CH. and HATT, P.-Y.: Ultrastructure de l'appareil juxtaglomérulaire du rat. Compt. rend. acad. sci., 250:929–930, 1960.

957. ODLAND, G. F.: The fine structure of the interrelationship of cells in the human epidermis. J. Biophys. Biochem. Cytol., 4:529–538, 1958.

958. ODLAND, G. F.: A submicroscopic granular component in human epidermis. J. Invest. Dermatol., 34:11–15, 1960.

959. ODOR, D. L.: Observations of the rat mesothelium with the electron and phase microscopes. Am. J. Anat., 95:433–466, 1954.

960. ODOR, D. L.: Uptake and transfer of particulate matter from the peritoneal cavity of the rat. J. Biophys. Biochem. Cytol., 2:105–108, 1956, Suppl.

961. ODOR, D. L.: Electron microscopic studies on ovarian oocytes and unfertilized tubal ova in the rat. J. Biophys. Biochem. Cytol., 7:567–574, 1960.

962. ODOR, D. L.: Electron microscopy of the postnatal histogenesis of the epithelium of the rat oviduct. Anat. Rec., 139:331, 1961. (Abstract.)

963. ODOR, D. L. and RENNINGER, D. F.: Polar body formation in the rat oocyte as observed with the electron microscope. Anat. Rec., 137:13–23, 1960.

964. OHMI, S.: Electron microscopy of peripheral nerve regeneration. Z. Zellforsch., 56:625–631, 1962.

965. OKSCHE, A.: Der histochemish nachweisbare Glykogenaufbau und -abbau in den Astrocyten und Ependymzellen als Beispiel einer funktionsabhängigen Stoffwechselaktivität der Neuroglia. Z. Zellforsch., 54:307–361, 1961.

966. OLSSON, R.: The skin of Amphioxus. Z. Zellforsch., 54:90–104, 1961.

967. ORNSTEIN, L.: Mitochondrial and nuclear interaction. J. Biophys. Biochem. Cytol., 2:351–352, 1956, Suppl.

968. ORNSTEIN, L.: A "new" connective tissue fibril. J. Biophys. Biochem. Cytol., 2:297–298, 1956, Suppl.

969. ORNSTEIN, L. and POLLISTER, A. W.: Applications of phase microscopy in cytology and electron micrography. Trans. N. Y. Acad. Sci., 14:194–199, 1952.

970. OTTOSON, D., SJÖSTRAND, F., STENSTRÖM, S., and SVAETICHIN, G.: Microelectrode studies on the E. M. F. of the frog skin related to electron microscopy of the dermo-epidermal junction. Acta Physiol. Scand., 29:Suppl. 106:611–624, 1953.

971. PAHLKE, G.: Elektronenmikroskopische Untersuchungen an der Interzellularsubstanz des menschlichen Sehnengewebes. Z. Zellforsch., 39:421–430, 1954.

972. PAK POY, R. K. F.: Electron microscopy of the marsupial renal glomerulus. Australian J. Exp. Biol. Med. Sci., 35:437–447, 1957.

973. PAK POY, R. K. F.: Electron microscopy of the amphibian renal glomerulus. Australian J. Exp. Biol. Med. Sci., 35:583–594, 1957.

974. PAK POY, R. K. F.: Electron microscopy of the mammalian renal glomerulus. The problems of intercapillary tissue and the capillary loop basement membrane. Am. J. Path., 34:885–895, 1958.

975. PAK POY, R. K. F.: Electron microscopy of the piscine (Carassius auratus) renal glomerulus. Australian J. Exp. Biol. Med. Sci., 36:191–210, 1958.

976. PAK POY, R. K. F.: Electron microscopy of the reptilian renal glomerulus. Australian J. Exp. Biol. Med. Sci., 37:153–162, 1959.

977. PAK POY, R. K. F. and BENTLEY, P. J.: Fine structure of the epithelial cells of the toad urinary bladder. Exp. Cell Res., 20:235–237, 1960.

978. PAK POY, R. K. F. and ROBERTSON, J. S.: Electron microscopy of the avian renal glomerulus. J. Biophys. Biochem. Cytol., 3:183–192, 1957.

979. PALADE, G. E.: A study of fixation for electron microscopy. J. Exp. Med., 95:285–297, 1952.

980. PALADE, G. E.: The fine structure of mitochondria. Anat. Rec., 114:427–451, 1952.

981. PALADE, G. E.: An electron microscope study of the mitochondrial structure. J. Histochem. Cytochem., 1:188–211, 1953.

982. PALADE, G. E.: Fine structure of blood capillaries. J. Appl. Phys., 24:1424, 1953. (Abstract.)

983. PALADE, G. E.: A small particulate component of the cytoplasm. J. Appl. Phys., 24:1419, 1953. (Abstract.)

984. PALADE, G. E.: Relations between the endoplasmic reticulum and the plasma membrane in macrophages. Anat. Rec., 121:445, 1955. (Abstract.)

985. PALADE, G. E.: A small particulate component of the cytoplasm. J. Biophys. Biochem. Cytol., 1:59–68, 1955.

986. PALADE, G. E.: Studies on the endoplasmic reticulum. II. Simple dispositions in cells in situ. J. Biophys. Biochem. Cytol., 1:567–582, 1955.

987. PALADE, G. E.: The endoplasmic reticulum. J. Biophys. Biochem. Cytol., 2:85–97, 1956, Suppl.

988. PALADE, G. E.: Intracisternal granules in the exocrine cells of the pancreas. J. Biophys. Biochem. Cytol., 2:417–422, 1956.

989. PALADE, G. E.: The endoplasmic reticulum. J. Biophys. Biochem. Cytol., 2:85–97, 1956, Suppl.

990. PALADE, G. E.: Electron microscopy of mitochondria and other cytoplasmic structures. In: Internat. Symposium on Enzymes: Units of Biological Structure and Function, pp. 185–215. Henry Ford Hospital, Detroit. Academic Press, New York, 1956.

991. PALADE, G. E.: A small particulate component of the cytoplasm. In: Frontiers in Cytology, pp. 283–304. Ed.: S. L. Palay. Yale University Press, New Haven, 1958.

992. PALADE, G. E.: Microsomes and ribonucleoprotein particles. In: Microsomal Particles and Protein Synthesis, pp. 36–61. Pergamon Press, New York, 1959.

993. PALADE, G. E.: Blood capillaries of the heart and other organs. Circulation, 24:368–384, 1961.

994. PALADE, G. E.: The secretory process of the pancreatic exocrine cell. In: Electron Microscopy in Anatomy, pp. 176–206. Eds.: J. D. Boyd, F. R. Johnson, and J. D. Lever. Williams and Wilkins, Baltimore, 1961.

995. PALADE, G. E. and PALAY, S. L.: Electron microscope observations of interneuronal and neuromuscular synapses. Anat. Rec., 118:335, 1954. (Abstract.)

996. PALADE, G. E. and PORTER, K. R.: Studies on the endoplasmic reticulum. I. Its identification in cells in situ. J. Exp. Med., 100:641–656, 1954.

997. PALADE, G. E. and SIEKEVITZ, P.: Liver microsomes. An integrated morphological and biochemical study. J. Biophys. Biochem. Cytol., 2:171–200, 1956.

998. PALADE, G. E. and SIEKEVITZ, P.: Liver microsomes: An integrated morphological and biochemical study. J. Biophys. Biochem. Cytol., 2:671–690, 1956.

1000. PALAY, S. L.: Synapses in the central nervous system. J. Biophys. Biochem. Cytol., 2:193–202, 1956, Suppl.

1002. PALAY, S. L.: The morphology of synapses in the central nervous system. Exp. Cell Res., Suppl. 5:275–293, 1958.

1003. PALAY, S. L.: The morphology of secretion. In: Frontiers in Cytology, pp. 305–342. Ed.: S. L. Palay. Yale University Press, New Haven, 1958.

1004. PALAY, S. L.: On the appearance of absorbed fat droplets in the nuclear envelope. J. Biophys. Biochem. Cytol., 7:391–392, 1960.

1005. PALAY, S. L., McGEE-RUSSELL, S. M., GORDON, S., and GRILLO, M.: Fixation of neural tissues for electron microscopy by perfusion with solutions of osmium tetroxide. J. Cell Biol., 12:385–410, 1962.

1006. PALAY, S. L. and KARLIN, L. J.: Absorption of fat by jejunal epithelium in the rat. Anat. Rec., 124:343, 1956. (Abstract.)

1007. PALAY, S. L. and KARLIN, L. J.: An electron microscope study of the intestinal villus. I. The fasting animal. J. Biophys. Biochem. Cytol., 5:363–372, 1959.

1008. PALAY, S. L. and KARLIN, L. J.: An electron microscopic study of the intestinal villus. II. The pathway of fat absorption. J. Biophys. Biochem. Cytol., 5:373–384, 1959.

1009. PALAY, S. L. and PALADE, G. E.: Fine structure of neuronal cytoplasm. J. Appl. Phys., 24:1419, 1953. (Abstract.)

1010. PALAY, S. L. and PALADE, G. E.: The fine structure of neurons. J. Biophys. Biochem. Cytol., 1:69–88, 1955.

1011. PANNESE, E.: Observations on the ultrastructure of the enamel organ. J. Ultrastructure Res., 4:372–400, 1960.

1012. PANNESE, E.: Observations on the morphology, submicroscopic structure and biological properties of satellite cells (S.C.) in sensory ganglia of mammals. Z. Zellforsch., 52:567–597, 1960.

1013. PANNESE, E.: Observations on the ultrastructure of the enamel organ. II. Involution of the stellate reticulum. J. Ultrastructure Res., 5:328–342, 1961.

1014. PANNESE, E.: Detection of neurofilaments in the perikaryon of hypertrophic nerve cells. J. Cell Biol., 13:457–461, 1962.

1015. PANNESE, E.: Observations on the ultrastructure of the enamel organ. III. Internal and external enamel epithelia. J. Ultrastructure Res., 6:186–204, 1962.

1016. PAPPAS, G. D.: The fine structure of the nuclear envelope of *Amoeba proteus*. J. Biophys. Biochem. Cytol., 2:431–434, 1956, Suppl.

1017. PAPPAS, G. D.: Helical structures in the nucleus of *Amoeba proteus*. J. Biophys. Biochem. Cytol., 2:221–222, 1956.

1018. PAPPAS, G. D. and SMELSER, G. K.: Studies on the ciliary epithelium and the zonule. II. Electron microscope observations on changes induced by alteration of normal aqueous humor formation in the rabbit. Am. J. Ophthal., 46:299–318, 1958.

1019. PAPPAS, G. D. and SMELSER, G. K.: The fine structure of the ciliary epithelium in relation to aqueous humor secretion. In: The Structure of the Eye, pp. 453–467. Ed.:

G. K. Smelser. Academic Press, New York, 1961.

1020. PAPPAS, G. D., SMELSER, G. K., and BRANDT, P. W.: Studies on the ciliary epithelium and the zonule. II. Electron and fluorescence microscope observations on the function of membrane elaborations. Arch. Ophthal., 62:959–965, 1959.

1021. PAPPAS, G. D. and TENNYSON, V. M.: An electron microscopic study of the passage of colloidal particles from the blood vessels of the ciliary processes and choroid plexus of the rabbit. J. Cell Biol., 15:227–239, 1962.

1022. PARKER, F.: An electron microscope study of coronary arteries. Am. J. Anat., 103:247–273, 1958.

1023. PARKER, F.: An electron microscopic study of experimental atherosclerosis. Am. J. Path., 36:19–53, 1960.

1024. PARKS, H. F.: The hepatic sinusoidal endothelial cell and its histological relationship. In: Stockholm Conf. Electron Micros., 1956. Proceed. pp. 151–153. Academic Press, New York, 1957.

1025. PARKS, H. F.: On the fine structure of the parotid gland of mouse and rat. Am. J. Anat., 108:303–329, 1961.

1026. PARKS, H. F.: Unusual formations of ergastoplasm in parotid acinous cells of mice. J. Cell Biol., 14:221–234, 1962.

1027. PARKS, H. F.: Morphological study of the extrusion of secretory materials by the parotid glands of mouse and rat. J. Ultrastructure Res., 6:449–465, 1962.

1028. PARKS, H. F. and CHIQUOINE, A. D.: Observations on early stages of phagocytosis of colloidal particles by hepatic phagocytes of the mouse. In: Stockholm Conf. Electron Micros. 1956. Proceed. pp. 154–156. Academic Press, New York, 1957.

1029. PARSONS, D. F.: A simple method for obtaining increased contrast in araldite sections by using postfixation staining of tissues with potassium permanganate. J. Biophys. Biochem. Cytol., 11:492–497, 1961.

1030. PARSONS, D. F.: An electron microscope study of radiation damage in the mouse oocyte. J. Cell Biol., 14:31–48, 1962.

1031. PARSONS, D. F. and DARDEN, E. B.: A technique for the simultaneous dirt-free lead staining of several electron microscope grids of thin sections. J. Biophys. Biochem. Cytol., 8:834–835, 1960.

1032. PEACH, R.: An electron optical study of experimental scurvy. J. Ultrastructure Res., 6:579–590, 1962.

1033. PEACH, R., WILLIAMS, G., and CHAPMAN, J. A.: A light and electron optical study of regenerating tendon. Am. J. Path., 38:495–513, 1961.

1034. PEACHEY, L. D. and PORTER, K. R.: Intracellular impulse conduction in muscle cells. Science, 129:721–722, 1959.

1035. PEACHEY, L. D. and RASMUSSEN, H.: Structure of the toad's urinary bladder as related to its physiology. J. Biophys. Biochem. Cytol., 10:529–553, 1961.

1036. PEARSON, R. and SPARGO, B.: Electron microscope studies on dermal-epidermal separation in human skin. J. Invest. Dermatol., 36:213–224, 1961.

1037. PEASE, D. C.: Electron microscopy of human skin. Am. J. Anat., 89:469–497, 1951.

1038. PEASE, D. C.: The electron microscopy of human skin. Anat. Rec., 112:373–374, 1952.

1039. PEASE, D. C.: Nodes of Ranvier in the central nervous system. J. Comp. Neurol., 103:11–15, 1955.

1040. PEASE, D. C.: Fine structures of the kidney seen by electron microscopy. J. Histochem. Cytochem., 3:295–308, 1955.

1041. PEASE, D. C.: Electron microscopy of the vascular bed of the kidney cortex. Anat. Rec., 121:701–721, 1955.

1042. PEASE, D. C.: Electron microscopy of the tubular cells of the kidney cortex. Anat. Rec., 121:723–743, 1955.

1043. PEASE, D. C.: Infolded basal plasma membranes found in epithelia noted for their water transport. J. Biophys. Biochem. Cytol., 2:203–208, 1956, Suppl.

1044. PEASE, D. C.: Histological Techniques for Electron Microscopy. New York, Academic Press, 1960.

1045. PEASE, D. C. and BAKER, R. F.: The fine structure of mammalian skeletal muscle. Am. J. Anat., 84:175–200, 1949.

1046. PEASE, D. C. and BAKER, R. F.: Electron microscopy of the kidney. Am. J. Anat., 87:349–390, 1950.

1047. PEASE, D. C. and BAKER, R. F.: Electron microscopy of nervous tissue. Anat. Rec., 110:505–529, 1951.

1048. PEASE, D. C. and MOLINARI, S.: Electron microscopy of muscular arteries: pial vessels of the cat and monkey. J. Ultrastructure Res., 3:447–468, 1960.

1049. PEASE, D. C. and PAULE, W. J.: Electron microscopy of elastic arteries; the thoracic aorta of the rat. J. Ultrastructure Res., 3:469–483, 1960.

1049a. PEASE, D. C. and QUILLIAM, T. A.: Electron microscopy of the Pacinian corpuscle. J. Biophys. Biochem. Cytol., 3:331–342, 1957.

1050. PEDLER, CH.: The fine structure of the corneal epithelium. Exp. Eye Res., 1:286–289, 1962.

1051. PETERS, A.: The formation and structure of myelin sheaths in the central nervous system. J. Biophys. Biochem. Cytol., 8:431–446, 1960.

1052. PETERS, A.: A radial component of central myelin sheaths. J. Biophys. Biochem. Cytol., 11:733–735, 1961.

1053. PETERS, A.: Myelogenesis in the central nervous system. In: European Regional Conf. Electron Micros., Delft 1960, Proceed. Vol. II, pp. 803–806. De Nederlandse Vereniging voor Electronenmicroscopie, Delft, 1961.

1054. PETERS, A. and MUIR, A. R.: The relationship between axons and Schwann cells during development of peripheral nerves in the rat. Quart. J. Exp. Physiol., 44:117–130, 1959.

1055. PETRY, G., OVERBECK, L., and VOGELL, W.: Sind Desmosomen statische oder temporäre Zellverbindungen? Naturwissenschaft, 48:166–167, 1961.

1056. Petry, G. and Zuleger, S.: Vergleichende Studie über den Bau der Eihüllen der Ratte. Z. Zellforsch., 47:683–712, 1958.

1057. Pfister, F.: Die Elektronenmikroskopie in der dermatologischen Forschung. Dermatol. Wochschr., 137:428–432, 1958.

1058. Pipan, N.: Licht- und elektronenmikroskopische Untersuchungen über die Differenzierung des embryonalen Pankreas der Maus. Z. Zellforsch., 52:291–314, 1960.

1059. Placková, A. and Štěpánek, J.: Zur Kenntnis der peritubulären Zone des Dentins. Z. Zellforsch., 52:730–738, 1960.

1060. Poche, R.: Submikroskopischer Beitrag zur Pathologie des Herzmuskels. Verhandl. deut. Ges. Pathol., 41:351–355, 1958.

1061. Poche, R.: Zur submikroskopischen Morphologie der Herzmuskelverfettung. Klin. Wochschr., 38:246–247, 1960.

1062. Poche, R. and Lindner, E.: Untersuchungen zur Frage der Glanzstreifen des Herzmuskelgewebes beim Warmblüter und beim Kaltblüter. Z. Zellforsch., 43:104–120, 1955.

1063. Pohl, W.: Die Leberzelle im Elektronenmikroskop. Med. Bild., 2:90–92, 1959.

1064. Pohl, W.: Zur Substruktur und Funktion von Leberzellorganellen. Münch. med. Wochschr., 101:334–336, 1959.

1065. Policard, A.: L'apport de la microscopie électronique à la connaissance d l'appareil de Golgi. Rev. Hématol., 11:471–473, 1956.

1066. Policard, A., Bessis, M., Collet, A., and Giltaire-Ralyte, L.: Une formation submicroscopique cellulaire peu connue: Les microvillosités, Bull. microsc. appl., 5:133–138, 1955.

1067. Policard, A. and Collet, A.: Apports de la microscopie électronique à la connaissance histophysiologique de la paroi alvéolaire. J. Physiol., 48:687–690, 1956.

1068. Policard, A. and Collet, A.: Les données nouvelles apportées par la microscopie électronique à la connaissance du fonctionnement des capillaires sanguins. Rev. franç. étud. clin. biol., 3:205–207, 1958.

1069. Policard, A. and Collet, A.: Étude au microscope électronique de l'appareil de Golgi dans diverses cellules de mammifères en voie de modification. Compt. rend. acad. sci., 246:1124–1127, 1958.

1070. Policard, A. and Collet, A.: A propos du problème des pores nucléaires. Bull. microsc. appl., 8:74–75, 1958.

1071. Policard, A., Collet, A., and Giltaire-Ralyte, L.: Étude au microscope électronique de la "bordure en brosse" du tube urinaire des mammifères. Compt. rend. acad. sci., 239:936–938, 1954.

1072. Policard, A., Collet, A., and Giltaire-Ralyte, L.: Étude au microscope électronique de la cellule alvéolaire de mammifère. Compt. rend. acad. sci., 239:573–575, 1954.

1073. Policard, A., Collet, A., and Giltaire-Ralyte, L.: Étude au microscope électronique des capillaires pulmonaires chez les mammifères. Compt. rend. acad. sci., 239:687–689, 1954.

1075. Policard, A., Collet, A., and Giltaire-Ralyte, L.: L'alvéole pulmonaire au microscope électronique. Presse Med., 62:1775–1777, 1954.

1076. Policard, A., Collet, A., and Giltaire-Ralyte, L.: Bordure superficielle de pseudopodes au niveau des cellules mésothéliales du revêtement peritonéal chez les mammifères. Experientia, 11:152, 1955.

1077. Policard, A., Collet, A., and Giltaire-Ralyte, L.: Constitution inframicroscopique des cils vibratiles des bronchioles du poumon des mammifères. Compt. rend. acad. sci., 241:148–150, 1955.

1078. Policard, A., Collet, A., and Giltaire-Ralyte, L.: Récherches au microscope électronique sur la structure du glomérule rénal des mammifères. Arch. anat. micr., 44:1–19, 1955.

1079. Policard, A., Collet, A., and Giltaire-Ralyte, L.: Structures péricapillaires et mésangium du glomérule rénal du rat observés au microscope électronique. Bull. microsc. appl., 5:5–6, 1955.

1080. Policard, A., Collet, A., and Giltaire-Ralyte, L.: Observations au microscope électronique sur la structure inframicroscopique des arterioles des mammifères. Bull. microsc. appl., 5:3–6, 1955.

1081. Policard, A., Collet, A., and Giltaire-Ralyte, L.: Étude au microscope électronique des cellules alvéolaires du poumon normal de mammifère. Compt. rend. acad. sci., 240:2363–2365, 1955.

1082. Policard, A., Collet, A., and Giltaire-Ralyte, L.: Observations microélectronique sur l'infrastructure des cellules bronchiolaires. Bronches, 5:187–196, 1955.

1083. Policard, A., Collet, A., and Giltaire-Ralyte, L.: Récherches au microscope électronique, sur la phagocytose des particules de silice. Rev. Hematol., 10:674–688, 1955.

1085. Policard, A., Collet, A. and Giltaire-Ralyte, L.: Étude au microscope électronique des reactions pulmonaires initiales aux agressions experimentales par la silice. Presse Med., 63:1775–1777, 1955.

1086. Policard, A., Collet, A., and Martin, J. C.: Récherches au microscope électronique sur diverses infrastructures des voies sanguines des ganglions lymphatiques. Z. Zellforsch., 56:203–212, 1962.

1087. Policard, A., Collet, A., and Martin, J. C.: La surface d'echange air-sang dans le poumon des oiseaux. Étude au microscope électronique. Z. Zellforsch., 57:37–46, 1962.

1088. Policard, A., Collet, A., and Prégermain, S.: Sur quelques dispositions inframicroscopiques de l'endothélium des capillaires pulmonaires chez les mammifères. Compt. rend. acad. sci., 243:8–11, 1956.

1089. Policard, A., Collet, A., and Prégermain, S.: Electron microscope studies on alveolar cells from mammals. In: Stockholm Conf. Electron Micros., 1956. Proceed.

pp. 244–246. Academic Press, New York, 1957.

1090. POLICARD, A., COLLET, A., and PRÉGERMAIN, S.: Structures alvéolaires normales du poumon examinées au microscope électronique. Semaine hôp. path-biol., 33:385–398, 1957.

1091. POLICARD, A., COLLET, A., and PRÉGERMAIN, S.: Études au microscope électronique des capillaires pulmonaires. Acta Anat., 30:624–638, 1957.

1092. POLICARD, A., COLLET, A., and PRÉGERMAIN, S.: Étude infrastructurale des thrombocytes du sang circulant chez le rat. Bull. microsc. appl., 9:26–29, 1959.

1093. POLICARD, A., COLLET, A., and PRÉGERMAIN, S.: Étude au microscope électronique d'un corpuscle nerveux du tissu fibreux peribronchique. Bull. microsc. appl., 9:77–80, 1959.

1094. POLICARD, A., COLLET, A., and PRÉGERMAIN, S.: Sur quelques observations au microscope électronique sur les fibres de réticuline du poumon. Bull. microsc. appl., 9:93–98, 1959.

1095. POLICARD, A., COLLET, A., and PRÉGERMAIN, S.: Récherches au microscope électronique sur les cellules parietales alvéolaires du poumon des mammifères. Z. Zellforsch., 50:561–587, 1959.

1096. POLICARD, A., COLLET, A., and PRÉGERMAIN, S.: Sur l'infrastructure des mitochondries du myocarde. Z. Zellforsch., 50:818–824, 1959.

1097. POLICARD, A., COLLET, A., and PRÉGERMAIN, S.: Le passage entre bronchioles et alvéoles pulmonaires. Étude au microscope électronique. Presse Méd., 26:999–1002, 1960.

1098. POLICARD, A., COLLET, A., and PRÉGERMAIN, S.: Observations au microscope électronique sur quelques vaisseaux pulmonaires. Bull. microsc. appl., 2:17–27, 1960.

1100. POLLISTER, A. W. and POLLISTER, P. F.: The structure of the Golgi apparatus. Int. Rev. Cytol., 6:85–106, 1957.

1101. PORTE, A. and BRINI, A.: Le ligament suspenseur du cristallin. Étude au microscope électronique. Compt. rend. acad. sci., 153:340–343, 1959.

1102. PORTE, A. and PETROVIC, A.: Étude au microscope électronique de la parathyroide de Hamster ordinaire (Cricetus cricetus) en culture organotypique. Compt. rend. soc. biol., 155:2025–2027, 1961.

1103. PORTE, A. and PETROVIC, A.: Sur les caractères ultrastructuraux de la thyroide d'embryons de Poulets en culture organotypique et leur signification fonctionnelle. Compt. rend. soc. biol., 155:1701–1705, 1961.

1104. PORTE, A. and ZAHND, J. P.: Structure fine du follicule ovarien de Lacerta stirpium. Compt. rend. soc. biol., 155:1058–1061, 1961.

1105. PORTER, K. R.: Observations on a submicroscopic basophilic component of cytoplasm. J. Exp. Med., 97:727–750, 1953.

1106. PORTER, K. R.: The submicroscopic structure of animal epidermis. J. Appl. Phys., 24:1424, 1953. (Abstract.)

1107. PORTER, K. R.: Electron microscopy of basophilic components of cytoplasm. J. Histochem. Cytochem., 2:346–375, 1954.

1108. PORTER, K. R.: Observations on the submicroscopic structure of animal epidermis. Anat. Rec., 118:433, 1954. (Abstract.)

1109. PORTER, K. R.: Observations on the fine structure of animal epidermis. In: Third Internat. Conf. Electron Micros., 1954. Proceed. pp. 539–546. Roy. Microscop. Soc., London, 1956.

1110. PORTER, K. R.: The sarcoplasmic reticulum in muscle cells of Amblystoma larvae. J. Biophys. Biochem. Cytol., 2:163–170, 1956, Suppl.

1111. PORTER, K. R.: The submicroscopic morphology of protoplasm. Harvey Lect., 51:175–228, 1957.

1112. PORTER, K. R.: Problems in the study of nuclear fine structure. In: Fourth Internat. Conf. Electron Micros. Berlin, 1958. Proceed. Vol. II, pp. 186–199. Springer Verlag, Berlin, 1960.

1113. PORTER, K. R.: The sarcoplasmic reticulum. Its recent history and present status. J. Biophys. Biochem. Cytol., 10:219–226, 1961, Suppl.

1114. PORTER, K. R.: The ground substance; observations from electron microscopy. In: The Cell. Vol. II, pp. 621–675. Eds.: J. Brachet and A. E. Mirsky. Academic Press, New York, 1961.

1115. PORTER, K. R. and BRUNI, C.: An electron microscopic study of the early effects of $3^1$-Me-DAB on rat liver cells. Cancer Res., 19:997–1009, 1959.

1116. PORTER, K. R. and KALLMAN, F.: The properties and effects of osmium tetroxide as a tissue fixative with special reference to its use for electron microscopy. Exp. Cell Res., 4:127–141, 1953.

1117. PORTER, K. R. and PALADE, G. E.: Studies on the endoplasmic reticulum. III. Its form and distribution in striated muscle cells. J. Biophys. Biochem. Cytol., 3:269–300, 1957.

1118. PORTER, K. R. and PAPPAS, G. D.: Collagen formation by fibroblasts of the chick embryo dermis. J. Biophys. Biochem. Cytol., 5:153–166, 1959.

1119. PORTER, K. R. and YAMADA, E.: Studies on the endoplasmic reticulum. V. Its form and differentiation in pigment epithelial cells of the frog retina. J. Biophys. Biochem. Cytol., 8:181–205, 1960.

1120. POTTS, B. P. and TOMLIN, S. G.: The structure of cilia. Biochim. Biophys. Acta, 16:66–74, 1955.

1121. POWERS, E. L., EHRET, C. F., ROTH, L. E., and MINICK, O. T.: The internal organization of mitochondria. J. Biophys. Biochem. Cytol., 2:341–346, 1956, Suppl.

1122. PRATT, C. W. M.: Observations on the fine structure of the cells of the periosteum. Anat. Rec., 136:261, 1960. (Abstract.)

1123. PRICE, Z., EIDE, B., PRINTZMETAL, M., and CARPENTER, C.: Ultrastructure of the dog cardiac muscle cell. Circulation Res., 7:858–865, 1959.

1124. PROSSER, C. L., BURNSTOCK, G., and KAHN, J.: Conduction in smooth muscle: comparative structural properties. Am. J. Physiol., 199:545–552, 1960.

1125. QUIGLEY, M. B.: Electron microscopy of the amelodentinal junction during early development of the molars of hamsters. J. Dent. Res., 38:558–568, 1959.
1126. QUIGLEY, M. B.: Electron microscopy of developing enamel matrix in the Syrian hamster. J. Dent. Res., 38:180–187, 1959.

1127. RAMSEY, H.: Electron microscopy of the developing cerebral cortex of the rat. Anat. Rec., 139:333, 1961. (Abstract.)
1128. RANDALL, J. T.: Observations on the collagen system. Nature, 174:853–855, 1954.
1129. RAUCH, S.: Physiologie and Pathologie der Regulationen der Speicheldrüsentätigkeit. Deut. zahnärztl. Z., 16:153–160, 1961.
1130. REGER, J. F.: Electron microscopy of the motor end-plate in rat intercostal muscle. Anat. Rec., 122:1–16, 1955.
1131. REGER, J. F.: The ultrastructure of normal and denervated neuromuscular synapses in mouse gastrocnemius muscle. Exp. Cell Res., 12:662–665, 1957.
1132. REGER, J. F.: The fine structure of neuromuscular synapses of gastrocnemii from mouse and frog. Anat. Rec., 130:7–24, 1958.
1133. REGER, J. F.: Studies on the fine structure of normal and denervated neuromuscular junctions from mouse gastrocnemius. J. Ultrastructure Res., 2:269–282, 1959.
1134. REGER, J. F., HUTT, M. P., and NEUSTEIN, H. B.: The fine structure of human hemoglobinuric kidney cells with particular reference to hyalin droplets and iron micelle localization. J. Ultrastructure Res., 5:28–43, 1961.
1135. RÉGNIER, CL. and BOUISSOU, H.: Étude histologique et électronique de l'embryologie du rein. Arch. franç. pédiat., 18:65–82, 1961.
1136. REID, R. T. W.: Observations on the structure of the renal glomerulus of the mouse revealed by the electron microscope. Australian J. Exp. Biol., Med. Sci., 32:235–240, 1954.
1137. REINAUER, H.: Morphologische Befunde an Lymphknoten bei infektiöser Mononukleose. Arch. pathol. anat. Physiol. Virchows, 332:56–82, 1959.
1138. REITH, E. J.: Ultrastructure of enamel organ of rat's incisor. Anat. Rec., 133:327–328, 1959. (Abstract.)
1139. REITH, E. J.: Arrangement of iron in the enamel organ of the rat's incisor. Anat. Rec., 136:264, 1960. (Abstract.)
1140. REITH, E. J.: The ultrastructure of ameloblasts from the growing end of rat incisors. Arch. Oral Biol., 2:253–262, 1960.
1141. REITH, E. J.: The ultrastructure of ameloblasts during matrix formation and the maturation of enamel. J. Biophys. Biochem. Cytol., 9:825–839, 1961.
1142. RESNIK, R. A., WANKO, T., and GAVIN, M. A.: Observations on a cytoplasmic component

in lens fibers. J. Biophys. Biochem. Cytol., 7:403–406, 1960.
1143. REVEL, J. P.: The sarcoplasmic reticulum of the bat cricothyroid muscle. J. Cell Biol., 12:571–588, 1962.
1144. REVEL, J. P., NAPOLITANO, L., and FAWCETT, D. W.: Identification of glycogen in electron micrographs of thin tissue sections. J. Biophys. Biochem. Cytol., 8, 575–589, 1960.
1145. RHODIN, J.: Correlation of ultrastructural organization and function in normal and experimentally changed proximal convoluted tubule cells of the mouse kidney. Thesis, Karolinska Institutet, Stockholm, pp. 1–76, 1954.
1146. RHODIN, J.: Electron microscopy of the glomerular capillary wall. Exp. Cell Res., 8:572–574, 1955.
1147. RHODIN, J.: Electron microscopy of the tracheal cilia. Bronches, 6:159–161, 1956.
1148. RHODIN, J.: Further studies on the nephron ultrastructure in mouse. Terminal part of proximal convolution. In: Stockholm Conf. Electron Micros. 1956. Proceed. pp. 180–182. Academic Press, New York, 1957.
1149. RHODIN, J.: Le tractus épithélial respiratoire, son ultra-structure et sa fonction. Bronches, 7:14–23, 1957.
1150. RHODIN, J.: Ergebnisse der elektronenmikroskopischen Erforschung von Struktur und Funktion der Zelle. Verhandl. deut. Ges. Pathol., 43:274–284, 1958.
1151. RHODIN, J.: Anatomy of kidney tubules. Int. Rev. Cytol., 7:485–534, 1958.
1152. RHODIN, J.: Electron microscopy of the kidney. Am. J. Med., 24:661–675, 1958.
1153. RHODIN, J.: Ultrastructure of the tracheal ciliated mucosa in rat and man. Ann. Otol. Rhinol. Laryngol., 68:964–974, 1959.
1154. RHODIN, J.: Fine structure of mammalian renal tubules. Proc. Ann. Conf. Nephrotic Syndrome, 10th Conf., pp. 30–57, 1959.
1155. RHODIN, J.: Microscopie électronique du rein. Bruxelles-Medical, 12:409–426, 1959.
1156. RHODIN, J.: Fine structure of the vascular pole of the renal corpuscle of the mouse. Anat. Rec., 136:345, 1960. (Abstract.)
1157. RHODIN, J.: Electron microscopy of the kidney. In: Edema: Mechanisms and Management, pp. 33–46. Eds.: J. H. Moyer and M. Fuchs. W. B. Saunders Company, Philadelphia, 1960.
1158. RHODIN, J. A. G.: The diaphragm of capillary endothelial fenestrations. J. Ultrastructure Res., 6:171–185, 1962.
1159. RHODIN, J. A. G.: Fine structure of vascular walls in mammals with special reference to smooth muscle component. Physiol. Reviews, 42:Suppl. 5, 48–87, 1962.
1160. RHODIN, J. A. G.: Electron microscopy of the kidney. In: Renal Disease, pp. 117–156. Ed.: D. A. K. Black. Blackwell Scientific Publ., Oxford, 1962.
1161. RHODIN, J. A. G.: The structure of the kidney. In: Diseases of the Kidney, pp. 10–55. Eds.: M. B. Strauss and L. G. Welt. Little, Brown and Company, Boston, 1963.

1162. RHODIN, J. and DALHAMN, T.: The ultrastructure of the epithelial cells in the trachea of the albino rat. J. Appl. Phys., 25:1463, 1954. (Abstract.)

1163. RHODIN, J. and DALHAMN, T.: Electron microscopy of collagen and elastin in lamina propria of the tracheal mucosa of rat. Exp. Cell Res., 9:371–375, 1955.

1165. RHODIN, J. and DALHAMN, T.: Electron microscopy of the tracheal ciliated mucosa in rat. Z. Zellforsch., 44:345–412, 1956.

1167. RHODIN, J. A. G., DEL MISSIER, P., and REID, L. C.: The structure of the specialized impulse-conducting system of the steer heart. Circulation, 24:349–367, 1961.

1168. RHODIN, J. A. G. and REITH, E. J.: Ultrastructure of keratin in oral mucosa, skin, esophagus, claw, and hair. In: Fundamentals of Keratinization, pp. 61–94. Eds.: E. O. Butcher and R. F. Sognnaes. AAAS, Publication No. 70. Washington, D. C., 1962.

1169. RHODIN, J. and TERZAKIS, J.: The ultrastructure of the human full-term placenta. J. Ultrastructure Res., 6:88–106, 1962.

1170. RICHARDSON, K. G.: Electronmicroscopic observations on Auerbach's plexus in the rabbit, with special reference to the problem of smooth muscle innervation. Am. J. Anat., 103:99–135, 1958.

1171. RICHTER, G. W.: A study of hemosiderosis with the aid of electron microscopy. With observations on the relationship between hemosiderin and ferritin. J. Exp. Med., 106:203–218, 1957.

1172. RICHTER, G. W.: Electron microscopy of hemosiderin: presence of ferritin and occurrence of crystalline lattices in hemosiderin deposits. J. Biophys. Biochem. Cytol., 4:55–58, 1958.

1173. RICHTER, G. W.: The nature of storage iron in idiopathic hemochromatosis and in hemosiderosis. Electron optical, chemical and serologic studies on isolated hemosiderin granules. J. Exp. Med., 112:551–570, 1960.

1174. RICHTER, G. W.: Intranuclear aggregates of ferritin in liver cells of mice treated with saccharated iron oxid. Their possible relation to nuclear protein synthesis. J. Biophys. Biochem. Cytol., 9:263–270, 1961.

1175. RINEHART, J. F., FARQUHAR, M. G., JUNG, C. H., and ABDUL-HAJ, S. K.: The normal glomerulus and its basic reactions in disease. Am. J. Path., 29:21–31, 1953.

1176. RINEHART, J. F.: Fine structure of the renal glomerulus as revealed by electron microscopy. Arch. Path., 59:439–448, 1955.

1177. ROBERTSON, D. M. and VOGEL, F. S.: Concentrical lamination of glial processes in oligodendrogliomas. J. Cell Biol., 15:313–334, 1962.

1178. ROBERTSON, J. D.: Ultrastructure of two invertebrate synapses. Proc. Soc. Exp. Biol. Med., 82:219–223, 1953.

1179. ROBERTSON, J. D.: The ultrastructure of adult vertebrate peripheral myelinated nerve fibers in relation to myelinogenesis. J. Biophys. Biochem. Cytol., 1:271–278, 1955.

1180. ROBERTSON, J. D.: The ultrastructure of the myelin sheath near nodes of Ranvier. J. Physiol., 135:56–57, 1956.

1181. ROBERTSON, J. D.: The ultrastructure of a reptilian myoneural junction. J. Biophys. Biochem. Cytol., 2:381–394, 1956.

1182. ROBERTSON, J. D.: Preliminary observations on the ultrastructure of a frog muscle spindle. In: Stockholm Conf. Electron Micros. 1956. Proceed. pp. 197–200. Academic Press, New York, 1957.

1183. ROBERTSON, J. D.: Some features of the ultrastructure of reptilian skeletal muscle. J. Biophys. Biochem. Cytol., 2:369–380, 1956.

1184. ROBERTSON, J. D.: New observations on the ultrastructure of the membranes of frog peripheral nerve fibers. J. Biophys. Biochem. Cytol., 3:1043–1048, 1957.

1185. ROBERTSON, J. D.: The ultrastructure of nodes of Ranvier in frog nerve fibers. J. Physiol., 137:8–9, 1957.

1186. ROBERTSON, J. D.: The cell membrane concept. J. Physiol., 140:58–59, 1957.

1187. ROBERTSON, J. D.: The ultrastructure of Schmidt-Lanterman clefts and related shearing defects of the myelin sheath. J. Biophys. Biochem. Cytol., 4:39–46, 1958.

1188. ROBERTSON, J. D.: Structural alterations in nerve fibers produced by hypotonic and hypertonic solutions. J. Biophys. Biochem. Cytol., 4:349–364, 1958.

1189. ROBERTSON, J. D.: The ultrastructure of cell membranes and their derivatives. Biochem. Soc. Symp., 16:3–43, 1959.

1190. ROBERTSON, J. D.: Preliminary observations on the ultrastructure of nodes of Ranvier. Z. Zellforsch., 50:553–560, 1959.

1191. ROBERTSON, J. D.: Electron microscopy of the motor end-plate and the neuromuscular spindle. Am. J. Phys. Med., 39:1–43, 1960.

1192. ROBERTSON, J. D.: The molecular biology of cell membranes. In: Molecular Biology: A Symposium, pp. 87–151. Ed.: D. Nachmansohn. Academic Press, New York, 1960.

1193. ROBERTSON, J. D.: The molecular structure and contact relationships of cell membranes. Progr. Biophys. and Biophys. Chem., 10:343–418, 1960.

1194. ROBERTSON, J. D.: The unit membrane. In: Electron Microscopy in Anatomy, pp. 74–99. Eds.: J. D. Boyd, F. R. Johnson, and J. D. Lever. Williams and Wilkins, Baltimore, 1961.

1195. ROBERTSON, J. S.: A morphological study with the electron microscope of sections of the normal mouse pancreas. Australian J. Exp. Biol. Med. Sci., 32:229–234, 1954.

1196. ROBINSON, R. A.: An electron microscope study of the crystalline inorganic component of bone and its relationship to the organic matrix. J. Bone and Joint Surg., 34A:389–434, 1952.

1197. ROBINSON, R. A. and CAMERON, D. A.: Electron microscopy of cartilage and bone matrix at the distal epiphyseal line of the femur in the newborn infant. J. Biophys. Biochem. Cytol., 2:253–260, 1956, Suppl.

Page 203

1198. ROBINSON, R. A. and CAMERON, D. A.: Electron microscopy of the primary spongiosa of the metaphysis at the distal end of the femur in the newborn infant. J. Bone and Joint Surg., 40A: 687–697, 1958.

1199. ROBINSON, R. A. and SHELDON, H.: Crystal-collagen relationships in healing rickets. In: Calcification in Biological Systems, pp. 261–279. Ed.: R. F. Sognnaes. AAAS, Publication No. 64. Washington, D. C., 1960.

1200. ROBINSON, R. A. and WATSON, M. L.: Crystal-collagen relationship in bone as observed in the electron microscope. Ann. N. Y. Acad. Sci., 60:596–628, 1955.

1201. ROBINSON, R. R., ASHWORTH, C. T., GLOVER, S. N., PHILLIPPI, P. J., LECOCQ, F. R., and LANGELIER, P. R.: Fixed and reproducible orthostatic proteinuria. Am. J. Path., 39: 405–417, 1961.

1202. RODMAN, N. F., MASON, R. G., McDEVITT, N. B., and BRINKHOUS, K. M.: Morphologic alterations of human blood platelets during early phases of clotting. Electron microscopic observations of thin sections. Am. J. Path., 40:271–284, 1962.

1203. ROGERS, G. E.: Electron microscopy of mast cells in the skin of young mice. Exp. Cell Res., 11:393–402, 1956.

1204. ROGERS, G. E.: Electron microscope observations on the glassy layer of the hair follicle. Exp. Cell Res., 13:521–528, 1957.

1205. ROGERS, G. E.: Some aspects of the structure of the inner root sheath of hair follicles revealed by light and electron microscopy. Exp. Cell Res., 14:378–387, 1958.

1206. ROGERS, G. E.: Electron microscope studies of hair and wool. Ann. N. Y. Acad. Sci., 83:378–399, 1959.

1207. ROGERS, G. E.: Electron microscopy of wool. J. Ultrastructure Res., 2:309–330, 1959.

1208. ROGERS, G. E.: Fine structure of keratin. J. Appl. Phys., 32:1637, 1961. (Abstract.)

1209. RÖHLICH, P. and KNOOP, A.: Elektronenmikroskopische Untersuchungen an den Hüllen des N. Ischiadicus der Ratte. Z. Zellforsch., 53:299–312, 1961.

1210. ROLLHÄUSER, H. and VOGELL, W.: Elektronenmikroskopische Untersuchungen über die aktive Stoffausscheidung in der Niere. Z. Zellforsch., 47:53–76, 1957.

1211. ROLLHÄUSER, H. and VOGELL, W.: Die tubuläre Phenolrotausscheidung und die Feinstrukturveränderungen der Glomerula bei der Rattenniere im traumatischen Schock. Z. Zellforsch., 52:549–566, 1960.

1213. RÖNNHOLM, E.: An electron microscopic study of the amelogenesis in human teeth. I. The fine structure of the ameloblasts. J. Ultrastructure Res., 6:229–248, 1962.

1214. RÖNNHOLM, E.: The amelogenesis of human teeth as revealed by electron microscopy. II. The development of the enamel crystallites. J. Ultrastructure Res., 6:249–303, 1962.

1215. RÖNNHOLM, E.: III. The structure of the organic stroma of human enamel during amelogenesis. J. Ultrastructure Res., 6:368–389, 1962.

1216. ROOS, B.: Die submikroskopische Struktur der Rattenschilddrüse. Ihre Beeinflussung durch hohe Dosen von thyreotropem Hormon. Ein Beitrag zum Studium der Sekretionsvorgänge in der Schilddrüse. Pathol. et Microbiol., 23:129–157, 1960.

1218. ROSENBERG, M., BARTL, P., and LESKO, J.: Water-soluble methacrylate as an embedding medium for the preparation of ultrathin sections. J. Ultrastructure Res., 4:298–303, 1960.

1219. ROSENBLUTH, J.: The fine structure of acoustic ganglia in the rat. J. Cell Biol., 12:329–359, 1962.

1220. ROSENBLUTH, J.: Subsurface cisterns and their relationship to the neuronal plasma membrane. J. Cell Biol., 13:405–421, 1962.

1221. ROSENBLUTH, J.: and PALAY, S. L.: Electron microscopic observations on the interface between neurons and capsular cells in dorsal root ganglia of the rat. Anat. Rec., 136:268, 1960. (Abstract.)

1222. ROSENBLUTH, J. and PALAY, S. L.: The fine structure of nerve cell bodies and their myelin sheaths in the eighth nerve ganglion of the goldfish. J. Biophys. Biochem. Cytol., 9:853–877, 1961.

1223. ROSS, L. L.: Electron microscopic observations of the carotid body of the cat. J. Biophys. Biochem. Cytol., 6:253–262, 1959.

1224. ROSS, L. L., BORNSTEIN, M. B., and LEHRER, G. M.: Electron microscopic observations of rat and mouse cerebellum in tissue culture. J. Cell Biol., 14:19–30, 1962.

1225. ROSS, M. H.: Electron microscopy of the human foetal adrenal cortex. In: The Human Adrenal Cortex, pp. 558–569. Eds.: A. R. Currie, T. Symington, and G. K. Grand. Livingstone Ltd., Edinburgh, 1960.

1226. ROSS, M. H., PAPPAS, G. D., LANMAN, J. T., and LIND, J.: Electron microscope observations on the endoplasmic reticulum in the human fetal adrenal. J. Biophys. Biochem. Cytol., 4:659–662, 1958.

1227. ROSS, R. and BENDITT, P.: Wound healing and collagen formation. I. Sequential changes in components of guinea pig skin wounds observed in the electron microscope. J. Biophys. Biochem. Cytol., 11:677–700, 1961.

1228. ROSS, R. and BENDITT, E. P.: Wound healing and collagen formation. II. Fine structure in experimental scurvy. J. Cell Biol., 12:533–551, 1962.

1229. ROTH, L. E.: A method for reducing methacrylate sublimation from thin sections. J. Ultrastructure Res., 5:142–150, 1961.

1230. ROTH, S. I.: Pathology of the parathyroids in hyperparathyroidism. Arch. Path., 73: 495–510, 1962.

1231. ROUILLER, CH.: Les canalicules biliares. Étude au microscope électronique. Compt. rend. soc. biol., 148:2008–2011, 1954.

1232. ROUILLER, CH.: Les canalicules biliares. Étude au microscope électronique. Acta Anat., 26:94–109, 1956.

1233. ROUILLER, CH. Contribution de la microscopie électronique a l'étude du foie normal et pathologique. Ann. anat. pathol., 2:548–562, 1957.

1234. ROUILLER, CH.: La contribution de la microscopie électronique à l'étude du rein normal et pathologique. Schweiz. med. Wochschr., 91:65–73, 1961.

1235. ROUILLER, CH. and BERNHARD, W.: Microbodies and the problem of mitochondrial regeneration in liver cells. J. Biophys. Biochem. Cytol., 2:355–360, 1956, Suppl.

1236. ROUILLER, CH., DANON, D., and RYTER, A.: Application de la microscopie électronique à l'étude de la cornée. Acta Anat., 20:39–52, 1954.

1237. ROUILLER, CH. and GANSLER, H.: Les modifications des mitochondries du foie et du rein chez le rat a jeun et réalimenté. Étude au microscope électronique. In: Symposium on the Fine Structure of Cells. 8th Congress of Cell Biology, Leiden, Holland, 1954, pp. 82–85. Noordhoff, Groningen, 1955.

1238. ROUILLER, CH. and GANSLER, H.: Contribution à la pathologie des mitochondries. Bull. microsc. appl., 5:17–18, 1955.

1239. ROUILLER, CH., HUBER, L., and RUTISHAUSER, E.: La structure de la dentine. Étude comparée de l'os et de l'ivoire au microscope électronique. Acta Anat., 16:16–28, 1952.

1240. RUSKA, C.: Die Zellstrukturen des Dünndarmepithels in ihrer Abhängigkeit von der physikalisch-chemischen Beschaffenheit des Darminhalts. I. Wasser und Natriumchlorid. Z. Zellforsch., 52:748–777, 1960.

1241. RUSKA, C.: Die Zellstrukturen des Dünndarmepithels in ihrer Abhängigkeit von der physikalisch-chemischen Beschaffenheit des Darminhalts. II. Wasserlösliche, grenzflächenaktive Stoffe. Z. Zellforsch., 53:867–878, 1961.

1242. RUSKA, C.: Die Zellstrukturen des Dünndarmepithels in ihrer Abhängigkeit von der physikalisch-chemischen Beschaffenheit des Darminhalts. V. Lipoidlösungsmittel verschiedener Wasserlöslichkeit. Z. Zellforsch., 56:762–788, 1962.

1243. RUSKA, H.: The morphology of muscle fibers and muscle cells with different properties of conduction of excitation. Exp. Cell Res., Suppl. 5:560–567, 1958.

1244. RUSKA, H.: Struktur und Funktion der Zelle. Deut. med. J., 12:711–714, 1961.

1245. RUSKA, H., EDWARDS, G.A., and CAESAR, R.: A concept of intracellular transmission of excitation by means of endoplasmic reticulum. Experientia, 14:117–120, 1958.

1246. RUSKA, H., MOORE, D. H., and WEINSTOCK, J.: The base of the proximal convoluted tubule cells of the rat kidney. J. Biophys. Biochem. Cytol., 3:249–254, 1957.

1247. RÜTTNER, J. R. and VOGEL, A.: Elektronmikroskopische Untersuchungen an der Lebersinusoidwand. Verhandl. deut. Ges. Pathol., 41:314–319, 1958.

1248. SABATINI, D. D. and DE ROBERTIS, E.: Ultrastructural zonation of adrenocortex in the rat. J. Biophys. Biochem. Cytol., 9:105–119, 1961.

1249. SAKAGUCHI, H.: Fine structure of the renal glomerulus. Keio J. Med., 4:103–112, 1955.

1250. SAKAGUCHI, H. and SUZUKI, Y.: Fine structure of renal tubule cells. Keio J. Med., 7:17–26, 1958.

1251. SALPETER, M. M. and SINGER, M.: Differentiation of the submicroscopic adepidermal membrane during limb regeneration in adult triturus, including a note on the use of the term basement membrane. Anat. Rec., 136:27–39, 1960.

1252. SAMPAIO, M. M.: The use of Thorotrast for the electron microscopic study of phagocytosis. Anat. Rec., 124:501–518, 1956.

1253. SAMPAIO, M. M., BRUNNER, A., JR., and FILHO, B. O.: Aspects of the ultrastructure of the brush border of the kidney of normal mouse. J. Biophys. Biochem. Cytol., 4:335–336, 1958.

1254. SANDERS, E. and ASHWORTH, C. T.: A study of particulate intestinal absorption and hepatocellular uptake. Exp. Cell Res., 22:137–145, 1961.

1255. SATIR, P.: On the evolutionary stability of the 9 + 2 pattern. J. Cell Biol., 12:181–184, 1962.

1256. SAWASAKI, C., MORI, T., INONE, T., and SHINMI, K.: Observations on the human placental membrane under the electron microscope. Endocrinologia Japonica, 4:1–11, 1957.

1257. SCHAFFNER, F. and POPPER, H.: Electron microscopic studies of normal and proliferated bile ductules. Am. J. Path. 38:393–410, 1961.

1258. SCHAFFNER, F., STERNLIEB, I., BARKA, T., and POPPER, H.: Hepatocellular changes in Wilson's disease. Histochemical and electron microscopic studies. Am. J. Path., 41:315–327, 1962.

1259. SCHLIPKÖTER, H. W.: Elektronenoptische Untersuchungen ultradünner Lungenschnitte. Deut. med. Wochschr., 79:1658–1659, 1954.

1260. SCHLIPKÖTER, H. W.: Elektronenoptische Untersuchungen von Gewebeschnitten aus silikotischen Granulomen. Klin. Wochschr., 3:54–56, 1955.

1261. SCHLIPKÖTER, H. W.: Eigenschaften und Wirkung von Staubaerosolen unter besonderer Berücksichtigung der Gewerbestaube. In: Bekämpfung der Silikose, Vol. II, pp. 20–151. Verlag Glückauf GMBH, Essen, 1956.

1262. SCHLIPKÖTER, H. W.: Normales Lungengewebe im elektronenoptischen Bild. Z. Aerosol-Forsch. Therap., 6:121–129, 1957.

1263. SCHLOTE, F.-W.: Submikroskopische morphologie von Gastropodennerven. Z. Zellforsch., 45:543–568, 1957.

1264. SCHLOTE, F.-W.: Die Kontraktion glatter Muskulatur auf Grund von Torsionsspannungen in den Myofilamenten. Z. Zellforsch., 52:363–395, 1960.

1265. SCHMIDT, F. C.: Electron microscopic observations of the sinusoid wall cells (Kupffer stellate cells) of white mice. Anat. Rec., 136:274, 1960. (Abstract.)

1266. SCHMIDT, W.: Elektronenmikroskopische Untersuchungen über die Speicherung von

Trypanblau in den Zellen des Haupt-stücks der Niere. Z. Zellforsch., 52:598–603, 1960.

1267. SCHMIDT, W.: Elektronenmikroskopische Un-tersuchung des intrazellulären Stofftrans-portes in der Dünndarmepithelzelle nach Markierung mit Myoffer. Z. Zellforsch., 54:803–806, 1961.

1268. SCHMITT, F. O.: The fibrous protein of the nerve axon. J. Cell. Comp. Physiol., 49:165–174, 1957, Suppl. 1.

1269. SCHMITT, F. O.: Axon-satellite cell relation-ships in peripheral nerve fibers. Exp. Cell Res., Suppl. 5:33–57, 1958.

1270. SCHMITT, F. O.: Interaction properties of elongate protein macromolecules with particular reference to collagen (tropo-collagen). Rev. Modern Phys., 31:349–358, 1959.

1271. SCHMITT, F. O.: Molecular organization of the nerve fiber. Rev. Modern Phys., 31:455–465, 1959.

1272. SCHMITT, F. O. and GEREN, B. B.: The fibrous structure of the nerve axon in relation to localization of "neurotubules." J. Exp. Med., 91:499–504, 1950.

1273. SCHMITT, F. O. and GESCHWIND, N.: The axon surface. Progress in Biophysics, 8:165–215, 1957.

1274. SCHROFF, F. R., WILLIAMSON, K. I., and BERTAUD, W. S.: Electron microscope studies of dentine. The true nature of dentinal canals. Oral Surg., Oral Med., Oral Pathol., 7:662–670, 1954.

1275. SCHULTZ, R. L., MAYNARD, E. A., and PEASE, D. C.: Electron microscopy of neurons and neuroglia of cerebral cortex and corpus callosum. Am. J. Anat., 100:369–407, 1957.

1276. SCHULTZ, R. L. and PEASE, D. C.: Cicatrix formation in rat cerebral cortex as re-vealed by electron microscopy. Am. J. Path., 35:1017–1041, 1959.

1277. SCHULTZ-LARSEN, J.: The morphology of the human sperm. Electron microscopic in-vestigations of the ultrastructure. Acta Pathol. Microbiol. Scand., Suppl. 128:1–121, 1958.

1278. SCHULZ, H.: Über den Gestaltwandel der Mitochondrien im Alveolarepithel unter $CO_2$- und $O_2$-Atmung. Naturwissenschaf-ten, 43:205–206, 1956.

1279. SCHULZ, H.: Elektronenoptische Unter-suchungen der normalen Lunge und der Lunge bei Mitralstenose. Arch. pathol. Anat. Physiol., Virchow's, 328:582–604, 1956.

1280. SCHULZ, H.: Elektronenmikroskopische Unter-suchungen der Lunge des Siebenschläfers nach Hibernation. Z. Zellforsch., 46:583–597, 1957.

1281. SCHULZ, H.: Elektronenmikroskopische Unter-suchungen der Lunge des Siebenschläfers im Winterschlaf und der embryonalen Rattenlunge. Verhandl. deut. Ges. Pathol., 41:342–344, 1957.

1282. SCHULZ, H.: Die Pathologie der Mitochondrien im Alveolarepithel der Lunge. Beitr. pathol. Anat. allgem. Pathol., 119:45–70, 1958.

1283. SCHULZ, H.: Die submikroskopische Anatomie und Pathologie der Lunge. Springer Verlag, Berlin, 1959.

1284. SCHULZ, H.: Submikroskopische Beiträge zur Orthologie und Pathologie der Thrombo-cyten. Verhandl. deut. Ges. inn. Med., 66:832–848, 1960.

1285. SCHULZE, W.: Elektronenmikroskopische Studie zur Frage der Entstehung von primären Bindegewebsfibrillen im embryonalen Hundeherzen. Acta Biol. et Med. Ger., 6:491–497, 1961.

1286. SCHWARTZ, W., MERKER, H.-J., and KIRTZ-SCHE, A.: Elektronenmikroskopische Un-tersuchungen über die Fibrillogenese in Fibroblastenkulturen. Z. Zellforsch., 56:107–124, 1962.

1287. SCHWARZ, W.: Elektronenmikroskopische Untersuchungen über den Aufbau der Sklera und der Cornea des Menschen. Z. Zellforsch., 38:26–49, 1953.

1288. SCHWARZ, W.: Elektronenmikroskopische Un-tersuchungen über die Differenzierung der Cornea- und Sklera-fibrillen des Men-schen. Z. Zellforsch., 38:78–86, 1953.

1289. SCHWARZ, W.: Elektronenmikroskopische Un-tersuchungen an Sehnenfibrillen verschie-dener Wirbeltiere. Z. Zellforsch., 48:309–323, 1958.

1290. SCHWARZ, W.: Elektronenmikroskopische Un-tersuchungen über die Bildung der elas-tischen Membranen in der embryona-len Aorta des Menschen. Verhandl. Anat. Ges., 56:308–330, 1959.

1291. SCHWARZ, W.: Electron microscopical studies of the fibrillogenesis in the human cornea. Anat. Rec., 136:275, 1960. (Abstract.)

1292. SCHWARZ, W.: Electron microscopical studies of the fibrillogenesis in the human cornea. In: The Structure of the Eye, pp. 393–403. Ed.: G. K. Smelser. Academic Press, New York, 1961.

1293. SCHWARZ, W. and HOFMANN, M.: Das Dop-pellamellen-System in den Drüsenzellen der Parotis. In: Fourth Internat. Conf. Electron Micros. Berlin 1958. Proceed. Vol. II, pp. 369–371. Springer Verlag, Berlin, 1960.

1294. SCHWARZACKER, H. G.: Untersuchungen über die Skeletmuskel-Sehnenverbindung. I. Elektronenmikroskopische und licht-mikroskopische Untersuchungen über der Feinbau der Muskelfaser-Sehnenverbin-dung. Acta Anat., 40:59–86, 1960.

1295. SCOTT, B. L. and PEASE, D. C.: Electron microscopy of the salivary and lacrimary glands of the rat. Am. J. Anat., 104:115–161, 1959.

1296. SCOTT, D. B.: Recent contributions in dental histology by use of the electron microscope. Int. Dent. J., 4:64–95, 1953.

1297. SCOTT, D. B.: The electron microscopy of enamel and dentine. Ann. N. Y. Acad. Sci., 60:575–584, 1955.

1298. SCOTT, D. B.: The crystalline component of dental enamel. In: Fourth Internat. Conf. Electron Micros. Berlin 1958. Proceed. Vol. II, pp. 348–351. Springer Verlag, Berlin, 1960.

1299. SCOTT, D. B., NYLEN, M. U., and TAKUMA,

S.: Electron microscopy of developing and mature calcified tissues. Rev. belge sci. dent., 14:329–342, 1959.

1300. SEBRUYNS, M.: Study of the ultrastructure of the retinal epithelium by means of the electron microscope. Am. J. Ophthal., 34:989–992, 1951.

1301. SEBRUYNS, M.: The ultrastructure of the cornea and lens studied by means of electron microscope. Am. J. Ophthal., 34:1437–1442, 1951.

1302. SEDAR, A. W.: Fine structure of parietal cells. Anat. Rec., 121:365, 1955. (Abstract.)

1303. SEDAR, A. W.: Further studies on the fine structure of parietal cells. Anat. Rec., 127:482–483, 1957. (Abstract.)

1304. SEDAR, A. W.: An attempt to correlate the fine structure of the parietal cell with the func-. tional state of the gastric mucosa. Anat. Rec., 133:337, 1959. (Abstract.)

1305. SEDAR, A. W.: Electron microscopy of the granular cells in the gastric glands of the bullfrog (Rana catesbiana) secreting in response to histamine. Anat. Rec., 136:275, 1960. (Abstract.)

1306. SEDAR, A. W.: Electron microscopy of the oxyntic cell in the gastric glands of the bullfrog (Rana catesbiana). I. The non-acid secreting gastric mucosa. J. Biophys. Biochem. Cytol., 9:1–18, 1961.

1307. SEDAR, A. W.: Electron microscopy of the oxyntic cell in the gastric glands of the bullfrog Rana catesbiana. II. The acid-secreting gastric mucosa. J. Biophys. Biochem. Cyto., 10:47–57, 1961.

1308. SEDAR, A. W.: Electron microscopy of the oxyntic cell in the gastric glands of the bullfrog Rana catesbiana. III. Permanganate fixation of the endoplasmic reticulum. J. Cell Biol., 14:152–156, 1962.

1309. SEDAR, A. W. and FRIEDMAN, M. H.: Electron microscopy of the parietal cell in the dog gastric glands proper secreting in response to histamine or vagus stimulation. Federation Proc., 18:141, 1959. (Abstract.)

1310. SEDAR, A. W. and FRIEDMAN, M. H. F.: Correlation of the fine structure of the gastric parietal cell (dog) with functional activity of the stomach. J. Biophys. Biochem. Cytol., 11:349–363, 1961.

1311. SELBY, C. C.: Electron microscopy: a review. Cancer Res., 13:753–755, 1953.

1312. SELBY, C. C.: An electron microscopic study of the epidermis of mammalian skin in thin sections. I. Dermo-epidermal junction and basal cell layer. J. Biophys. Biochem. Cytol., 1:429–444, 1955.

1313. SELBY, C. C.: An electron microscope study of the epidermis of mammalian skin in thin sections. II. Superficial cell layers. J. Appl. Phys., 26:1393, 1955. (Abstract.)

1314. SELBY, C. C.: The fine structure of human epidermis as revealed by the electron microscope. J. Soc. Cosmetic Chemists, 7:584–599, 1956.

1315. SELBY, C. C.: An electron microscope study of thin sections of human skin. II. Superficial cell layers of foot pad epidermis. J. Invest. Dermat., 29:131–150, 1957.

1316. SELBY, C. C.: Electron microscopy: Techniques and applications in cytology. In: Analytical Cytology, 2nd ed., pp. 273–341. Ed.: R. C. Mellors. McGraw-Hill Book Co., New York, 1959.

1317. SETÄLÄ, K., MERENMIES, L., STJERNVALL, L., and NYHOLM, M.: Mechanism of experimental tumorigenesis. IV. Ultrastructure of interfollicular epidermis of normal adult mouse. J. Natl. Cancer Inst., 24:329–353, 1960.

1318. SHELDON, H.: An electron microscope study of the epithelium in the normal mature and immature mouse cornea. J. Biophys. Biochem. Cytol., 2:253–262, 1956.

1319. SHELDON, H. and KIMBALL, F. B.: Studies on cartilage. III. The occurrence of collagen within vacuoles of the Golgi apparatus. J. Cell Biol., 12:599–613, 1962.

1320. SHELDON, H. and ROBINSON, R. A.: Electron microscope studies of crystal collagen relationships in bone. IV. The occurrence of crystals within collagen fibrils. J. Biophys. Biochem. Cytol., 3:1011–1016, 1957.

1321. SHELDON, H. and ROBINSON, R. A.: Studies on cartilage. Electron microscope observations on normal rabbit ear cartilage. J. Biophys. Biochem. Cytol., 4:401–406, 1958.

1322. SHELDON, H. and ROBINSON, R. A.: Studies on cartilage. II. Electron microscope observations on rabbit ear cartilage following the administration of papain. J. Biophys. Biochem. Cytol., 8:151–163, 1960.

1323. SHELDON, H. and ROBINSON, R. A.: Studies on rickets. I. The fine structure of uncalcified bone matrix in experimental rickets. Z. Zellforsch., 53:671–684, 1961.

1324. SHELDON, H. and ROBINSON, R. A.: Studies on rickets. II. The fine structure of the cellular components of bone in experimental rickets. Z. Zellforsch., 53:685–701, 1961.

1325. SHELDON, H., SILVERBERG, M., and KERNER, I.: On the differing appearance of intranuclear and cytoplasmic glycogen in liver cells in glycogen storage disease. J. Cell Biol., 13:468–473, 1962.

1326. SHOENBERG, C. F.: An electron microscope study of smooth muscle in pregnant uterus of the rabbit. J. Biophys. Biochem. Cytol., 4:609–614, 1958.

1327. SHROFF, F. R., WILLIAMSON, K., and BERTAUD, W. S.: Electron microscope studies of dentine. Oral Surg., Oral Med., Oral Pathol., 7:662–670, 1954.

1328. SIADAT-POUR, A.: Die Ultrastruktur des Blut-Harnweges in verschiedenen Abschnitten des Nephrons bei der Maus. Beitr. pathol. Anat. allgem. Pathol., 120:382–398, 1959.

1329. SIEKEVITZ, P. and PALADE, G. E.: A cytochemical study on the pancreas of the guinea pig. VI. Release of enzymes and ribonucleic acid from ribonucleoprotein particles. J. Biophys. Biochem. Cytol., 7:631–644, 1960.

1330. SIEKEVITZ, P. and PALADE, G. E.: Cytochemical study on the pancreas of the guinea pig. VII. Effects of spermine on ribosomes. J. Cell Biol., 13:217–232, 1962.

1331. SIEKEVITZ, P. and WATSON, M. L.: Cyto-

Page 207

chemical studies of mitochondria. II. Enzymes associated with a mitochondrial membrane fraction. J. Biophys. Biochem. Cytol., 2:653–670, 1956.

1332. SILBERBERG, R., SILBERBERG, M., VOGEL, A., and WETTSTEIN, W.: Ultrastructure of articular cartilage of mice of various ages. Am. J. Anat., 109:251–275, 1961.

1333. SILK, M. H., HAWTREY, A. O., SPENCE, I. M., and GEAR, J. H. S.: A method for intracellular autoradiography in the electron microscope. J. Biophys. Biochem. Cytol., 10:577–587, 1961.

1334. DA SILVA SASSO, W. and DE SOUZA SANTOS, H.: Electron microscopy of enamel and dentin of teeth of the *Odontaspis* (*Selachii*). J. Dent. Res., 40:49–57, 1961.

1335. SIMPSON, F. O. and OERTELIS, S. J.: Relationship of the sarcoplasmic reticulum to sarcolemma in sheep cardiac muscle. Nature, 189:758–759, 1961.

1336. SIMPSON, F. O. and OERTELIS, S. J.: The fine structure of sheep myocardial cells; Sarcolemmal invaginations and the transverse tubular system. J. Cell Biol., 12:91–100, 1962.

1337. SINGER, S. J. and SCHICK, A. F.: The properties of specific stains for electron microscopy prepared by the conjugation of antibody molecules with ferritin. J. Biophys. Biochem. Cytol., 9:519–537, 1961.

1338. SITTE, H.: Veränderungen im Glomerulum der Rattenniere nach Fremdeiweissgaben und hypothetische Erklärung der glomerulären Ultrafiltration. Verh. deut. Ges. Pathol., 43:225–234, 1959.

1339. SJÖSTRAND, F. S.: An electron microscopic study of the retinal rods of the guinea pig eye. J. Cell. Comp. Physiol., 33:383–404, 1949.

1340. SJÖSTRAND, F. S.: Electron microscopic demonstration of a membrane structure isolated from nerve tissue. Nature, 165:482–483, 1950.

1341. SJÖSTRAND, F. S.: The lamelated structure of the nerve myelin sheath as revealed by high resolution electron microscopy. Experientia, 9:68–69, 1953.

1342. SJÖSTRAND, F. S.: The ultrastructure of the outer segments of rods and cones of the eye as revealed by the electron microscope. J. Cell. Comp. Physiol., 42:15–44, 1953.

1343. SJÖSTRAND, F. S.: The ultrastructure of the inner segments of the retinal rods of the guinea pig eye as revealed by electron microscopy. J. Cell. Comp. Physiol., 42:45–70, 1953.

1344. SJÖSTRAND, F. S.: Electron microscopy of mitochondria and cytoplasmic double membranes. Nature, 171:30–32, 1953.

1345. SJÖSTRAND, F. S.: Electron microscopy of cells and tissues. Phys. Tech. Biol. Res., 3:241–298, 1956.

1346. SJÖSTRAND, F. S.: Ultrastructure of cells as revealed by the electron microscope. Int. Rev. Cytol., 5:455–533, 1956.

1347. SJÖSTRAND, F. S.: Ultrastructure of retinal rod synapses of the guinea pig eye as revealed by three-dimensional reconstructions from serial sections. J. Ultrastructure Res., 2:122–170, 1958.

1348. SJÖSTRAND, F. S.: Fine structure of cytoplasm: the organization of membranous layers. Rev. Modern Phys., 31:301–318, 1959.

1349. SJÖSTRAND, F. S.: The ultrastructure of the retinal receptors of the vertebrate eye. Ergeb. Biol., 21:128–160, 1959.

1350. SJÖSTRAND, F. S.: Electron microscopy of the retina. In: The Structure of the Eye, pp. 1–28. Ed.: G. K. Smelser. Academic Press, New York, 1961.

1351. SJÖSTRAND, F. S. and ANDERSSON, E.: The ultrastructure of skeletal muscle myofilaments at various conditions of shortening. Exp. Cell Res., 11:493–496, 1956.

1352. SJÖSTRAND, F. S. and ANDERSSON-CEDERGREN, E.: The ultrastructure of the skeletal muscle myofilaments at various stages of shortening. J. Ultrastructure Res., 1:74–108, 1957.

1353. SJÖSTRAND, F. S. and ANDERSSON-CEDERGREN, E.: Intercalated discs of heart muscle. In: The Structure and Function of Muscle. I. Structure, pp. 421–445. Ed.: H. G. Bourne. Academic Press, New York, 1960.

1354. SJÖSTRAND, F. S., ANDERSSON-CEDERGREN, E., and DEWEY, M.: The ultrastructure of the intercalated discs of frog, mouse and guinea pig cardiac muscle. J. Ultrastructure Res., 1:271–286, 1958.

1354a. SJÖSTRAND, F. S. and HANZON, V.: Electron microscopy of the Golgi apparatus of the exocrine pancreas cells. Experientia, 10:367–368, 1954.

1354b. SJÖSTRAND, F. S. and HANZON, V.: Membrane structures of cytoplasm and mitochondria in exocrine cells of mouse pancreas as revealed by high resolution electron microscopy. Exp. Cell Res., 7:393–414, 1954.

1354c. SJÖSTRAND, F. S. and HANZON, V.: Ultrastructure of Golgi apparatus of exocrine cells of mouse pancreas. Exp. Cell Res., 7:415–429, 1954.

1355. SJÖSTRAND, F. S. and RHODIN, J.: The ultrastructure of the proximal convoluted tubules of the mouse kidney as revealed by high resolution electron microscopy. Exp. Cell Res., 4:426–456, 1953.

1356. SMITH, C. A.: Electron microscopic studies of the organ of Corti. Anat. Rec., 121:451, 1955.

1357. SMITH, C. A.: Electron microscopic studies of cochlear and vestibular receptors. Anat. Rec., 127:483, 1957. (Abstract.)

1358. SMITH, C. A.: Structure of the stria vascularis and the spiral prominence. Ann. Otol. Rhinol. Laryngol., 66:521–536, 1957.

1359. SMITH, C. A. and DEMPSEY, E. W.: Electron microscopy of the organ of Corti. Am. J. Anat., 100:337–367, 1957.

1360. SMITH, C. A. and SJÖSTRAND, F. S.: A synaptic structure in the hair cells of the guinea pig cochlea. J. Ultrastructure Res., 5:184–192, 1961.

1361. SMITH, C. A. and SJÖSTRAND, F. S.: Structure of the nerve endings on the external hair cells of the guinea pig cochlea as studied by serial sections. J. Ultrastructure Res., 5:523–556, 1961.

1362. SMITH, D. S.: Reticular organizations within the striated muscle cell. An historical survey of light microscopic studies. J. Biophys. Biochem. Cytol., 10:61–87, 1961. Suppl.

1363. SMITH, D. E. and LEWIS, Y. S.: Electron microscopy of the tissue mast cell. J. Biophys. Biochem. Cytol., 3:9–14, 1957.

1364. SMITH, J. R., BURFORD, T. H., and CHIQUOINE, A. D.: Electron microscopic observations of the ventricular heart muscle of man obtained by surgical biopsy during thoracotomy. Exp. Cell Res., 20:228–232, 1960.

1365. SMITH, S. W.: "Reticular" and "areticular" Nissl bodies in sympathetic neurons of a lizard. J. Biophys. Biochem. Cytol., 6:77–84, 1959.

1366. SOGNNAES, R. F. and ALBRIGHT, J. T.: Preliminary observations on the fine structure of oral mucosa. Anat. Rec., 126:225–240, 1956.

1367. SOGNNAES, R. F. and ALBRIGHT, J. T.: Electron microscopy of the epithelial lining of the human oral mucosa. Oral Surg., Oral Med., Oral Pathol., 11:662–673, 1958.

1368. SOGNNAES, R. F., SCOTT, D. B., USSING, M. J., and WYCKOFF, W. G.: Electron microscopy of the enamel of teeth in various stages of development. J. Dent. Res., 31:85–93, 1952.

1369. SORENSON, G. D.: An electron microscopic study of hematopoiesis in the liver of the fetal rabbit. Am. J. Anat., 106:27–40, 1960.

1370. SORENSON, G. D.: An electron microscopic study of popliteal lymph nodes from rabbits. Am. J. Anat., 107:73–96, 1960.

1371. SOTELO, J. R.: An electron microscope study on the cytoplasmic and nuclear components of rat primary oocytes. Z. Zellf., 50:749–765, 1959.

1372. SOTELO, J. R. and PORTER, K. R.: An electron microscope study of the rat ovum. J. Biophys. Biochem. Cytol., 5:327–342, 1959.

1373. SOTELO, J. R. and TRUJILLO-CENOZ, O.: Electron microscope study of the vitelline body of some spider oocytes. J. Biophys. Biochem. Cytol., 3:301–310, 1957.

1374. SOTELO, J. R. and TRUJILLO-CENOZ, O.: Electron microscope study on spermatogenesis. Chromosome morphogenesis at the onset of meiosis (cyteI) and nuclear structure of early and late spermatids. Z. Zellforsch., 51:243–277, 1960.

1375. SPIRO, D.: The ultrastructure of striated muscle at various sarcomere lengths. J. Biophys. Biochem. Cytol., 2:157–162, 1956. Suppl.

1376. SPOENDLIN, H.: Elektronenmikroskopische Untersuchungen am Cortischen Organ des Meerschweinchens. Pract. oto-rhino-laryng., 19:192–234, 1957.

1377. SPOENDLIN, H.: Elektronenmikroskopische Untersuchungen am respiratorischen Epithel der oberen Luftwege Pract. oto-rhino-laryng., 21:484–498, 1959.

1378. SPOENDLIN, H.: Submikroskopische Organisation des Sinneselemente im Cortischen Organ des Meerschweinchens. Pract. oto-rhino-laryng., 21:34–48, 1959.

1379. SPOENDLIN, H.: Submikroskopische Strukturen im Cortischem organ der Kätze. Acta Oto-Laryng., 52:111–130, 1960.

1380. STAUBESAND, J. and SCHMIDT, W.: Zur Histophysiologie des Herzbeutels. I. Elektronenmikroskopische Beobachtungen an den Deckzellen des Peri- und Epikards. Z. Zellforsch., 53:55–68, 1960.

1381. STEGNER, H.-E.: Das Epithel der Tuba uterina des Neugeborenen. Elektronenmikroskopische Befunde. Z. Zellforsch., 55:247–262, 1961.

1382. STEGNER, H.-E. and WARTENBERG, H.: Elektronenmikroskopische und histotopochemische Befunde an menschlichen Eizellen. Arch. Gynäkol., 196:23–34, 1961.

1383. STEGNER, H.-E. and WARTENBERG, H.: Elektronenmikroskopische und histotopochemische Untersuchungen über Struktur und Bildung der Zona pellucida menschlicher Eizellen. Z. Zellforsch., 53:702–713, 1961.

1384. STEINER, J. W., and CARRUTHERS, J. S.: Studies on the fine structure of the terminal branches of the biliary tree. I. The morphology of normal bile canaliculi, bile pre-ductules (ducts of Hering) and bile ductules. Am. J. Path., 38:639–661, 1961.

1385. STENGER, R. J. and SPIRO, D.: Structure of the cardiac muscle cell. Am. J. Med., 30:653–665, 1961.

1386. STENGER, R. J. and SPIRO, D.: The ultrastructure of mammalian cardiac muscle. J. Biophys. Biochem. Cytol., 9:325–351, 1961.

1387. STENGER, R. S., SPIRO, D., SCULLY, R. E., and SHANNON, J. M.: Ultrastructural and physiologic alterations in ischemic skeletal muscle. Am. J. Path., 40:1–20, 1962.

1388. STICH, H.: Bau und Funktion der Nukleolen. Experientia, 12:7–14, 1956.

1389. STOCKINGER, L. and ZARZICKI, J.: Elektronenmikroskopische Untersuchungen der Milchdrüse des laktierenden Meerschweinchens mit Berücksichtigung des Saugaktes. Z. Zellforsch., 57:106–123, 1962.

1390. STOECKENIUS, W.: Morphologische Beobachtungen beim intracellularen Erythrocytenabbau und der Eisenspeicherung in der Milz des Kaninchens. Klin Wochschr., 35:760–763, 1957.

1391. STOECKENIUS, W.: Weitere Untersuchungen am lymphatischen Gewebe. Verhandl. deut. Ges. Pathol., 41:304–311, 1958.

1392. STOECKENIUS, W.: Elektronenmikroskopische Untersuchungen am Retikulum der Milz. Verhandl. deut. Ges. Pathol., 42:351–352, 1959.

1393. STOECKENIUS, W. and KRACHT, J.: Elektronenmikroskopische Untersuchungen an den Langerhans' schen Inseln der Ratte. Endokrinologie, 36:135–145, 1958.

1394. STOLL, R., BLANQUET, P., LACHAPELE, A. P., MAURAUD, R., and MAGIMEL, A.: Electron microscopy of chick embryo thyroid. In: Stockholm Conf. Electron Micros. 1956. Proceed. pp. 173–176. Academic Press, New York, 1957.

1395. Stoll, R., Maraud, R., and Blanquet, P.: Sur la différenciation de la thyroide de l'embryon de poulet, étudiée en microscopie électronique. Compt. rend. assoc. anatom., 44:911–912, 1957.

1396. Stoll, R., Maraud, R., Blanquet, P., Mounier, J. and Lachapèle, A.: Nouvelles données sur la physiologie thyroidienne étudiée avec le microscope électronique. Ann. endocrinol. Paris., 19:183–201, 1958.

1397. Stoll, R., Maraud, R., and Lacourt, P.: L'ultrastructure de la thyroide (revue d'ensemble). Ann. endocrinol. Paris., 22:281–304, 1961.

1398. Stoll, R., Maraud, R., and Sparfel, A.: Recherches sur le rôle des α-cytomembranes dans le développement de la thyroide et dans ses tumeurs. Arch. anat. microscop. morphol. exp., 48:1–24, 1959.

1399. Suzuki, Y.: An electron microscopy of the renal differentiation. I. Proximal tubule cells. J. Electronmicroscopy, 6:52–65, 1958.

1400. Suzuki, Y.: An electron microscopy of the renal differentiation. II. Glomerulus. Keio J. Med., 8:129–155, 1959.

1401. Suzuki, Y., Osada, M., and Watanabe, A.: Cytological and electron microscopical observations on the vascular system of the various organs and mesentery of guinea pigs with special reference to the endothelial cells. Arch. histol. Japon., 22:477–514, 1962.

1402. Swift, H.: The fine structure of annulate lamellae. J. Biophys. Biochem. Cytol., 2:415–418, 1956. Suppl.

1403. Swift, H. H.: Studies on nuclear function. In: A Symposium on Molecular Biology, pp. 266–303. Ed.: R. E. Zirkle. University of Chicago Press, Chicago, 1959.

1404. Swift, H.: RNA and nuclear fine structure. In: Fourth Internat. Conf. Electron Micros. Berlin 1958. Proceed. Vol. II, Springer Verlag, Berlin, 1960.

1405. Swigart, R. N. and Kane, D. J.: Electron microscopic observations of pulmonary alveoli. Anat. Rec., 118:57–72, 1954.

1406. Syrrist, A. and Gustafson, G.: A contribution to the technique of the electron microscopy of dentine. Odont. Tidskr., 59:500–513, 1951.

1407. Szollosi, D. G. and Ris, H.: Observations on sperm penetration in the rat. J. Biophys. Biochem. Cytol., 10:275–283, 1961.

1408. Takaki, F., Suzuki, H. Y., Aoyagi, S., Shimizu, Y., and Hagiwara, A.: Electronmicroscopic cyto-histopathology. II. Fine structure of thin segment of loop of Henle of rat's kidney as revealed by electron microscopy. Acta Pathol. Japon., 6:99–108, 1956.

1409. Takuma, S.: Electron microscopy of the developing cartilagenous epiphysis. Arch. Oral Biol., 2:111–119, 1960.

1410. Tandler, B.: The cell base in the striated duct of normal human submaxillary gland. J. Appl. Phys., 32:1634, 1961. (Abstract.)

1411. Tandler, B.: Ultrastructure of the human submaxillary gland. I. Architecture and histological relationships of the secretory cells. Am. J. Anat., 111:287–307, 1962.

1412. Taniguchi, Y.: Ultrastructure of pigment granules of retinal epithelium. I. Cow's eye. Am. J. Ophthal., 48:221–230, 1959.

1413. Taylor, J. J.: Observations on the ultrastructure of the goblet cell of the rat duodenum. Anat. Rec., 133:434, 1959. (Abstract.)

1414. Telkkä, A., Fawcett, D. W., and Christensen, K.: Further observations on the structure of the mammalian sperm tail. Anat. Rec., 141:231–245, 1961.

1415. Terry, R. D. and Harkin, J. C.: Regenerating peripheral nerve sheaths following Wallerian degeneration. Exp. Cell Res., 13:193–197, 1957.

1416. Terzakis, J. and Rhodin, J. A. G.: Ultrastructure of human term placenta. Anat. Rec., 139:279, 1961. (Abstract.)

1417. Thaemert, J. C.: Intercellular bridges as protoplasmic anastomoses between smooth muscle cells. J. Biophys. Biochem. Cytol., 6:67–70, 1959.

1418. Themann, H.: Elektronenmikroskopische Untersuchungen der normalen und der pathologisch veränderten Mundschleimhaut. Fortschr. Kiefer- u. Gesichtschir., 4:390–398, 1958.

1419. Themann, H.: Zur elektronenmikroskopischen Darstellung von Glykogen mit Best's carmin. J. Ultrastructure Res., 4:401–412, 1960.

1420. Themann, H.: Elektronenmikroskopische Darstellung von Glykogen. Naturwissenschaften, 47:155–157, 1960.

1421. Thoenes, W.: Zur Feinstruktur der Macula densa im Nephron der Maus. Z. Zellforsch., 55:486–499, 1961.

1422. Thoenes, W.: Die Mikromorphologie des Nephron in ihrer Beziehung zur Funktion. I. Funktionseinheit: Glomerulum-proximales und distales Konvolut. Klin. Wochschr., 39:504–518, 1961.

1423. Thoenes, W.: Die Mikromorphologie des Nephron in ihrer Beziehung zur Funktion. II. Funktionseinheit: Henlesche Schleife-Sammelrohr. Klin. Wochschr., 39:827–839, 1961.

1424. Thoenes, W.: Fine structure of lipid granules in proximal tubule cells of mouse kidney. J. Cell Biol., 12:433–437, 1962.

1425. Thoenes, W. und Ruska, H.: Über "leptomere Myofibrillen" in der Herzmuskelzelle. Z. Zellforsch., 51:560–570, 1960.

1426. Thomas, O. L.: Electron microscopy of the Golgi apparatus. Nature, 185:703–704, 1960.

1427. Thomas, W. A. and O'Neal, R. M.: Electron microscopy studies of butter and corn oil in jejunal mucosa. Arch. Path., 69:121–129, 1960.

1428. Thornburg, W. and De Robertis, E.: Polarization and electron microscopy study of frog nerve axoplasm. J. Biophys. Biochem. Cytol., 2:475–482, 1956.

1429. Toji, Y.: Electron microscope studies on ciliary apparatus of oviduct (I). J. Electronmicroscopy, 5:43–46, 1957.

1430. Toji, Y.: Studies on the ciliary apparatus of the oviduct in mouse as revealed with the electron microscope. J. Osaka City Med. Center, 7:39–54, 1958.

1431. Tokuyasu, K. and Yamada, E.: The fine structure of the retina studied with the electron microscope. IV. Morphogenesis of outer segments of retinal rods. J. Biophys. Biochem. Cytol., 6:225–230, 1959.

1432. Tokuyasu, K. and Yamada, E.: The fine structure of the retina. V. Abnormal retinal rods and their morphogenesis. J. Biophys. Biochem. Cytol., 7:187–190, 1960.

1433. Tousimis, A. J. and Fine, B. S.: Ultrastructure of the iris: an electron microscopic study. Am. J. Ophthal. 48:397–417, 1959.

1434. Tousimis, A. J. and Fine, B. S.: Ultrastructure of the iris: the intercellular stromal components. Arch. Ophthal., 62:974–976, 1959.

1435. Tousimis, A. J. and Fine, B. S.: Electron microscopy of the pigment epithelium of the iris. In: The Structure of the Eye, pp. 441–452. Ed.: G. K. Smelser. Academic Press, New York, 1961.

1436. Tokuyasu, K. and Yamada, E.: The fine structure of the retina. V. Abnormal retinal rods and their morphogenesis. J. Biophys. Biochem. Cytol., 7:187–190, 1960.

1437. Tremble, G. E.: Observations of respiratory cilia with the electron microscope. Brit. Med. J., 2:127, 1955.

1438. Trier, J. S.: The fine structure of the parathyroid gland. J. Biophys. Biochem. Cytol., 4:13–22, 1958.

1439. Trujillo-Cenóz, O.: Electron microscope study of the rabbit gustatory bud. Z. Zellforsch., 46:272–280, 1957.

1440. Trujillo-Cenóz, O.: Some aspects of the structural organization of the arthropod ganglia. Z. Zellforsch., 56:649–682, 1962.

1441. Trujillo-Cenóz, O. and Sotelo, J. R.: Relationships of the ovular surface with follicle cells and origin of the zona pellucida in rabbit oocytes. J. Biophys. Biochem. Cytol., 2:347–350, 1959.

1442. Trump, B. F.: An electron microscope study of the uptake, transport, and storage of colloidal materials by the cells of the vertebrate nephron. J. Ultrastructure Res., 5:291–310, 1961.

1443. Trump, B. F., Smuckler, E. A., and Benditt, E. P.: A method for staining epoxy sections for light microscopy. J. Ultrastructure Res., 5:343–348, 1961.

1444. Turunen, M. and Stjernvall, L.: Submicroscopic structure of the pulmonary capillaries in patent ductus arteriosus. Acta Chir. Scand., 117:131–136, 1959.

1445. Ueberberg, H.: Elektronenmikroskopische Untersuchungen an der Nebennierenrinde der cortisonbehandelten Ratte. In: European Regional Conf. Electron Micros., Delft 1960, Proceed. Vol. II, pp. 857–861. De Nederlandse Vereniging voor Electronenmicroscopie, Delft, 1961.

1446. Usuku, G., Simonagayosi, S., Kodama, Y., and Aratake, H.: Ultrastructure of the lamina elastica interna of rabbit's femoral artery. Kumamoto Med. J., 12:285–287, 1959.

1447. Uzmann, B. G.: The formation of myelin in the peripheral nerves of vertebrates. J. Biophys. Biochem. Cytol., 2:219, 1956. Suppl.

1448. Uzmann, B. G. and Nogueira-Graf, G.: Electron microscope studies of the formation of nodes of Ranvier in mouse sciatic nerves. J. Biophys. Biochem. Cytol., 3:589–598, 1957.

1449. Uzmann, B. G. and Villegas, G. M.: A comparison of nodes of Ranvier in sciatic nerves with node-like structures in optic nerves of the mouse. J. Biophys. Biochem. Cytol., 7:761–762, 1960.

1450. Vecchietti, G. and Morano, E.: Investigation of human endometrium by the electron microscope. Int. J. Fertility, 4:109–114, 1959.

1451. Veratti, E.: Investigations on the fine structure of striated muscle fiber. J. Biophys. Biochem. Cytol., 10:1–60, 1961. Suppl.

1452. Vial, J. D. and Orrego, H.: Electron microscope observations on the fine structure of parietal cells. J. Biophys. Biochem. Cytol., 7:367–372, 1960.

1453. Virágh, S. and Porte, A.: Le noeud de Keith et Flack et les différentes fibres auriculaires du coeur de rat. Étude en microscopie optique et électronique. Compt. rend. acad. sci., 251:2086–2088, 1960.

1454. Virágh, S. and Porte, A.: Structure fine du tissu vecteur dans le coeur de rat. Z. Zellforsch., 55:263–281, 1961.

1455. Virágh, S. and Porte, A.: Elements nerveux intracardiaques et innervation du myocarde. Étude au microscope électronique dans le coeur de rat. Z. Zellforsch., 55:282–296, 1961.

1456. Vogel, A.: Zelloberfläche und Zellverbindung im elektronenmikroskopischen Bild. Verh. deut. Ges. Pathol., 43:284–295, 1958.

1457. Vogel, A.: Zur Struktur des Peritoneal-Mesothels. Experientia, 13:54–55, 1957.

1458. Vogel, A.: Zellgrenzstrukturen im elektronenmikroskopischen Bild. Therap. Ber., 31:67–71, 1959.

1459. Vogel, A.: Zum Feinbau der Interzellularbrücken nach Kontrastierung mit Phosphorwolframsäure. In: Fourth Internat. Conf. Electron Micros. Berlin 1958. Proceed. Vol. II, pp. 286–289. Springer Verlag, Berlin, 1960.

1460. Vokaer, R.: Étude du placenta au microscope électronique. In: Le placenta humaine, pp. 149–155. Ed.: J. Snoeck. Masson, Paris, 1958.

1461. Vrabec, F.: The amorphous substance in the trabecular meshwork. Brit. J. Ophthal., 41:20–24, 1957.

1462. Wainrach, S. and Sotelo, J. R.: Electron microscope study of the developing chick embryo heart. Z. Zellforsch., 55:622–634, 1961.

Page 211

1463. WALD, F. and DE ROBERTIS, E.: The action of glutamate and the problem of the "extra-cellular space" in the retina. An electron microscope study. Z. Zellforsch., 55:649–661, 1961.

1464. WALKER, B. E.: Electron microscopic observations on transitional epithelium of the mouse urinary bladder. J. Ultrastructure Res., 3:345–361, 1960.

1465. WALLER, U.: Zur submikroskopischen Struktur der Rattenschilddrüse. Elektronenmikroskopische Untersuchungen an der Basis des Schilddrüsenfollikels. Acta Endocrinologica, 35:334–350, 1960.

1466. WALTHARD, B.: Elektronenmikroskopische Strukturen der Schilddrüse. Bull. schweiz. Akad. med. Wiss., 11:346–351, 1955.

1467. WALTHARD, B.: Zur Elektronenmikroskopie der Parathyreoidea. Arch. "De Vecchi" anat. patol. med. clin., 31:441–448, 1960.

1468. WALTHARD, B. and ROOS, B.: Elektronenmikroskopische Untersuchungen der Schilddrüse. Verhandl. deut. Ges. Pathol., 42:335–343, 1959.

1469. WANKO, T. and GAVIN, M. A.: The fine structure of the lens epithelium: an electron microscopic study. Arch. Ophthal., 60:868–879, 1958.

1470. WANKO, T. and GAVIN, M. A.: Electron microscope study of lens fibers. J. Biophys. Biochem. Cytol., 6:97–102, 1959.

1471. WANKO, T. and GAVIN, M. A.: Cell surfaces in the crystalline lens. In: The Structure of the Eye, pp. 221–233. Ed.: G. K. Smelser. Academic Press, New York, 1961.

1472. WANKO, T., VON SALLMAN, L., and GAVIN, M. A.: Early changes in the lens epithelium after roentgen irradiation. A correlated light and electron microscopic study. Arch. Ophthal., 62:977–984, 1959.

1473. WARTENBERG, H. and SCHMIDT, W.: Elektronenmikroskopische Untersuchungen der strukturellen Veränderungen im Rindenbereich des Amphibieneies im Ovar und nach der Befruchtung. Z. Zellforsch., 54:118–146, 1961.

1474. WARTENBERG, H. and GUSEK, W.: Elektronenoptische Untersuchungen über die Feinstruktur des Ovarialeies und des Follikelepithels von Amphibien. Exp. Cell Res., 19:199–209, 1960.

1475. WARTENBERG, H. and STEGNER, H. E.: Über die elektronenmikroskopische Feinstruktur des menschlichen Ovarialeies. Z. Zellforsch., 52:450–474, 1960.

1476. WASSERMANN, F.: The structure of the wall of the hepatic sinusoids in the electron microscope. Z. Zellforsch., 49:13–32, 1958.

1477. WASSERMANN, F. and KUBOTA, L.: Observations on fibrillogenesis in the connective tissue of the chick embryo with the aid of silver impregnation. J. Biophys. Biochem. Cytol., 2:67–70, 1956. Suppl.

1478. WASSERMANN, F., ROTH, L. E., and MINICK, O. T.: The fine structure of native collagen in thin sections. Exp. Cell Res., 13:407–410, 1957.

1479. WATRACH, A. M. and VATTER, A. E.: Electron microscopy of the pulmonary alveolar wall. Am. J. Vet. Res., 20:723–735, 1959.

1480. WATSON, M. L.: Spermatogenesis in the albino rat as revealed by electron microscopy. Biochim. Biophys. Acta, 8:369–374, 1952.

1481. WATSON, M. L.: Pores in the mammalian nuclear membrane. Biochim. Biophys. Acta, 15:475–479, 1954.

1482. WATSON, M. L.: The use of carbon films to support tissue sections for electron microscopy. J. Biophys. Biochem. Cytol., 1:183–184, 1955.

1483. WATSON, M. L.: The nuclear envelope. Its structure and relation to cytoplasmic membranes. J. Biophys. Biochem. Cytol., 1:257–270, 1955.

1484. WATSON, M. L.: Staining of tissue sections for electron microscopy with heavy metals. J. Biophys. Biochem. Cytol., 4:475–478, 1958.

1485. WATSON, M. L.: Staining of tissue sections for electron microscopy. II. Application of solutions containing lead and barium. J. Biophys. Biochem. Cytol., 4:727–730, 1958.

1486. WATSON, M. L.: Further observations on the nuclear envelope of the animal cell. J. Biophys. Biochem. Cytol., 6:147–156, 1959.

1487. WATSON, M. L.: The extracellular nature of enamel in the rat. J. Biophys. Biochem. Cytol., 7:489–492, 1960.

1488. WATSON, M. L.: Observations on a granule associated with chromatin in the nuclei of cells of rat and mouse. J. Cell Biol., 13:162–167, 1962.

1489. WATSON, M. L. and ALDRIDGE, W. G.: Methods for the use of indium as an electron stain for nucleic acids. J. Biophys. Biochem. Cytol., 11:257–272, 1961.

1490. WATSON, M. L. and AVERY, J. K.: The development of the hamster lower incisor as observed by electron microscopy. Am. J. Anat., 95:109–162, 1954.

1491. WATSON, M. L. and ROBINSON, R. A.: Collagencrystal relationships in bone. II. Electron microscope study of basic calcium phosphate crystals. Am. J. Anat., 93:25–59, 1953.

1492. WATSON, M. L. and SIEKEVITZ, P.: Cytochemical studies of mitochondria. I. The separation and identification of a membrane fraction from isolated mitochondria. J. Biophys. Biochem. Cytol., 2:639–652, 1956.

1493. WATSON, M. L. and SIEKEVITZ, P.: The isolation and analysis of a mitochondrial membrane fraction. J. Biophys. Biochem. Cytol., 2:379–382, 1956. Suppl.

1494. WEBSTER, H. F.: Transient, focal accumulation of axonal mitochondria during the early stages of Wallerian degeneration. J. Cell Biol., 12:361–383, 1962.

1495. WEBSTER, H. F. and SPIRO, D.: Phase and electron microscopic studies of experimental demyelination. I. Variations in myelin sheath contour in normal guinea pig sciatic nerve. J. Neuropathol. Exp. Neurol., 19:42–69, 1960.

1496. WEINSTEIN, H. J.: An electron microscope study of cardiac muscle. Exp. Cell Res., 7:130–146, 1954.

1497. WEISBLUM, B., HERMAN, L., and FITZGERALD, P. J.: Changes in pancreatic acinar cells during protein deprivation. J. Cell Biol., 12:313–327, 1962.

1498. WEISS, J. M.: The ergastoplasm; its fine structure and relation to protein synthesis as studied with the electron microscope in the pancreas of the Swiss albino mouse. J. Exp. Med., 98:607–618, 1953.

1499. WEISS, J. M.: Intracellular changes due to neutral red as revealed in the pancreas and kidney of the mouse by the electron microscope. J. Exp. Med., 101:213–224, 1955.

1500. WEISS, J. M.: The role of the Golgi complex in fat absorption as studied with the electron microscope with observations on the cytology of the duodenal absorptive cells. J. Exp. Med., 102:775–781, 1955.

1501. WEISS, J. M.: Mitochondrial changes induced by potassium and sodium in the duodenal absorptive cell as studied with the electron microscope. J. Exp. Med., 102:783–788, 1955.

1502. WEISS, L.: A study of the structure of splenic sinuses in man and in the albino rat with the light microscope and electron microscope. J. Biophys. Biochem. Cytol., 3:599–610, 1957.

1503. WEISS, L.: Aspects of the reticuloendothelial system studied with the light microscope and the electron microscope. Ann. N. Y. Acad. Sci., 73:131–138, 1958.

1504. WEISS, L.: The organization of the connective tissues in the bone marrow. II. Reticular cells. Anat. Rec., 136:300, 1960. (Abstract.)

1505. WEISS, L.: An electron microscopic study of the vascular sinuses of the bone marrow of the rabbit. Bull. Johns Hopkins Hosp., 108:171–199, 1961.

1506. WEISS, L.: Observations on the red pulp of the spleen of rabbits and dogs by electron and light microscopy. Anat. Rec., 139:286, 1961. (Abstract.)

1507. WEISS, L.: The structure of fine splenic arterial vessels in relation to hemoconcentration and red cell destruction. Am. J. Anat., 111:131–180, 1962.

1508. WEISS, P.: Cell contact. Int. Rev. Cytol., 7:391–423, 1958.

1509. WEISS, P. and FERRIS, W.: Electron-microscopic study of the texture of the basement membrane of larval amphibian skin. Proc. Natl. Acad. Sci., 40:528–540, 1954.

1510. WEISS, P. and FERRIS, W.: Electronmicrograms of larval amphibian epidermis. Exp. Cell Res., 6:546–549, 1954.

1511. WELLINGS, S. R. and DeOME, K. B.: Milk protein droplet formation in the Golgi apparatus of the C₃H/Crgl mouse mammary epithelial cells. J. Biophys. Biochem. Cytol., 9:479–485, 1961.

1512. WELLINGS, S. R., DeOME, K. B., and PITELKA, D. R.: Electron microscopy of milk secretion in the mammary gland of the C₃H/-Crgl mouse. J. Natl. Cancer Inst., 25:393–242, 1960.

1513. WELLINGS, S. R., GRUNBAUM, B. W., and De OME, K. B.: Electron microscopy of milk secretion in the mammary gland of the C₃H/Crgl mouse. J. Natl. Cancer Inst., 25:423–438, 1960.

1514. WERSÄLL, J.: Studies on the structure and innervation of the sensory epithelium of the cristae ampullares in guinea pig. Acta-Oto-Laryngol., 126:1–85, 1956. Suppl.

1515. WERSÄLL, J., HILDING, D. A., and LUNDQUIST, P. G.: Ultrastruktur und Innervation der cochlearen Haarzellen. Arch. Ohr. Nas. Kehlkopfheilk., 178:106–126, 1962.

1516. WESSEL, W.: Das elektronenmikroskopische Bild menschlicher endometrialer Drüsenzellen während des menstruellen Zyklus. Z. Zellforsch., 51:633–657, 1960.

1517. WESSEL, W.: Über die Form der Mitochondrien in elektronenmikroskopischen Bildern. Z. Zellforsch., 52:712–714, 1960.

1518. WETZEL, B. K.: Sodium permanganate fixation for electron microscopy. J. Biophys. Biochem. Cytol., 9:711–716, 1961.

1519. WETZSTEIN, R. and WAGNER, H.: Elektronenmikroskopische Untersuchungen am menschlichen Endometrium. Anat. Anz., 108:362–375, 1960.

1520. WHALEY, W. G., MOLLENHAUER, H. H., and LEECH, J. H.: Some observations on the nuclear envelope. J. Biophys. Biochem. Cytol., 8:233–245, 1960.

1521. WHITE, J. C. and ELMES, P. C.: Fibrous proteins of pathological bronchial secretions studied by optical and electron microscopy: deoxyribonucleo-protein and muco-protein in bronchial secretions. J. Pathol. Bacteriol., 67:105–108, 1954.

1522. WHITEAR, M.: An electron microscope study of nerves in the corneal epithelium. Experientia, 13:287, 1957.

1523. WHITTAKER, V. P. and GRAY, E. G.: The synapse. Brit. Med. Bull., 18:223–228, 1962.

1524. WILHELM, G.: Elektronenoptische Untersuchungen zur Verknöcherung. Z. Kinderheilk., 76:73–78, 1955.

1525. WILLIAMSON, J. R.: Electron microscopy of glycogenic changes in beta cells in experimental diabetes. Diabetes, 9:471–480, 1960.

1526. WILLIAMSON, J. R. and GRISHAM, J. W.: Electron microscopy of leukocytic margination and emigration in acute inflammation in dog pancreas. Am. J. Path., 39:239–256, 1961.

1527. WILLIAMSON, J. R. and LACY, P. E.: Electron microscopy of islet cells in alloxan-treated rabbits. Arch. Path., 67:102–109, 1959.

1528. WILLIAMSON, J. R. and LACY, P. E.: Electron microscopy of glycogen infiltration in the islets of the cat; effects of repeated injections of glucose. Arch. Path., 72:637–647, 1961.

1529. WISCHNITZER, S.: An electron microscope study of the nuclear envelope of amphibian oocytes. J. Ultrastructure Res., 1:201–222, 1958.

1531. WISCHNITZER, S.: Observations on the annulate lamellae of immature amphibian oocytes. J. Biophys. Biochem. Cytol., 8:558–563, 1960.

1532. WISCHNITZER, S.: An electron microscopic

study of the Golgi apparatus of amphibian oocytes. Z. Zellforsch., 57:202–212, 1962.

1533. WISLOCKI, G. B. and DEMPSEY, E. W.: Electron microscopy of the placenta of the rat. Anat. Rec., 123:33–64, 1955.

1534. WISLOCKI, G. B. and DEMPSEY, E. W.: Electron microscopy of the human placenta. Anat. Rec., 123:133–168, 1955.

1535. WISLOCKI, G. B. and LADMAN, A. J.: The demonstration of a blood-ocular barrier in the albino rat by means of the intravitam deposition of silver. J. Biophys. Biochem. Cytol., 1:501–510, 1955.

1536. WISSIG, S. L.: The anatomy of secretion in the follicular cells of the thyroid gland. I. The fine structure of the gland in the normal rat. J. Biophys. Biochem. Cytol., 7:419–432, 1960.

1537. WISSIG, S. L.: The sequence of cytological changes induced in the thyroid gland by a single injection of thyrotrophic hormone. Anat. Rec., 139:287, 1961. (Abstract.)

1538. WOHLFARTH-BOTTERMANN, K.-E. and KUHNKE, E.: Zur Darstellung der Kollagen-Querstreifung in Dünnschnitten. Naturwissenschaften, 44:595, 1957.

1539. WOLLENBERGER, A. and SCHULZE, W.: Mitochondrial alterations in the myocardium of dogs with aortic stenosis. J. Biophys. Biochem. Cytol., 10:285–288, 1961.

1540. WOLPERS, C.: Elektronenmikroskopische Kollagenbefunde. Leder, 1:3–12, 1950.

1541. WOLPERS, C.: Der Strukturwandel der Kollagenquerstreifung. Klin. Wochschr., 28:317–318, 1950.

1542. WOOD, R. L.: Some structural features of the bile canaliculus. Anat. Rec., 140:207–215, 1961.

1543. WOOD, R. L.: The fine structure of the junction between bile canaliculi and bile ducts in mammalian liver. Anat. Rec., 139:287, 1961. (Abstract.)

1544. WOODSIDE, G. L. and DALTON, A. J.: The ultrastructure of lung tissue from newborn and embryo mice. J. Ultrastructure Res., 2:28–54, 1958.

1545. WORLEY, L. G., FISCHBEIN, E., and SHAPIRO, J. E.: The structure of ciliated epithelial cells as revealed by the electron microscope and in phase-contrast. J. Morph., 92:545–578, 1953.

1546. WYBURN, G. M.: The capsule of spinal ganglion cells. J. Anat., 92:528–533, 1958.

1547. WYBURN, G. M.: An electron microscopic survey of a sympathetic ganglion. Scot. Med. J., 3:385–391, 1958.

1548. WYCKOFF, R. W. G.: The electron microscope in biology. Nature, 173:419–422, 1954.

1549. YAMADA, E.: The fine structure of the gall bladder epithelium of the mouse. J. Biophys. Biochem. Cytol., 1:445–458, 1955.

1550. YAMADA, E.: The fine structure of the renal glomerulus of the mouse. J. Biophys. Biochem. Cytol., 1:551–566, 1955.

1551. YAMADA, E.: The fine structure of the mega-karyocyte in the mouse spleen. Acta Anat., 29:267–290, 1957.

1552. YAMADA, E.: The fine structure of retina studied with electron microscope. I. The fine structure of frog retina. Kurume Med. J., 4:127–147, 1957.

1553. YAMADA, E.: Some observations on the fine structure of centriole in the mitotic cell. Kurume Med. J., 5:36–38, 1958.

1554. YAMADA, E.: A peculiar lamellated body observed in the cells of the pigment epithelium of the retina of the bat, *Pipistrellus abramus*. J. Biophys. Biochem. Cytol., 4:329–330, 1958.

1555. YAMADA, E.: A crystalline body found in the rod inner segment of the frog's eye. J. Biophys. Biochem. Cytol., 6:517–518, 1959.

1556. YAMADA, E.: Collagen fibrils within the renal glomerulus. J. Biophys. Biochem. Cytol., 7:407–408, 1960.

1557. YAMADA, E.: Observations on the fine structure of photoreceptive elements in the vertebrate eye. J. Electronmicroscopy, 9:1–14, 1960.

1558. YAMADA, E.: The fine structure of the paraboloid in the turtle retina as revealed by electron microscopy. Anat. Rec., 136:352, 1960. (Abstract.)

1559. YAMADA, E.: The fine structure of the pigmented epithelium in the turtle eye. In: The Structure of the Eye, pp. 73–84. Ed.: G. K. Smelser. Academic Press, New York, 1961.

1560. YAMADA, E. and ISHIKAWA, T. M.: The fine structure of the corpus luteum in the mouse ovary as revealed by electron microscopy. Kyushu J. Med. Sci., 11:235–259, 1960.

1561. YAMADA, E., MUTA, T., MOTOMURA, A., and KOGA, H.: The fine structure of the oocyte in the mouse ovary studied with electron microscope. Kurume Med. J., 4:148–171, 1957.

1562. YAMADA, E., TOKUYASU, K., and IWAKI, S.: The fine structure of retina studied with electron microscope. II. Pigment epithelium and capillary of the choriocapillary layer. J. Electronmicroscopy, 6:42–46, 1958.

1563. YAMADA, E., TOKUYASU, K., and IWAKI, S.: The fine structure of retina studied with electron microscope. III. Human retina. Kurume Med. J., 21:1979–2027, 1958.

1564. YAMAMOTO, T.: On the relationship between mitochondria and fat droplets in the hepatic cells of the mouse after administration of hydrocortisone. Arch. Histol. Japon., 15:625–631, 1958.

1565. YAMAMOTO, T.: Electron microscope investigation on the relationship between the smooth muscle cell of the Proc. vermiformis and the autonomic peripheral nerves. Acta Neuroveget. Vienna, 21:406–425, 1960.

1566. YAMAMOTO, T.: An electron microscope study on development of uterine smooth muscle. J. Electronmicroscopy, 10:145–160, 1961.

1567. YAMORI, T., MATSUURA, S., and SAKAMOTO, S.: An electron microscopic study of the normal and stimulated adrenal cortex in the rat. Z. Zellforsch., 55:179–199, 1961.

1568. YASUDA, H.: Electron microscopic cyto-histopathology. IV. A study of normal adult and fetus lung in mammals as revealed by electron microscopy. Acta Pathol. Japon., 8:189–213, 1958.

1569. YASUTAKE, S.: The fine structure of the olfactory epithelium studied with the electron microscope. J. Kurume Med. Assoc., 22:1279–1304, 1959.

1570. YASUZUMI, G.: Spermatogenesis in animals as revealed by electron microscopy. I. Formation and submicroscopic structure of the middle-piece of the albino rat. J. Biophys. Biochem. Cytol., 2:445–450, 1956.

1571. YASUZUMI, G. and OBATA, Y.: Electron microscopy of human dentine. J. Dent. Res., 34:808–813, 1955.

1572. YASUZUMI, G., SAWADA, T., SUGIHARA, R., KIRIYAMA, M., and SUGIOKA, M.: Electron microscope researches on the ultrastructure of nucleoli in animal tissues. Z. Zellforsch., 48:10–23, 1958.

1573. YASUZUMI, G. and TANAKA, H.: Electron microscope studies of the fine structure of the ovary. I. Studies on the origin of yolk. Exp. Cell Res., 12:681–685, 1957.

1574. YASUZUMI, G. and WAKISAKA, I.: A comparative study of kino-cilia and stereocilia as revealed by electron microscope. Cytologia Tokyo, 21:157–164, 1956.

1575. YOLAC, A. B.: Elektronenmikroskopische Untersuchungen zur Morphologie der Hauptstückepithelien der Mäuseniere nach Injektion von hypertoner Saccharoselösung. Verhandl. deut. Ges. Pathol., 43:235–240, 1959.

1576. YOSHIMURA, F. and IRIE, M.: Licht- und elektronenmikroskopische Studie an den Kristalloiden in der Schilddrüsenzelle. Z. Zellforsch., 55:204–219, 1961.

1577. YOUNG, J. Z.: The organization within nerve cells. Endeavour, 15:5–19, 1956.

1578. ZACKS, S. I., BAUER, W. C., and BLUMBERG, J. M.: Abnormalities in the fine structure of the neuromuscular junction in patients with myasthenia gravis. Nature, 190:280–281, 1961.

1579. ZACKS, S. I. and BLUMBERG, J. M.: Observations on the fine structure and cytochemistry of mouse and human intercostal neuromuscular junctions. J. Biophys. Biochem. Cytol., 10:517–528, 1961.

1580. ZACKS, S. I. and BLUMBERG, J. M.: The histochemical localization of acetylcholinesterase in the fine structure of neuromuscular junctions of mouse and human intercostal muscle. J. Histochem. and Cytochem., 9:317–324, 1961.

1581. ZAMBONI, L.: Electron microscopic investigation of cell web and desmosomes in the epithelial cells of the rat small intestine. Anat. Rec., 139:290, 1961. (Abstract.)

1582. ZAMBONI, L. and PEASE, D. C.: The vascular bed of red bone marrow. J. Ultrastructure Res., 5:65–85, 1961.

1583. ZEBRUN, W. and MOLLENHAUER, H. H.: Electron microscopic observations on mitochondria of rat testes fixed in potassium permanganate. J. Biophys. Biochem. Cytol., 7:311–314, 1960.

1584. ZEIGEL, R. F. and DALTON, A. J.: Speculations based on the morphology of the Golgi systems in several types of protein-secreting cells. J. Cell Biol., 15:45–54, 1962.

1585. ZELANDER, T.: The ultrastructure of the adrenal cortex of the mouse. Z. Zellforsch., 46:710–716, 1957.

1586. ZELANDER, T.: Ultrastructure of articular cartilage. Z. Zellforsch., 49:720–738, 1959.

1587. ZELANDER, T.: Ultrastructure of mouse adrenal cortex. An electron microscopical study in intact and hydrocortisone-treated male adults. J. Ultrastructure Res., Suppl. 2:1–111, 1959.

1588. ZELANDER, T.: Ultrastructure of the adrenal cortex in the mouse. In: Fourth Internat. Conf. Electron Micros. Berlin 1958. Proceed. Vol. II, pp. 384–388. Springer Verlag, Berlin, 1960.

1589. ZELANDER, T., EKHOLM, R., and EDLUND, Y.: The ultrastructural organization of the rat exocrine pancreas. III. Intralobular vessels and nerves. J. Ultrastructure Res., 7:84–101, 1962.

1590. ZELICKSON, A. S. and HARTMANN, J. F.: An electron microscope study of human epidermis. J. Invest. Dermatol., 36:65–72, 1961.

# INDEX

# INDEX

# INDEX